D1095956

Activation
and
Behavior

Activation
and
Behavior

ELIZABETH DUFFY
The Woman's College
of the University of North Carolina

John Wiley & Sons, Inc., New York · London

to John and Betsy

Preface

This manuscript is released for publication with a combination of enthusiasm and apology on my part—enthusiasm for its aims and apology for the extent to which it falls short of fulfilling them.

The book has been long in the making, far too long. The germ of its thesis began to grow as long as thirty years ago. Indeed, I was publishing in the ninteen-thirties and nineteen-forties articles which presented the basic concept developed here, though the terms employed for it were variously, "degree of excitation," "energy level," and "energy mobilization." The notion, based upon behavioral phenomena, found relatively little acceptance among psychologists until the nineteen-fifties, when neural findings (particularly in regard to the functioning of the reticular activating system) lent plausibility to the conception.

In the meantime, I had written a first draft of the present book and had shown it privately to an eminent physiological psychologist who was so critical of it that I was discouraged from submitting it to a publisher. The criticism, however, bore fruit. Still convinced that the conception was basically correct, I was led to a more thorough search of the psychological literature to see whether there was more experimental evidence which might indirectly support the suggestion and to check on whether I had, as my critic suggested, overlooked negative evidence. Just when I thought I knew the literature of the field fairly well, and had written another version of the book, investigations in the area began to multiply so rapidly that I could not keep up with them and still have time left for writing. Friends, who had almost begun to think the book was a myth, jokingly suggested that I publish what I had and save new investigations for a second edition. At this point it was decided that the area covered by the book was so broad, and knowledge about it growing so rapidly, that the book should indeed be published even though no complete review of relevant studies was possible. I apologize to my colleagues, especially to those who may have conducted important experiments which have been omitted, for this state of affairs. I regret that some recent and important studies are in this category. It is believed, however, that the coverage of the literature has been sufficiently complete to give reasonable assurance that the position taken here would not have been altered in basic respects by further reading.

The situation in the field of activation, with respect to writing and publishing, is much like that described by Bishop (1953) in his review of a book on neurophysiology by Eccles. He said, "In these unsettled times, he who would achieve the impeccable synopsis of nervous system activity should have written his first draft at the age of thirty, revised it every ten years without publication, and finally have left it in his literary remains for the next generation to finish; or to further revise. The last edition might turn out to be the simplest, and the easiest to read" (p. 626). The present author has complied with approximately all except the last step of this advice. Therefore, I can say to my readers, "This is the best that I can do now, with our limited information and my finite time. Take it, if you will, and make of it something better, either now or in the next generation." Perhaps the book will at least take the place of the reprints of articles requested by many of my colleagues.

It is now high time to say, not only how the book came into being, but what it is about. Its purpose is to develop more fully than has been possible in journal articles a previously advocated concept, that of "energy mobilization." This concept has been rechristened "activation" in order to get rid of some of the unintended connotations of the earlier term and to take advantage of the acceptance and familiarity which the term "activation" has acquired through its use in Woodworth and Schlosberg's (1954) *Experimental Psychology*. I believe that the concept is a unifying one, bringing under a single heading phenomena discussed by psychologists under many different rubrics. It is an attempt to point out similarities where, it is believed, differences may often have been emphasized to the point of obscuring the characteristics which a number of psychological phenomena have in common.

The organism is conceived of as characteristically an energy system, storing energy and releasing it in activity of one form or another. The behavior which occurs apparently varies with (1) the extent of, and the fluctuations in, energy release or activation, and (2) the parts of the body maximally activated, as well as the direction of the activity upon the external environment.

A basic purpose of the present volume (strayed from many times because of the necessity of using the language employed by others in describing their experiments) is to present psychological phenomena in terms which will harmonize with those of the other sciences, and to show the relationship of psychology to the foundation sciences upon which it rests. As D. E. Cameron (1941) has pointed out, "the organism is essentially a specialized part of its environment, . . . the materials which compose it are without exception those which are found at large around it, and . . . consequently in some respects the organism may reasonably be expected to react to forces in a way similar to that shown by the less specialized environment" (p. 22).

In this book, behavior is considered to be a function of the entire organism, which itself is a function of its entire previous history, including the genes which constantly interact with environmental factors. It is the organism, and not some individual part, which is considered to be activated. Nevertheless, patterning in activation, rather than a massive, undifferentiated activation of the individual, is described. Interrelations of one part or system with another are stressed, and adjustment of the pattern of activation to the particular stimulating situation, as interpreted by the individual, is recognized. The neural and endocrine basis of activation is briefly discussed, and the problem of the measurement of activation is explored. Experimental evidence is presented to show the many factors, physiological and psychological, which may affect activation. Activation, in turn, is considered in relation to simple sensory and motor processes and also more complex responses. Individual differences in activation, explored less by psychologists than their significance warrants, are discussed and, where possible, experimental evidence is presented in regard to their origin and their behavioral correlates. Finally, there is a discussion of activation in relation to the functional disorders.

Though in recent years there have been studies of activation, the main purpose of which was to throw light on some of the problems discussed here, in the early years of work on the book I was dependent in large measure upon the gleaning of information from studies conducted for other purposes. Hence, I have ranged widely but not systematically over psychological and experimental psychiatric publications, often using suggestive evidence where no direct evidence on a problem was available.

Activation and Behavior presents a group of related hypotheses which, though they may or may not be correct, are testable. It attempts to summarize a considerable portion of our knowledge of activation and to present a unified view of the field as conceived by the author. Some parts of the book have already been published as articles, and many of the hypotheses presented here have been suggested in the articles. The full development of the hypotheses, presentation of the experimental evidence tending to support them, and consideration of the significance of these hypotheses for all areas of psychology could, however, be elaborated only in a book. While I know how small the chance is that I can be altogether right in my conclusions, I am equally convinced that I cannot be altogether wrong. As a prejudiced critic, I am of the opinion that the theoretical structure has general validity, however necessary it may prove to be to alter some of its parts. I leave to my colleagues the joy of finding and correcting my errors, though I hope that, by good fortune, my statements may even prove reliable at the .05 level of confidence.

ELIZABETH DUFFY

Greensboro, North Carolina
June, 1962

Acknowledgments

My greatest debt is to the authors whose names are recorded in the
forty odd pages of references at the end of the book. They have fur-
nished the data, and in some instances the theoretical suggestions,
which have given the book its present form. I am especially grateful
to the relatively few psychologists who have, over a period of years,
continued to work in a significant area of psychology which was not
receiving the attention or acclaim afforded to work in many other areas.

I should like to express my appreciation to those who have read
the manuscript in part or in its entirety, and to absolve them from all
blame where I have not heeded their advice. The late R. C. Davis read
the entire manuscript and was, over the years, until his recent death,
a source to which I could turn for advice. Dr. R. B. Malmo, in 1955,
read the manuscript and discussed it with students in his seminar.
Others who have been kind enough to read the whole manuscript are
Dr. Kendon Smith and, by arrangement of the publisher, Dr. John I.
Lacey and Dr. Leonard Uhr. Dr. Harold Schlosberg read a part of
the manuscript in early years and offered encouragement. Dr. Walter
D. Obrist more recently read a part of it and supplied me with many
references in the field of neurology, only a few of which, regrettably,
I had the time to consult. To all these psychologists I should like to
express my gratitude.

For financial assistance, in the form of supplies and services, I wish
to thank the Research Council of the Woman's College of the University of North Carolina; and for a grant for a summer's work, I should
like to express my appreciation to the Southern Fellowships Fund.

Many individuals have assisted me in the project. Miss Betty Jo
Stancil performed a major part of the work in getting the bibliography
in order, and also did some reference work for me. For indispensable
assistance in compiling the subject index, I am deeply grateful to Dr.

Mary Bynum Pierson. For work on the author index, I wish to thank Miss Rita Caudle and Miss Diane Pfaff. Mrs. Marjorie Memory checked the proof for the references. The Woman's College Library staff in general has been most co-operative. Two persons upon whom I have called frequently are Miss Virginia Trumper and Miss Mary Seawell. Many students, too numerous to mention, have "given me a hand." Among these, Miss Diana Evans worked with me longest. For a superb job in typing the entire manuscript and the lengthy bibliography, I am indebted to Mrs. Jeanelle Lovern. Others have from time to time assisted in the typing of my various revisions.

Several colleagues have aided me in the translation of articles in foreign languages. Among these are Dr. Malcolm Hooke, Dr. Meta Miller, and Dr. Elisabeth Jastrow.

The dedication acknowledges assistance in many forms from my husband, John Bridgers, and my daughter, Betsy. And it is no mere formality to say that without the faithful help on the domestic front of Mrs. Mary Alston and Mrs. Margaret Scott, this book could never have been written.

Finally, for permission to use quotations, I wish to express my indebtedness to the authors quoted and to the following journals and publishers: American Journal of Physiology (American Physiological Society); American Journal of Psychiatry (American Psychiatric Association); American Journal of Psychology; Annals of the New York Academy of Sciences (New York Academy of Sciences); Annual Review of Physiology (Annual Reviews, Inc.); Annual Review of Psychology (Annual Reviews, Inc.); Archives of Neurology and Psychiatry (American Medical Association); British Journal of Psychology (British Psychological Society); Diseases of the Nervous System (Physicians Postgraduate Press); Endocrinology (Charles C. Thomas); Genetic Psychology Monographs (Journal Press); Harcourt, Brace, and World, Inc.; Holt, Rinehart and Winston, Inc.; Journal of Comparative and Physiological Psychology (American Psychological Association); Journal of Comparative Psychology (Williams and Wilkins Co.); Physiological Reviews (American Physiological Society); Psychological Bulletin (American Psychological Association); Psychological Monographs (American Psychological Association); Psychological Reports; Psychological Review (American Psychological Association); Psychosomatic Medicine (Hoeber Medical Division of Harper and Brothers); Ronald Press Co.; Routledge and Kegan Paul Ltd.; Charles C. Thomas; University of Leyden Press; University of

Minnesota Press; Wistar Institute of Anatomy and Biology; Yale University Press.

I am particularly indebted to the *Psychological Review,* published by the American Psychological Association, for permission to reprint small portions of two articles of mine published in that journal, one "The Concept of Energy Mobilization," published in 1951, and the other "The Psychological Significance of the Concept of 'Arousal' or 'Activation,'" published in 1957.

E. D.

Contents

part I
THE NATURE OF ACTIVATION

chapter 1

Introduction

GENERAL INTRODUCTION

The terms "activation," "arousal," "energy mobilization," and "excitation" (used here with the same meaning) have recently occurred with increasing frequency in psychological literature.[1] Discovery of the arousal function of certain lower brain centers, such as the reticular formation (Moruzzi and Magoun, 1949; Lindsley, Bowden, and Magoun, 1949), has given impetus to the study of behavioral phenomena long before noted and described by such terms as the "degree of excitation" (Duffy, 1934)[2] or "energy mobilization" (Duffy, 1941a, 1951), or the "energetics of behavior" (G. L. Freeman, 1948a). Some of the phenomena covered by these terms have been traditionally described by the concepts of "drives," "motives," and "emotions"—though it is through no fault of the author's that terms of this sort were not

[1] "Activation" and "arousal," as used here, do not refer specifically to the activation pattern of the EEG. On the contrary, they refer to variations in the excitation of the individual as a whole, as indicated roughly by any one of a number of physiological measures (e.g., skin resistance, muscle tension, EEG, cardiovascular measures, and others). The degree of activation appears to be best indicated by a combination of measures. These points will be discussed later.

[2] The "degree of excitation," as the term was employed by the author in 1934 (Duffy, 1934), was defined as "the extent to which the organism as a whole is activated or aroused, not as measured by overt behavior but as measured by the activity of those processes which supply the energy for overt behavior." A more adequate definition would appear to be the activity in the various organs and tissues of the organism. Such activity in itself constitutes energy release.

3

abandoned long ago (Duffy, 1934, 1941a, 1941b, 1948, 1949, 1951, 1957).

Changes in the degree of activation, defined here in terms much broader than those of changes in the electroencephalogram, are found in studies of sleep, of "fatigue," and of various psychiatric conditions. They have been investigated as effects produced by changes in endocrine secretions and by the administration of drugs. A unifying concept which covers the range of physiological changes from deep sleep to extreme excitement would appear to offer hope of dealing with these phenomena more effectively. Such a concept would not only permit economy in the treatment of this subject matter but would no doubt serve also to reveal relationships now obscured by traditional descriptive categories (Duffy, 1941a, 1951, 1957, 1934). Some degree of acceptance accorded these suggestions has led to the present attempt to develop more completely the concept previously referred to as "energy mobilization" and now called "activation."

This book is divided into three sections. In the first and most basic section, there is a discussion of the nature of activation: the measurement of activation, the patterning of activation, the neurohumoral basis of activation, and the physiological and psychological factors which produce changes in activation. The conclusions reached in this section rest, in most instances, on rather solid ground, though detailed aspects of our conceptions are changing as further facts come to light. The second section of the book discusses some of the probable sensory and motor correlates of variations in activation. The chief aim of this section is to show the possible scope of the topic. Here some of the conclusions are tenuous, though many have a solid basis in fact. In order to suggest possible relationships, data of many sorts have been brought together—it may seem to some in an unjustifiable unity. However, since it is at least as easy to overlook similarities as to overlook differences, it is conceivably of value to consider whether many different kinds of factors, physiological and psychological, may not, through exerting a similar influence upon activation, exert a similar influence upon the functioning of the organism. In the third section of the book, there is a discussion of individual differences in activation. Here an attempt is made to establish the fact that there are consistent differences in arousal among individuals. These individual differences are shown to have certain behavioral correlates. The behavioral correlates are, however, less clearly established than the presence of consistent differences in activation among individuals.

Any discussion of the concept of activation necessitates consideration of the relationship between this concept and other descriptive categories in psychology. It is necessary to specify what contribution to the description of behavior may be expected of this construct and what aspects of behavior are properly describable by other constructs; for activation, like any psychological concept, represents an abstraction from the total behavior of the organism.

Observation of behavior, as well as the analysis of current psychological concepts, suggests that there are only two basic respects in which behavior shows variation. These are direction and intensity. An organism may approach or withdraw from a stimulus situation, and this approach or withdrawal may take place at any one of many possible degrees of intensity. Argument for this proposition has been offered previously by the author and by Stagner (Stagner, 1937; Duffy, 1941a, 1949). In brief, it has been argued that, while there are many objects, persons, and situations, and many aspects of all these which may be approached or withdrawn from, the behavior of the organism may always be described as approach or withdrawal with respect to some condition of the environment. This characteristic of behavior may be designated as the direction of behavior.[3] It will be discussed more fully later.

The behavior of the organism may also be described as occurring always with some particular degree of intensity. Approach or withdrawal may occur, for example, at a low degree of intensity, at a high degree of intensity, or at an intermediate degree of intensity. The intensity of response is measurable as the force of overt action, or as changes in the internal processes associated with the release of energy. Because of the frequent intervention of inhibitory activity, the two measures do not show a one-to-one correspondence. For most purposes, a concept of intensity based on the measurement of internal processes appears to be a more useful psychological construct than one based on the force of overt response. The behavioral correlates of internal arousal appear to be more numerous, its predictive value greater. Such a concept (i.e., the degree of energy release within the organism), referred to here as the level of activation, the degree of arousal, or the degree of energy mobilization, is the principal subject of the present discussion. The construct describes a condition conceived to vary in a continuum from a low point in deep sleep to a high point in extreme effort or intense excitement. Since this concept will be developed in some detail in the following chapter, it will not be

[3] The concept of direction in behavior has, of course, been employed by Lewin (1938), by Tolman (1932), and by others.

discussed further here. The directional aspect of behavior should, however, receive further attention at the present time. Despite its basic importance, it will be discussed later only to the extent necessary for a discussion of activation.

THE DIRECTIONAL ASPECT OF BEHAVIOR

The construct "direction" derives from the fact that behavior characteristically shows selectivity. The organism approaches certain objects, persons, or situations, or certain aspects of objects, persons, or situations. It withdraws from other objects, persons, or situations, or aspects of these. For example, it approaches food; it withdraws from electric shock. Behavior may be described as directed toward or away from any number of environmental stimuli.

Approach or withdrawal may be either overt or covert. For example, an individual may pick up a pear and eat it; he may be set to pick up the pear in a moment; or he may have a liking for pears, or a favorable attitude toward them, which represents a readiness in general to pick up and eat pears. Covert directional responses, such as sets or attitudes, may be conceived of as constituting a preparation or readiness for corresponding overt responses. In fact, John Dewey (1895) regarded attitudes as "reduced" movements. He said, "Certain movements, formerly useful in themselves, become reduced to tendencies to action, to attitudes."

The direction of behavior is conceived to be basically goal-direction. Selectivity of response, which is the observable fact, shows certain consistencies which have led to the inference of orientation toward a goal, whether the goal be defined as drive-reduction or in other terms. The organism's responses seem to be directed toward bringing about a particular condition: more of this stimulus or less of that, or more of stimulation in general or less of it (Hebb, 1955b; Leuba, 1955). Environmental objects or situations are responded to in the light of the requirements ("motives," "drives," "needs") of the organism and the perceived promise of various aspects of the environment with respect to satisfying these requirements. Behavior appears to be based upon what Tolman (1932) has called "expectancies" in regard to the outcome of various possible modes of response. The individual approaches "this" or withdraws from "that" on the basis of these expectations. More specifically, he appears to approach, or to be set to approach, an aspect of the environment if he interprets it to be a means to the end of reaching his goal; he appears to ignore it if it seems to be of no significance in relation to his goal; he appears to avoid or attack it if it seems to interpose an obstacle.

The maintenance of direction in behavior requires responses to relationships. Present stimuli are responded to in terms of their relationship to each other, their relationship to past experiences, and their relationship to present goals. An individual's movements in space, his manipulations of objects, his perception of his surroundings, his thinking about his problems, all show "response to relationships." Such responses to relationships are presumably the same as the "cognitive maps" of Tolman (1932) or the "cue functions" of Hebb (1955b). These various concepts imply that behavior is based upon certain discriminations. There is no implication that either discriminations or goals need be conscious.

The various situations (or groups of stimuli) to which the individual responds differ in the nature and the degree of their significance or, if the terminology is more acceptable, in their cue-function and in the intensity of the response which they produce. Those situations which bear a relationship to the individual's goals may be conceived to have either incentive-value or threat-value, and to have these in varying degrees.[4] Some situations he approaches, others he withdraws from. The nature of the significance of a situation may be defined as the direction it produces in behavior, if the unit of behavior is conceived as a cycle beginning with a need and ending with a consummatory response, or behavior aimed at such a response.

Direction is observable in both overt behavior and covert behavior. It is seen in physical movements, in the pattern of muscle tension preparatory to making a given movement, and in the sequence of symbolic processes involved in thinking or problem-solving.

Lewin (1935) suggests a distinction between the physical direction of behavior (overt approach or withdrawal) and the psychological direction of behavior, which is defined as the desire to have more, or to have less, of the stimulating condition. He points out, for example, that physical approach may be directed, not toward having more of an object, but toward having less of it through destruction of it. "Psychological" approach or withdrawal is less directly measurable than physical approach or withdrawal, and is a construct rejected by many psychologists. Nevertheless, direction in behavior, defined in some fashion, is a necessary conception for psychologists of all persuasions.

[4] Presumably, incentive-value and threat-value may be either conscious or unconscious and may be either learned or unlearned.

The most radical operationalist must, along with his more mentalistic colleagues, conceive of an animal's doing "this" rather than "that," of his responding positively to certain stimuli and negatively to others. The term "direction of behavior" is employed to distinguish this aspect of response from the other basic aspect, that of intensity.

Measurement of the direction of behavior may take many forms since there are many things and many aspects of things toward or away from which the individual may be oriented. Direction is not describable in general, but only with reference to something. The particular thing or things with reference to which it is described will depend upon the purposes of the investigator—whether he wishes, for example, to determine the effect of certain factors upon a bar-pressing response, to aid an individual in making a vocational choice, or to inform a manufacturer concerning public reaction to his product. But always there is measurement of approach or withdrawal, or of the set or tendency to approach or withdraw, with respect to something. Among the techniques of measurement which have been employed are the time-sampling of certain varieties of overt behavior (with chimpanzees and children, for example) and the administration (usually to human adults) of questionnaires, association tests, and projective tests designed to reveal the covert direction of behavior—i.e., attitudes, desires, habitual modes of thinking.

The directional aspect of behavior may be conceived to have various measurable subcategories. Among these are (1) the ability to respond to relationships of various kinds and (2) the consistency with which a given direction in behavior is maintained. The former comprises the nature and complexity of the cues to which "correct" responses can be made, and the speed with which these cue-responses are acquired. The latter includes the degree of integration of behavior, or the extent to which part-responses are co-ordinated with each other, as shown, for example, in smooth motor responses, in well-organized thinking, or in the absence of conflict of "motives." It includes also the degree of consistency which the individual shows in the long-range pursuit of goals.

Except in the case of "instinctive" behavior, consistent maintenance of goal-direction depends upon the ability of the individual to learn responses to cues, and upon the opportunity for such learning to occur, but it depends also upon other factors. Significant among these, it would seem, is the ability to inhibit responses until a number of factors have had the opportunity to participate in the final determination of the form of the behavior. Impulsive behavior is, as a rule, not well-integrated. No doubt the topic of inhibitory ability deserves more attention than it has received from psychologists.

Description of the direction of an individual's behavior at a given moment occurs when we describe his movements in space, his set, or the goal-direction of his thinking. Description of the persistent direction of his behavior occurs when we describe his habits, his interests, and his attitudes or values. These are characteristic of him and differentiate him from other individuals. They indicate his general orientation in his environment, and they may be used for predicting, within limits, many of his future responses. They constitute a significant part of what is referred to as "personality."

THE DEGREE OF ACTIVATION

The degree of significance of a situation, as opposed to the nature of its significance (i.e., the direction it produces in behavior) may be defined as the degree of activation or arousal occurring in the situation when all factors affecting activation except the incentive-value or threat-value of the situation are held constant. Situations having a high degree of significance will, if other factors are constant, produce a high degree of activation, while situations having a low degree of significance will, if other factors are constant, produce a low degree of activation. Data bearing on this point will be presented in Chapter 4.

Activation is, however, affected by many factors other than the incentive-value or the threat-value of a situation. For example, it is affected by the metabolic condition of the individual as this is influenced by drugs, hormones, the products of fatigue, and other agents. It is affected to a marked degree by the muscular movements required by the activity in which he is engaged or for which he is set. To the psychologist it is of particular interest that the level of activation is affected to a striking degree by the incentive-value or the threat-value of situations. An exhausted man, walking at a low level of activation toward his home, would suddenly become highly activated if he noticed that his home was on fire. Even if he were restrained from any increase in overt activity in the situation, he would still show a high degree of arousal. This type of response has traditionally been referred to as "motivation" or "emotion." If it is desired to measure the intensity (as opposed to the direction) of the motivation, measurement should be made of the physiological processes indicative of the level of activation. When variables other than the incentive-value or the threat-value of a situation are controlled, measurement of the degree of activation should afford the basic means of measuring the intensity of "motives." It would appear that any other measure of this condition must of necessity be less direct. Conversely, if it is desired to measure the effect of drugs or other agents upon the physiological processes of the individual, it would appear that the incentive-value or the threat-value of the situation should be held constant. Just as the "sedation threshold" of an individual may indicate the degree of his activation (Shagass, 1954), so the degree of an individual's prior activation may influence the measured effect of a particular drug.

INTERACTION BETWEEN THE DIRECTION OF BEHAVIOR AND THE DEGREE OF ACTIVATION

There is interaction between the direction of behavior and the degree of activation of behavior. If other factors are constant, integration of behavior (i.e., consistent goal-direction) seems less likely to be maintained when the degree of activation is very low or very high. Instances of in-co-ordination of response may be observed in states of drowsiness or extreme fatigue, even when the act is a well-practiced one and there is no conflict of goals. Similarly, if other factors are constant, co-ordination of response seems less likely to be maintained when the degree of activation is very high.[5] Examples of this phenomenon may be observed after large doses of stimulants, during hyperactivity of certain endocrine glands, and during conditions commonly referred to as "excessive motivation" or "excited emotion." It would appear, however, that disorganization of response does not always occur when the level of activation is high. Even during the excitement of "emotion" there may be good organization of behavior on occasion—or so it seems from the sketchy evidence that is available (Stratton, 1925, 1928; Cannon, 1936).

Interaction between the direction of behavior and the level of activation is to be observed also in the fact that the extent of arousal has as one of its determinants (and often the major one) the organism's responses to cues. The individual is aroused or not aroused or, more precisely, is aroused to a given degree, according to the cues with which he is confronted—provided, of course, other factors are held constant. We may conclude, then, that the level of arousal depends in part upon the responses to cues, and that the ability to respond to

[5] For a discussion of these questions, see Chapter 8.

cues, and to inhibit and co-ordinate reactions, depends in part upon the level of arousal.

DIRECTION AND ACTIVATION AS THEY APPEAR IN PSYCHOLOGICAL CONCEPTS

If behavior varies in the two basic respects described above, and in these respects only, it is not surprising to find that the psychological concepts employed to describe behavior have as their content a description of these variations. Unfortunately, many of these constructs incorporate in a single descriptive category both of these aspects of variation. Since the direction and the degree of arousal of behavior may vary independently, "compound" concepts, describing both aspects of variation, lead to confusion. The replacement of such concepts by concepts describing a single phase of variation should promote clarity. This subject has been discussed more fully elsewhere (Duffy, 1934, 1941a, 1949) and will be treated only briefly here.

The concept of "motivation" incorporates a description of both the direction taken by behavior (selectivity of response) and the intensity or "drive level" of behavior. Studies of motivation have employed two basically different kinds of measures to indicate the presence and the strength of "motives." In one, changes in the directional aspect of behavior have been observed; in the other, changes in the activity level have been observed. An example of the former is the study of choice responses under varying conditions. In this instance the experimenter determines what direction an animal's behavior will take with variations in "motivating" conditions. An example of the latter, intensity, is the measurement of the number of revolutions of a drum produced by an animal confined in a cage under varying conditions of motivation. This measure of activity level may be regarded as a very rough indicator of the degree of activation. While certain stimulating conditions, such as hunger, characteristically affect both the level of activation and the direction of behavior, these two aspects of response are basically different and can show independent variation.

The concept of "emotion" affords a particularly striking example of the failure to differentiate clearly between the degree of activation and the direction of behavior. Both aspects of response are included in a single concept. The term "emotion," as commonly used, refers to a condition in which activation is unusually high (excitement) or unusually low (depression without agitation), and in which behavior is directed toward approach or withdrawal with respect to some aspect of the environment (Duffy, 1941b, 1934). Reference to the first part of this compound concept (degree of activation) is made when psychologists wish to differentiate between emotion and nonemotion, though no clear differentiation can be made since activation occurs in a continuum, from a very low degree to a very high degree. Reference to the second part of the concept (the direction or patterning of overt or covert response) is made when psychologists wish to differentiate between specific emotions, such as fear and rage. In certain experiments the investigators have found it difficult to decide whether or not true emotion was present. When, for example, adrenalin was administered, a number of subjects had difficulty in deciding whether or not they were experiencing an emotion (Cantril and Hunt, 1932). A few said they felt "as if afraid." Others denied having an emotional experience. Though no doubt they felt "stirred-up," there was nothing in the environment toward which emotion could be meaningfully directed. The level of activation had been affected, but not the direction of behavior. In another experiment on emotion, the effect of the experimental variable was to alter the direction of behavior (Bard, 1928). Removal of the cerebral cortex of cats caused the cats, when prodded by the experimenter, to hiss and claw as was usual under prodding, but to direct the attack inappropriately—as for example, toward the table leg rather than toward the source of the prodding. This behavior was called "sham" rage. It seems clear that in emotional behavior, as in other behavior, the direction and the intensity of response may vary independently.

The concepts of perceiving and thinking apparently incorporate only the directional aspect of response. "Selectivity," "patterning," and "response to relationships," constitute the primary content of these constructs. While perceiving and thinking may be said to produce arousal, they are not themselves usually defined in terms of arousal.

The concepts of maturation and learning refer to modifications in behavior, and to the variables upon which these modifications are presumed to depend. The modifications referred to must be changes in the direction of behavior, or in activation, or both. The phenomena of maturation and learning are therefore included in the descriptive categories suggested.

Many psychologists have tried to content themselves with the traditional categories of psychology and have attempted to fit their findings into these categories. The fit has not been a comfortable one, and recently we have seen an increasing amount of squirming from some of those who have persisted in squeezing new ideas into old shoes. Such an outcome is to be expected since the traditional descriptive categories, taken over from common usage, are vaguely defined and overlapping (Duffy, 1941a). In other words, they are unsuited to scientific investigation.

Certain other psychologists have rejected the traditional categories in favor of a precise description of what occurs under a given set of stimulating conditions. This would certainly appear to be the direction in which psychology should move. There is a limit, however, to the usefulness of descriptions which are too particularistic. Grouping and systematization of phenomena have always been found necessary in science. No one, I think, denies this. Some psychologists, nevertheless, are fearful that any attempt at conceptualizing will lead us back where we came from—that is, to concepts which handicap us in our investigations. For my own part, I should like to see poor concepts replaced by better ones, with the conviction that as our knowledge increases these better concepts will in turn be modified or replaced as new information may indicate. We must not shrink from theoretical ventures, for if we do so we shall be handicapped in the assimilation and interpretation of empirical data.

PURPOSE OF THE PRESENT DISCUSSION

In the spirit described above, I have proposed that two operationally defined concepts, activation and direction, be employed in the description of behavior, and I have made use of these constructs in the discussion which follows. While a complete description of behavior would require a full discussion of both the activation and the direction of behavior—and an account of the factors (genetic and environmental) which determine their variation—only one of these aspects of behavior, activation, is the focus of the present discussion. The choice of topic was dictated, not by the relative importance of the two aspects of behavior, but by the relative neglect. Psychological investigation has been oriented primarily toward the study of the direction of behavior and its modifying factors. In instances where the degree of activation has been investigated, it has been studied usually as a special condition, such as that of sleep, of fatigue, of exercise, of stress, of motivation, or of emotion; or it has been studied as an effect produced by changes in endocrine secretions or by the administration of drugs. The probable common factor in these various conditions has apparently not been recognized, or at any rate it has not been clearly pointed out. The present discussion stems from the hope that when the basic similarity of certain of these phenomena is appreciated, the differences between them may become more meaningful.

No attempt will be made to present a systematic review of the changes occurring in activation under each of the conditions mentioned above. Instead, this book is confined to citing a few of the studies where, under various conditions, changes in one or more of the indicators of the degree of activation, or in the presumed effects of the degree of activation, have been reported. It suggests that variations in the degree of activation produced by many different agents may have much in common: they apparently have a similar neurohumoral basis and, when other factors are constant (as often they are not), they appear to exert a similar effect upon behavior. Conceivably, they affect sensory sensitivity, reaction time, and various other aspects of performance. Finally, data are presented which suggest a continuum in the degree of activation, from sleep, through moderate effort, to strong "motivation" or "emotion." Any difference in behavior under these various conditions is considered to be due to variations in the degree of activation or in the direction of behavior, or both, and not to properties peculiar to any one of the conditions in itself.[6] Thus it is suggested that events customarily treated in separate categories may advantageously be considered together.

If propositions such as these are examined, the requirements for the discussion of activation, so far as general psychology is concerned, will have been met. There remains, however, the question of individual differences in activation. It appears that, for a variety of reasons, individuals differ markedly with respect to their activation in the same stimulus situation, and that the differences shown in one situation tend to carry over to other situations. Moreover, it seems that consistent differences in activation show some relationship to other aspects

---

[6] Such peculiar properties are often attributed to the condition called "emotion." Emotion remains, I believe, undefined in any precise and useful fashion. It is, no doubt, undefinable in such a fashion. This point was made as well as I am capable of making it in an article published some time ago, in which various types of definition of emotion were examined and all were shown to fail to establish a clear demarcation between emotion and nonemotion (Duffy, 1934). Definition by "pointing" remains common. Emotion is said to comprise "such states as fear, rage, etc." In other words, emotion is what everyone knows it to be, but no one knows what that is. I myself have attempted to describe what "everyone means by emotion" (Duffy, 1941b), but the description fails to delimit a unique state.

of behavior, and are therefore of special interest to those concerned with differences in personality, as, for example, the clinical psychologist.

It is thus apparent that the purpose of the present discussion is two-fold: (1) to show the place of the concept of activation in general psychology, and (2) to show the significance of this concept for the understanding of individual differences in behavior. Committed to the position that personality differences are describable by the same concepts as those appropriate for psychology in general (since they are merely differences in the forms of behavior described in general psychology), the author finds no conflict in this dual purpose (Duffy, 1949).[7]

[7] Some of the material used in this chapter has been taken directly from articles of mine published in the *Psychological Review* and in the *Journal of Abnormal and Social Psychology*, or more precisely, the articles were in some instances taken directly from this manuscript, which has been long in the making.

chapter 2

The concept of activation

THE GENERAL NATURE OF ACTIVATION

Psychological systems of almost every type have incorporated concepts dealing with the effects of variations in the extent of energy release of the organism. Such constructs have variously been labeled "drives," "tensions," "motives," "emotions," or "libido." These various constructs are by no means synonymous. Some of them are reasonably well anchored physiologically; others are not. The characteristic they have in common is that none of them has ever been defined satisfactorily, and most of them incorporate into a single concept phenomena which may vary independently (a defect pointed out in the previous chapter). Though all contain something analogous to the concept of activation, this concept has never been fully developed.[1] It requires separation from the directional aspect of behavior and firm anchorage in experimental data.

In developing a concept of activation it is apparent that our prob-

[1] The concept, and its further development, were suggested by the author in 1950 in an address before the Southern Society for Philosophy and Psychology (Duffy, 1951). Here the construct was referred to as "energy mobilization." In earlier papers I had called it "excitation," "arousal," "activation," or "energy mobilization" (Duffy, 1932a, 1934, 1941a, 1949). Since some have objected to the term "mobilization" as misleading, and others have feared that the "energy" referred to might be conceived to be something non-physiological, as for example psychic energy, I have adopted the term "activation" used by Lindsley (1951) and by Woodworth and Schlosberg (1954). The phenomena referred to by this term are identical, however, with those discussed earlier under other headings. Moreover, the terms "energy release" and "energy mobilization" will continue to be employed in the present discussion to emphasize the fact that we are concerned with metabolic processes in the tissues.

16

lem is rooted in the storage and release of energy in animals. Normal animals achieve from day to day a fairly constant energy balance, yet there are four important variables involved in this balance which increase or decrease at one time or another. These are (1) food, (2) stored energy, (3) work production, and (4) heat production (Brobeck, 1948). Mammals appear to be able to make choices among these four to some extent. For example, they may increase or decrease their food intake; they may dispose of more or less energy as work, as heat, or as stored fat or carbohydrates. In an experiment performed upon German working men during the war when only limited quantities of food were available, the work output of the men was found in general to be proportional to the energy intake in the form of food. However, it was influenced also by a psychological factor which was referred to as "incentive pay." When cigarettes were promised to the men in return for extra work, there was a sharp rise in their work output. This increase in work was accompanied by a loss in body weight, for the men were, under these conditions, drawing upon their stored energy reserves (Brobeck, 1948).

The construct energy mobilization, or activation, derives from and emphasizes the fact that a living organism is characteristically an energy-system. The process of living, in any of its aspects, requires energy release in varying degrees. Every response of the organism is fundamentally concerned with energy transformation and release, as Gesell and his co-workers, among others, have pointed out. Even growth, when thought of in its most general aspects, is a method of assimilating and transforming energy (Gesell, A., Castner, B. M., Thompson, H., and Amatruda, C. S., 1939). Activity of all types, whether covert or overt, requires the release of energy. Attending and thinking, as well as locomotion and manipulation, can be shown to involve increased release of energy, or a higher degree of activation.

The level of activation of the organism may be defined, then, as the extent of release of potential energy, stored in the tissues of the organism, as this is shown in activity or response. The degree of activation of the organism is not synonymous with the degree of overt activity, though the two phenomena bear a necessary relationship to each other. Vigorous overt activity requires a high degree of energy release, but a high degree of energy release may take place without an accompanying high degree of overt activity, as for example in conditions of excitement when the individual inhibits overt responses. Nor is the degree of activation of the organism synonymous with the vitality of the organism, or the ready availability of energy for response, for under suitable stimulating conditions an individual of low vitality, or in an exhausted condition, may function for relatively long periods of time at a high level of activation. The level of activation is, rather, *the extent of release of the stored energy of the organism through metabolic activity in the tissues.*

The variations which are observed in the degree of activation appear to occur in a continuum, one end of which is found in the condition of deep sleep or of coma, and the other end of which is found during the performance of tasks requiring extreme effort or during states of great excitement. The level of activation at which a given response occurs appears to be an important factor in determining various characteristics of the response, as will be shown later. And the relationship between energy intake and storage and energy output in the form of heat and work (or activities of all types) is an important factor in the general health and well-being of the individual.

Energy output which takes different forms (e.g., physical exercise versus internal arousal with a minimum of overt activity) may perhaps have different effects upon behavior, and will, no doubt, show a difference in the patterning of energy release within the organism; nevertheless, the similarities as well as the differences between such conditions should be recognized. They produce similar chemical effects within the organism. For example, it has been shown that changes in the blood-sugar level may be induced by any of a number of factors which affect the essential equilibria of the organism—by "emotion," by intense physical activity, or by a change in temperature (Silvette and Britton, 1932). Silvette and Britton (1932) made the following observation:

> It is pertinent to emphasize that the influences of emotion on important chemical constituents of the body are essentially similar to those which are brought about by severe muscular exertion. Both motion and emotion result in release to the bloodstream and degradation in the tissues of energy-supplying substances, and concurrent accumulation of the products of tissue oxidation or metabolities (p. 691).

Some psychologists object to a definition of activation based upon energy release because it presumably places states of arousal such as "motivation" and "emotion" in the same category as physical exertion, which also involves the release of energy and perhaps to a greater degree. Since psychologists are interested primarily in the arousal which is not the result of physical activity, but is rather, as Darrow (1936) has suggested, "preparatory and facilitative," it may be advantageous for our purposes to define activation as the arousal which occurs in the absence of overt activity. Such a distinction seems, however, somewhat arbitrary in view of the fact that covert activity is merely a preparation for anticipated overt activity, and might be said, in a sense, to "flow over" into overt activity under ordinary conditions. The increase in activation often occurs, nevertheless, without a corresponding increase in overt activity. This point is well brought out in a study of brain metabolism in "emotional excitement" made by Richter and Dawson (1948). They state that:

> The lactic acid content of the rat brain is reduced in sleep and increased in emotional excitement. The rise in lactic acid in the brain in emotion is not due to concomitant muscular activity, since the effect was still observed in animals immobilized by tubocurarine. The brain lactic acid was not raised by muscular exercise in trained animals. The rise in lactic acid in the brain in emotion is a transient effect, followed by a rapid return to normal when the stimulus is discontinued (p. 79).

It would be possible to define activation as the arousal which occurs in the absence of physical exertion, or the arousal found when we subtract from measures of activation the effects of physical activity.

An alternative to this position is to make no distinction between the activation of physical exertion and any other sort of activation but to say that, if we are interested in the energy release produced by factors other than overt movement, we must hold constant the factor of physical exertion, just as we must hold constant in any experiment the variables whose effect we do not wish to include in our measurements. Many factors affect energy release—among them drugs, hormones, and exercise. It is the problem of the experimenter to hold constant all variables except the one which he is interested in manipulating. If he wishes, for example, to secure a measure of the incentive-value or the threat-value of a situation, he must hold constant other factors known to affect the level of activation. If, however, he wishes merely to determine the effect of variation in activation upon some response, he need concern himself with the way in which the variation was produced only if it can be shown that variations in activation have different effects upon performance if they are produced in different ways. At present, there is relatively little information about the similarities and differences between the energy release of routine physical activities and that of internal arousal unaccompanied by a corresponding degree of overt activity. It is known that both involve metabolic activity in the tissues. What, if any, differences there may be in the patterning of the energy release and the effect of the energy release upon various performances is not yet known with any certainty. Perhaps, with overt action, the energy is dissipated more quickly and relaxation is more likely to follow, but the similarities between motion and emotion should not be overlooked.

Some psychologists prefer a definition of activation, not in terms of energy release, but in terms of neural activity in the ascending reticular activating system (Malmo, 1959), the functioning of which will be discussed in the following chapter. Their measures of activation, other than the EEG, are, however, always measures of peripheral functions such as heart rate, skin conductance, muscle tension, etc., which are regarded as indicants of central functioning. These measures are the same as those employed in the present discussion. Empirical procedures would, so far as the author is aware, be affected in no way by accepting the one rather than the other definition of activation. The choice of definition depends perhaps upon whether one feels there is more security in speaking in neural terms or more in being strictly operational. Preference is given to the latter type of definition in this book, that is, to a definition of activation closer to actual measurements, with full recognition accorded the fact that all activity of the organism has a neurohumoral basis, and that further investigation will no doubt make clearer the relationship between peripheral and central events.

As the term "activation" is employed in the present discussion, it refers, as mentioned, to organismic arousal, not merely to the activation pattern of the EEG. Perhaps to electroencephalographers this will appear to be an unwarranted extension of one of their concepts but such an extension serves to emphasize the fact of the interrelation of central and peripheral processes, and it places the emphasis upon the organism, and not merely upon one part of the organism, however basic its role may be.

MEASUREMENT OF THE LEVEL OF ACTIVATION

The crucial question in regard to activation is: *How is the condition to be measured?*

The answer to the question proves to be more difficult than might be expected. Since we are interested in the degree of excitation of the organism as a whole, recognizing that different tissues, or the same kinds of tissue in different parts of the body, may be activated to different degrees, it might appear that the most suitable measure would be the metabolic activity of the organism as a whole, such as would be obtained through determining oxygen consumption. Such a line of thinking might be reinforced by considering the fact that "the most fundamental physiological property of all plants and animals, the rate at which they are living, is reflected quantitatively in their metabolic rates" (Pearson, 1948).

The most commonly used measure of metabolic rate is that obtained under basal conditions, i.e., when the individual is resting quietly. Oxygen consumption under these conditions indicates the rate of oxidation of stored materials, with the consequent release of energy, when the individual is subjected to as little stimulation as possible. While this measure is not without significance, the psychologist is interested particularly in the energy release in various tissues when the organism is subjected to the varieties of stimulation experienced in the ordinary course of life—and indeed under extraordinary conditions. But would such a measure as that of oxygen consumption during nonbasal states afford the measure desired?

G. L. Freeman (1948a) has pointed out a source of difficulty in using measures of total metabolism as measures of the energy release occasioned by stimulation. He says: "The fundamental difficulty with well-recognized measures of total metabolism is that there normally exists in the organism sufficient local energy reserves to effect adequate adjustments to displacing stimuli without occasioning an immediate increase in the general level of vital activity." He suggests an approach which, it would seem, is the most satisfactory way of solving the problem—i.e., the study of the many significant but minute energy transformations which occur in specific tissues without being adequately reflected immediately in conventional measures of total metabolic activity. These measures (to be discussed shortly) correlate with other, less refined, measures of energy transformation such as weight loss (Freeman and Darrow, 1935) and oxygen consumption (Freeman and Giffin, 1939).

It is apparent that energy release takes place in all physiological processes. As Freeman (1948a) has pointed out, these processes are aspects of the functioning of one or the other of two interdependent systems: (1) the neuromuscular system, with central nervous control of the skeletal muscles, and (2) the digestive-circulatory system, with autonomic control of smooth muscles and glands. The higher nerve centers play a major role in assessing stimulus situations, or determining the response to cues, and hence in determining the extent of energy release. The individual's responses to situations which produce increased release of energy ordinarily demand postural changes and consequent tensions of the skeletal muscles. Muscular contraction, in turn, is accompanied by changes in the blood supply and in the temperature of the active parts so there are many different physiological processes which are involved in changes in the degree of excitation or arousal of the organism.[2] Measurement of these processes is assumed to afford an indication of the degree of activation of the organism at a given moment.

Measurement of the level of activation presents, however, a number of problems, some of which will be discussed subsequently. The organism is not equally activated in all its parts at any given time. We do not know with certainty what aspects of the organism's activity provide the most useful indices of the general level of activation, or even in some instances what may be the best means of measuring a particular aspect of activation. Yet the striking fact emerges, from any survey of the literature, that *a wide variety of measures of physiological processes show relatively consistent changes with changes in what appear to be the energy requirements of the situation. The direction of the change in these measures seems, in general, to be consistent as the individual goes from the sleeping to the waking state, from waking relaxation to work on easy tasks, and from work on easy tasks to frantic effort or extreme excitement.* Moreover, it appears that a change in any one of these measures is ordinarily correlated with changes in the other measures, though the degree of *inter*correlation of measures in different individuals, as opposed to the *intra*correlation of measures, is frequently not high, for reasons which will be discussed later. It thus appears that we are dealing, not with isolated or independent processes, but with interrelated processes, the measurement of almost any one of which may ordinarily, in a given organism, serve as a rough indicator of a condition which may be called the general level of activation.

[2] Kuntz (1951) has pointed out that "The demands of the body musculature due to environmental factors and general activity necessitate continuous adjustments in the dynamics of the circulatory and respiratory organs, the metabolic processes and general visceral activity. . . . Somatic and visceral functions do not represent clearly delimited spheres of activity, but are closely interrelated. Every tonic or motor response of skeletal-muscle probably is accompanied by a visceral response. Visceral reactions, consequently, may be regarded as part of the organism's total reaction to its environment. Visceral activity also exerts a conditioning influence on somatic reactions. . . . Such interdependence of visceral and somatic functions in the peripheral fields is entirely in keeping wth the concept that the central control of somatic and visceral functions is exerted through neural mechanisms which are located at common levels in the spinal cord, the brain stem, the diencephalon and the cerebral cortex" Kuntz (1951), p. 67.

Concurrence in this view, proposed earlier by the author,[3] has been expressed by Woodworth and Schlosberg (1954). These authors compare the general level of activation with the general level of prosperity of a community, which may be indicated by a number of indices based on key processes in the economic life of the community. While it might be argued that the activities of the organism are more highly integrated than the economic processes of a community, and differ from it in certain other respects also, the parallel is illuminating if not pressed too far.

What we must seek are measures of physiological processes which, taken singly, afford a rough indication of the degree of arousal of the organism as a whole and, when taken in combination, afford a more adequate measure of this condition. Many possibilities present themselves. There are a number of physiological conditions which show variation in one direction with increased stimulation or increased demands upon the organism, and variations in the opposite direction with decreased stimulation or decreased demands. The conditions to be discussed here are those which have been most frequently investigated as physiological correlates of behavioral changes.

Tension of the Skeletal Muscles

Since any action upon the environment necessitates the contraction of skeletal muscles, it is to be expected that these muscles would show increased contraction when the organism becomes highly activated. A number of studies have shown that such increased contraction of the muscles occurs when the individual responds to stimulation, whether the responses made are overt or covert—that is to say, it is found as regularly in attending and thinking as in locomotion or manual movements.[4]

The degree of tension of the skeletal muscles has been measured in four ways chiefly, though other means of measurement have on occasion been employed. The four ways referred to are the graphic recording of one of the following: (1) grip pressure, (2) point pressure during writing or similar manual activity, (3) changes in the thickening of some group of muscles, and (4) electrical potentials from the muscles (the electromyogram or EMG). The earliest studies employed one or both of the first two techniques. Later studies sometimes employed the third technique, and the most recent studies have employed the fourth technique. Action potentials from the muscles, or the electri-

---

[3] See Footnote 1.
[4] See Chapter 4 for support of this statement.

cal changes which occur when a muscle contracts, constitute by far the most sensitive measure of muscular activity.[5] It appears, however, that there is a lack of complete correspondence between muscular contraction and the EMG (Inman, Ralston, Saunders, Feinstein, and Wright, 1952).

For purposes of the present discussion, the term "muscle tension" will be used to refer to electrical potentials from the muscles, to grip pressure, to point pressure, or to muscle thickening. While almost all current investigations make use of the EMG, changes in muscle tension under certain conditions, or with certain types of subjects (e.g., children or neurotics), seem to be so gross as to make either grip pressure or point pressure a reasonably adequate indicator of a general state of arousal.

Fluctuations in muscle tension appear to be of at least as great psychological interest as the degree of muscle tension. These fluctuations may be observed as irregularities in the graphic record of grip pressure on an object held in the hand, or of downward pressure on a key or pencil; they may be observed as certain changes in the EMG; and they may be observed also in measures of steadiness of the hand and of postural steadiness. It appears to the author that gross changes of relatively infrequent occurrence are likely to be of less psychological significance than frequent changes of smaller magnitude.

Electrical Resistance of the Skin

One of the most frequently used indicators of changes in the level of activation of the individual is the degree of resistance afforded by certain parts of the body to the passage of a minute electric current through their surface.[6] The work on this phenomenon has been exten-

---

[5] Muscular relaxation should not produce action potentials since experiments reviewed by A. V. Hill (1950) indicate that muscular relaxation is an inactive process.

[6] A less commonly used measure of the electrical phenomena of the skin, but one which seems to parallel closely in some respects the measure described here (Jeffress, 1928), is one in which electrodes are placed on the skin and differences in potential between two points are recorded when no external current is applied. This method is called the Tarchanoff method, while the method which makes use of an external source of current is known as the method of Féré. Wilcott (1958) has confirmed the finding of Jeffress that there is a high degree of correspondence between the skin-resistance response (GSR) and the skin-potential response. He found, however, no apparent relationship between the base levels of skin resistance and of skin potential, or between skin-potential responses and the skin-potential base level.

Studies of living organisms by means of the Tarchanoff method have demon-

sive and has been going on for many years. It appears that the electrical resistance of the skin depends upon some aspect of activity of the sweat glands (McCleary, 1950). The sweat-gland activity produces increased permeability of the cell membrane, which results in a polarization change, and thus a change in electrical resistance.[7] The widest variations in resistance, it has been suggested, are probably dependent upon the content of extracellular water and electrolyte balance, which may in turn be controlled by certain hormones (Hemphill, 1942).

The resistance of the palms of the hands and the soles of the feet has been reported to vary somewhat independently of resistance in other parts of the body (Richter, 1929, 1928). The sweating of other parts of the body is said to be primarily for the purpose of regulating body temperature, and to occur most profusely when the body temperature is raised through exercise or an increase in the atmospheric temperature. Palmar sweating, on the contrary, while not unaffected by variations in temperature, is said to be most responsive to changes in muscular activity (overt or covert) or in the perceived degree of significance of the stimulus situation, and has been interpreted by Darrow (1936) as serving a "facilitative" function.[8] It may be, however, that the difference between the reaction of palmar and plantar areas and other areas of the body is chiefly a difference in the ease with which the various areas are excited to activity (Darrow and Freeman, 1934). The palmar and plantar areas appear to become more active

strated that in all organisms from plants to man there is a relatively stable voltage gradient between any two points, and that these patterns are characteristic of the species and, to some extent, of the individual (Burr, 1944). Potential differences increase during the growth of the organism until a maximum is reached. Since, when corn and cotton seeds are measured, those potentials permit prediction of future plant size and productivity, Burr suggests that they may represent a reservoir of stored energy which can be rapidly drained to meet the demands of activity, and that they may be an index of the vigor of the organism. It has been suggested that all living systems may be viewed as responsive to the same fundamental forces as nonliving systems.

[7] The reciprocal of resistance, i.e., *conductance*, appears to be the better unit of measurement of the physiological processes involved. However, since our measuring instruments are calibrated in units of *resistance* (ohms), and since many investigators have reported their findings in these terms, the present discussion will in most instances refer to resistance rather than conductance.

[8] This conclusion has been questioned in a study in which conductance in both palmar and non-palmar areas reflected temperature changes, and the percentage change in conductance was reported to be not significantly different between the two (Conklin, 1951). For a fuller discussion of the relationship between temperature and skin conductance, see Woodworth and Schlosberg (1954), pp. 144–145.

first and then to approach their limit of responsiveness as the non-palmar and non-plantar areas become increasingly more responsive. Richter is said, however, to have shown that changes in resistance in the palmar areas of the hand, as compared with the dorsal areas, are often different in both amplitude and direction (McCleary, 1950). Whatever the cause of the differences in their reactions, the palmar and plantar areas have been found more useful than other areas in the study of behavioral correlates of changes in resistance. These areas respond quickly to changes in the energy demands of the situation, and they respond to small differences in such demands.

It is generally agreed that palmar skin-resistance changes are dependent upon the organism's having an intact sympathetic nervous system, and that they may be produced by stimuli which affect the level of activity of the central nervous system. It has been pointed out that for various reasons it is questionable whether palmar skin resistance provides an uncomplicated measure of sympathetic activity (Darrow, 1943). In fact, Darling and Darrow (1938) suggested that changes in skin resistance summate both sympathetic and parasympathetic activity. Wang (1957, 1958) concludes that the indispensable central neural structures for the galvanic skin response are to be found in the brain stem.

Studies of the electrical phenomena of the skin have distinguished between the general level of skin resistance before stimulation is applied and the change in resistance which occurs upon the presentation of a stimulus. The change in resistance (most frequently investigated) is known as the galvanic skin response, or GSR. However, the GSR is by no means independent of the level of skin resistance at the time the stimulus is presented. In general, it is said that the largest drops in resistance occur when the resistance level is highest and the smallest drops occur when the resistance level is lowest (Seward and Seward, 1935), or conductance has approached its ceiling. It has been reported, in fact, that the means and the standard deviations of galvanic skin responses at the various base levels of resistance are almost linear functions of the base level (Ellson, Davis, Saltzman, and Burke, 1952; R. C. Davis, Buchwald, and Frankmann, 1955). Measurement of the GSR must therefore take into account the level of resistance at which the change occurs. R. C. Davis et al. (R. C. Davis, Buchwald, and Frankmann, 1955) have suggested that the GSR be recorded as the ratio obtained by dividing the decrease in resistance by the base level of resistance. Other investigators, however, have questioned this procedure, and various mathematical models have been suggested, among them a regression model to be described later (J. I. Lacey, 1956).

Electroencephalogram (EEG)

The electroencephalogram, referred to as the EEG, is a record of electrical potentials from the brain. Activity of nerve tissue, like activity of muscle tissue, produces electrical changes in the tissue. If electrodes are attached to the surface of the scalp, these electrical changes, popularly known as "brain-waves," may be recorded. Actually, it has been said that the electrical rhythms of the brain might more accurately be described as "inaction" potentials rather than action potentials since they appear most clearly when the part of the brain concerned is at rest (W. G. Walter, 1944). It has been demonstrated that the electrical potentials are due to the activity of the brain itself rather than to extraneous factors (H. Berger, 1929; Adrian and Matthews, 1934). It has also been shown that the potentials recorded from the surface of the scalp show considerable similarity to those recorded from the exposed surface of the brain, although they are of smaller amplitude and frequently of greater duration (Abraham and Marsan, 1958).

Electrical potentials of the brain are said to be due largely to aggregates of cortical nerve cells and nerve fibers whose activity is influenced by the action of subcortical centers (Jasper, 1954). The electrical activity is often of a rhythmic nature. It is thought to represent oscillations in the local membrane potentials of nerve cells and to reflect changes in the excitability of the nerve cell body (Werre, 1957). With the exception of "evoked" potentials, the electrical activity has been said not to represent action potentials of impulses coursing in nerve fibers (Werre, 1957). Many neurones must discharge in unison in order to produce the relatively high voltages of the waves or oscillations observed in the EEG.[9]

It was suggested in the early stages of investigation that the rhythms might be "autonomous"—i.e., there might be a natural period of excitability of, and discharge by, cortical cells. It was also suggested that impulses from a diencephalic pacemaker might be responsible for rhythmic stimulation of the cortex (Bishop, 1936; Bremer, 1949). Vari-

---

[9] It has been reported that the electrical potentials ordinarily regarded as an index of cortical activity may, under certain conditions, show little relationship to the active discharge of individual cortical cells as indicated by records obtained from microelectrodes (Li, McLennan, and Jasper, 1952).

ous other suggestions have been offered as to the origin of "spontaneous" cortical rhythms—for example, that they are derived from activity in neuronal chains (Eccles, 1951).

Brain potentials vary in two dimensions, frequency and amplitude—that is to say, they may be fast or slow, and they may be large or small. While they appear to vary in a continuum, so that there is no sharp break between waves of one frequency or amplitude and those of another, it has been customary to divide them into several roughly defined categories to which names have been given (J. D. N. Hill and Parr, 1950; F. A. Gibbs and E. L. Gibbs, 1950).[10] Alpha waves are large, rhythmic waves with an average frequency of about 10 per second, and a normal range, in the adult, of 8 to 13 per second. The magnitude of these waves is about 10 to 100 millionths of a volt. Beta waves are smaller and faster, their frequency ranging from about 18 to 50 per second (predominantly, 18 to 30 per second) and their voltage from 5 to 30 microvolts. They are often superimposed on the alpha waves. Either type of wave can be recorded from most regions of the head, but alpha waves are more prominent from the occipital, parietal, and temporal regions, while the largest beta waves are usually found in the frontal region, particularly over the motor area. Slow waves, with a frequency of less than about 8 per second (the lower limit of alpha waves in normal adults), have been classified as theta waves if the frequency is between 4 and 7 cycles per second, and as delta waves if the frequency is between 0.5 and 3.5 cycles per second (W. G. Walter, 1950a). More rapid waves, with a frequency greater than that of beta waves, have also on occasion been reported, but the information about such waves is very meager.

EEG frequency, voltage, and phase relationships are said to depend to a considerable degree upon the relative strength or dominance of activity in the various areas of the brain (Darrow, 1952). It appears that the frequency of waves is the aspect of electrical activity of the cortex which has been found most significant in relation to behavior. The amplitude of the waves also seems, however, to be of importance. The EEG, and the factors which affect it, will be further discussed later.

[10] It would appear that there is little to recommend the practice of dividing a continuum of frequencies into more or less arbitrary categories to which various names are assigned. The author is in sympathy with the suggestion that the EEG be described in terms of (1) mean amplitude, (2) mean frequency, and (3) persistence (number of waves of a certain amplitude following without interruption) (Motokawa, 1943; Motokawa, Hukuda and Ohinata, 1949).

Other Measures

A number of other physiological measures are indicative of the degree of activation. Among these are measures of respiration, blood
pressure, pulse, body temperature, skin temperature, and the volume
of various parts of the body. Some of these offer difficulty in measurement, in interpretation, or in both. R. C. Davis et al. have reported, for
example, that blood pressure is one of the most difficult circulatory responses to measure (R. C. Davis, Buchwald, and Frankmann, 1955).
They have pointed out also that the circulatory system is a physical response system in which there are negative feed-back mechanisms, and
in which the activity of one part may bear an inverse relationship to the
activity of another part, as for example, the heart rate to the blood
pressure. These factors complicate the interpretation of circulatory
measures. Recorded variations in respiration have been said to depend
on so many different factors, some of them apparently uncontrollable,
that it has been concluded that differences in the results of different
investigators should be expected to occur (Altschule, 1953). Although
many compensatory feed-back mechanisms are involved in cardiovascular measures, and measures of respiration have certain deficiencies, these measures have often shown predictable relationships to
overt behavior, as will be pointed out later. It would appear, however,
that measures of the EEG, of muscular tension, and of palmar skin
conductance have, on the whole, shown more dependable relationships
to stimulus situations and to overt behavior and are therefore especially
to be recommended in psychological studies of activation. Such a conclusion must be regarded as highly tentative, and any adequate discussion of the measurement of the degree of activation must await the
discussion of the patterning of activation, which is the subject of a later
chapter.

MEASUREMENT OF CHANGES IN ACTIVATION

As the preceding discussion has indicated, measures of activation
may be measures of the "basal" or resting level of activation,[11] or they

[11] It is, of course, erroneous to suppose that the individual is in a truly "basal"
state of activation until the experimenter introduces the stimulus which serves
as the independent variable. On the contrary, the level of activation varies continuously with variations in a wide variety of factors. The rest period usually required before physiological measurements are made does not in fact reduce the
degree of activation to a level which might be considered "basal." It serves merely
to lower somewhat the degree of arousal and to make somewhat more comparable

may be measures of the change in activation which occurs when some experimentally manipulated stimulus is introduced. They may also, and significantly, be "spontaneous" changes in activation not correlated with any known stimulus variation.

Measurement of changes in activation presents many problems. Raymond Dodge (1913) long ago pointed out that a particular change in a physiological measure is meaningful only if we know the conditions antecedent to the change. To use his example, if we say that walking causes an increase in pulse rate, we should know whether the subject was previously standing quietly or was running.

In addition to the need of a meaningful reference point, there is another cogent reason for knowing the initial level from which a given change is measured. The "base" level of a function determines to a considerable degree the extent of change in the function which will occur. This fact has been generally recognized in regard to measures of the galvanic skin response, or the change in skin resistance which occurs in response to a stimulus. Many investigators have suggested various means of computing the response which are designed to obtain a measure independent of the initial level of skin resistance, together with a normal distribution of scores.[12] J. I. Lacey (1956) maintains that these transformations have turned out to be specific to the data on which they were developed. It seems clear, as Lacey points out, that measures of physiological changes other than changes in skin resistance involve the same problem. For example, the initial level of skin temperature was found to affect the magnitude, rate, and duration of changes in temperature (Plutchik and Greenblatt, 1956).

Lacey (1956) contends that computing algebraic or percentage changes in autonomic functions ignores the fact that a chief function of the autonomic nervous system and the endocrine glands associated with it is to maintain a homeostatic norm. Since any excitation or inhibition of a structure innervated by the autonomic nervous system apparently sets off a series of changes that serve to counteract the disturbance, Lacey (1956) concludes that *"the recorded autonomic response is a function both of the induced magnitude of autonomic innervation (as it would be seen in the absence of contrary changes) and of the promptness and vigor of secondarily induced autonomic changes that serve to restrain and limit the effects of the initial disturbance."* He says that, in general, a high degree of autonomic ex-

the condition of different subjects at the time the experimental stimulus is introduced.

[12] See, for example, Darrow (1937), O. L. Lacey and P. S. Siegel (1949), Haggard (1945, 1949), and Paintal (1951).

citation before stimulation has been found correlated with a low degree of autonomic reaction to the stimulation.[13] As a measure of autonomic reaction he proposes to obtain for each individual the solution of an equation which takes account of the individual's initial level of response and his level of response after stimulation, expressed in units of sigma deviation in the total sample. The equation takes account also of the correlation for the sample between the initial level of functioning and the level after stimulation is introduced.[14] Lacey says his findings indicate that whenever such "autonomic lability scores" show a significant variation with an independent variable, scores representing an absolute or percentage change in the autonomic measure also show a significant variation, but scores based on an absolute or percentage change may give results that do not hold up when the effect of base level is removed.

Wilder (1957), in a number of papers, has emphasized the "law" of initial value. Studying changes in, for example, blood pressure, foot temperature, and blood-sugar value produced by various pharmacological agents and various types of stimulation, he has shown that, when the initial levels of the function were low, there was a tendency toward an increased level of functioning; whereas, when the initial levels were high, there was a tendency toward either a minimal change or a paradoxical decrease in the case of agents which usually stimulated the function under consideration. Inhibitory agents produced autonomic changes that were the opposite of those produced by excitatory agents.

While all investigations, including not merely those of autonomic functions, but also those of the EEG and of muscular tension, suggest a relationship between the initial level of a physiological function and the degree of change in the function which will be produced by stimulation, either because of homeostatic regulation or because a "ceiling" in the function is being approached, not all investigators have agreed that the relationship between the initial level and the degree of change is always a linear relationship, with the largest changes occur-

[13] There is said to be a high positive relationship for the group, but not always for the individual, between initial level of excitation and the level of excitation produced by stress (J. I. Lacey, 1956).

[14] The equation is as follows:

"Autonomic Lability Score $= 50 + 10\ [Y_z - X_z\ r_{xy}/(1 - r_{xy})\frac{1}{2}]$, where X_z and Y_z are the individual's initial and stress levels, respectively, expressed in units of sigma deviation in the total sample, r_{xy} is the correlation for the sample between initial level and stress level, and the constants 10 and 50 translate the resulting scores to a distribution with a mean of 50 and a standard deviation of 10" (J. I. Lacey, 1956, p. 139).

ring where the initial level is lowest. G. L. Freeman and Katzoff (1942a) have suggested that the increase in activity due to a particular stimulus will be greatest when the "basal" level of activity is in the middle range and least at the extremes of the range. Perhaps, if this is the case, it may be due to the fact that at a very low level of activation, the individual is presumably less sensitive to stimulation; at a very high level of activation, he is approaching his ceiling of response. A curvilinear relationship between the base level and the extent of response is suggested by the report of Ax and Wenger (1955) that the product-moment correlation between the base level and the ballisto-cardiograph decrement was .574, while the curvilinear eta for the two measures was .797. Studies of the galvanic skin response also offer some support for this conclusion. It was found that there was a significant decrease in the extent of the response when the body was in a relaxed reclining position as compared with a normal sitting condition, and a significant decrease also under conditions of "tension" (muscular and "attitudinal") as compared with normal sitting (Staudt and Kubis, 1948). The investigators did not, however, interpret their findings in the way suggested here.

It seems somewhat uncertain whether the relationship between the initial level of functioning and the level of functioning after stimulation is linear or curvilinear. If a sufficiently limited range of values of activation is under consideration (and most studies appear to have imposed stimulation upon a level of activation ranging from low to middle values), a curvilinear relationship might appear to be a linear one since only one part of the U-shaped curve would be represented. On the other hand, it is obvious that there is less room for change in any measure as it approaches its ceiling. Autonomic measures in particular would appear to be strongly affected by homeostatic regulation. Measures of muscle tension or of brain potentials might be somewhat less so, though here too organismic factors might exert a regulatory influence. In any case, a change in a physiological measure of any kind, including measures of brain potentials, and muscular tension, must take into account the pre-existing excitatory state of the system in which the change in functioning is being recorded.

CONCLUSIONS

It is proposed that the degree of activation of the organism and the changes in activation, whether "spontaneous" or stimulus-induced, constitute a significant part of the organism's response. Measurement of this aspect of behavior is still relatively crude, but current investigations are daily throwing light upon some of the problems which have plagued studies in this area. The general direction which should be taken in the measurement of activation is relatively clear, but many of the details remain to be worked out.

As R. C. Davis (1957b) has suggested, activation, if given a quantitative physiological definition, might fit into a transfer equation in which the purpose might be either to state the degree of activation "consequent upon a certain input, say the intensity or character of certain sensory stimuli" or to state how a given response such as reaction time or response rate would depend upon the degree of activation. In any case, the concept appears to refer to phenomena which possess major significance for the understanding of behavior.

chapter 3

The neurohumoral basis of activation

The regulation of the level of activation has a neural and chemical basis; for the nervous system and the blood stream are the agencies by which the activities of the organism are integrated. Since chemical conditions affect the activity of nerve cells, and neural stimulation produces glandular secretion and in other ways determines the chemical constitution of the blood stream, we may say that the level of activation of the organism has a neurohumoral basis.

It is becoming increasingly clear that activation is an organismic phenomenon. Cortex and subcortex function in interrelated fashion. Central neurones affect the functioning of peripheral neurones, and peripheral functioning "feeds back" upon central functioning. Endocrine secretions are controlled in part by neural action, and hormones, in turn, affect the activity of the nervous system. A complex system of interactions, neural and chemical, determines the activational status of the organism at a given moment. This status, it will be shown, can be modified through intervention with drugs or with electrical stimulation of certain brain centers.

NEURAL BASIS OF ACTIVATION

Activation of the organism involves changes in neural, muscular, and glandular tissues. Some of these changes, as, for example, increased tension of the skeletal muscles, apparently serve the function of acting, or preparing to act, upon the external environment. Others apparently serve the function of so regulating visceral processes as to maintain

34

homeostasis and to supply the internal support required for actual or possible overt activity. It appears that, when the situation demands a high degree of activation of the individual, or is interpreted to make such a demand, various physiological processes are speeded up and others are slowed down. For example, glycogen is released from the liver in the form of blood sugar, which may be burned to supply energy for the activity of the muscles; respiration is likely to become either more rapid or deeper, thus supplying more oxygen for burning food materials; the heart is likely to beat faster or more strongly, with the result that the blood is circulated more rapidly through the body, carrying its supply of food and removing the waste products of muscular action. There has been said to be a tendency for more of the blood to leave the viscera and go to the brain and the skeletal muscles; digestion may be slowed down or stopped; there is likely to be increased tension of the skeletal muscles, presumably in preparation for activity; there is a decrease in the secretion of the salivary glands, and an increase in the secretion of the sweat glands, especially those on the palms of the hands and the soles of the feet. Many, but by no means all, of these physiological changes are regulated by the autonomic nervous system.

Walter B. Cannon (1936) described a number of the physiological phenomena involved in an increased level of activation in his studies of the bodily changes which occur during the excited "emotions." It has been demonstrated, however, in many experiments that these changes occur, at least to some extent, not only during the excited emotions but also during great physical or mental effort, or whenever the activities of the organism demand increased release of energy. In fact, some degree of change in physiological processes can be detected upon the slightest stimulation. As the individual "attends," or makes ready for response, there is an increase in his level of activation as measured by various physiological processes. If he engages in a "difficult" activity, his level of activation is greater than it is for an "easy" performance. If he is "anxious," or anticipates difficulty, his level of activation is higher than if he feels assured that no difficulty will arise. If strong stimulation occurs unexpectedly, as in "startle" situations, the organism releases energy both quickly and to an extreme degree, since such situations frequently demand prompt and strong response if disaster is to be averted. If the startle stimulus proves to be of no significance, the individual relaxes; if it proves to be of significance, he maintains a high level of activation while he attempts to cope with the problem. The level of activation is characteristically higher in "new" situations than in habitual ones, in significant situations than in unimportant ones, in "emergency" situations than in situations which the individual is prepared to meet. In other words, the degree of activation of the organism appears to be adjusted to the demands of the situation, as interpreted by the individual, within the limits of his capacities. It thus appears to vary in a continuum from a very low level to a very high level.

Neural control of the activity of various organs and systems is exerted from the subcortex and from the cortex. Within the brain stem are found nuclei of the reticular formation, which, together with the hypothalamus, the thalamus, and the cortex, play significant parts in the regulation and integration of various bodily processes. The reticular system and the hypothalamus appear to be of particular importance in determining the level of activation of the organism.

In recent years it has been shown that striking effects on the level of activation are exerted by the meso-diencephalic activating system, composed of the reticular formation of Moruzzi and Magoun (1949) and the diffuse thalamic projection system of Jasper (1949). Ascending fibers from the subcortical areas exert a regulatory influence upon the activity of the cortex. Though the exact pathway of the ascending reticular system is still not clearly established, there is evidence of a diffuse activating system, with its core in the brain stem reticular formation and the nonspecific, midline thalamic nuclei, which projects to the cortex and many other parts of the brain (Morrison and Dempsey, 1942; Delafresnaye, 1954). Studies summarized by Magoun (1950, 1952b, 1953) show that the classical sensory pathways, as they pass through the lower brain stem, give off collaterals which presumably set up recurrent discharges in the reticular formation. The effects of this lateral stimulation are transmitted upward in the brain, where it produces widespread cortical "activation"[1] (i.e., fast, low-amplitude, desynchronized activity) associated with behavioral arousal (Ingram, Knott, Wheatley, and Summers, 1951; Magoun, 1952a). Behavioral arousal has been said, however, not to bear an invariable direct relationship to the pattern of the EEG, though some degree of correlation between the two is indicated by the evidence (Sheer, 1957).

Behavioral arousal may be observed in greater activity in the skeletal

[1] It has been suggested, as a result of experiments with cats, that the amygdala, like the brain stem reticular formation, is capable of exerting diffuse regulatory effects on other cerebral regions (Feindel and Gloor, 1954). Lindsley (1956) concludes that the diencephalic, or limbic, system has some properties in common with the reticular activating system of the lower brain stem, and that the two may function together in maintaining wakefulness, states of attention, and consciousness.

muscles and the viscera. It has sometimes been described as "alertness" or "apprehension." Changes in arousal may be noted in the human being as he goes from sleep or relaxation to an alert, waking state. In fact, it has been suggested that the brain stem reticular formation possesses the characteristics of the "wakefulness center" postulated by Kleitman (Ellingson, 1956; Kleitman, 1939). A reduction of activity, produced, for example, by anesthesia or by lesions of the brain stem, apparently brings on somnolence or unconsciousness, a striking paucity of behavior, and the EEG characteristics of sleep (Lindsley, Bowden, and Magoun, 1949; Lindsley, Schreiner, Knowles, and Magoun, 1950). Lindsley (1956) has suggested that activity of the ascending reticular activating system may well underlie the energizing aspects of "emotion," "motivation," and "drive." However, it would appear that too much emphasis has been placed upon the two extremes of activation, sleep and excited "emotion," and that a more adequate conceptualization of the phenomena of activation would describe activation as occurring in a continuum, from sleep or coma to conditions of extreme excitement.

An ascending reticular inhibitory system is also being hypothesized by many workers to account for their experimental findings (Brazier, 1957). Apparently inhibitory units are said to have been found in the cortex by Jasper and in the nucleus ventralis anterior of the thalamus by Machne, Calma, and Magoun.

No account of the relationship between the cortex and the reticular formation would be complete without mention of the fact that, just as stimulation of the reticular formation may produce cortical stimulation, so cortical stimulation may produce responses in the reticular formation, and through these responses affect the activity of motor organs. Scattered throughout the reticular formation of the brain stem are cells which, through descending fibers, are concerned with the control of muscular activity, both somatic and visceral (Samuels, 1959). Some of these cells are excitatory since, when they discharge, they lower the thresholds of the motor cells to which they project or cause the cells to fire off, thus producing muscular contraction. Others of these cells are inhibitory since, when they discharge, they increase the thresholds of the motor neurones to which they project or cause an actual inhibition or blocking of muscular activity (Mountcastle, 1958). The cerebral cortex may either activate or block the excitatory systems of the brain stem, and may cause either discharge or blocking in the inhibitory mechanisms of this region, thus tending to cause either excitation or inhibition of the activity of motor organs.

Cortical stimulation, interacting with sensory influences in the

reticular formation, may also affect the action of the reticular formation upon the cortex (J. D. French, Hernández-Peón, and Livingston,
1955). It has been suggested that such interaction in moderation could
lead to facilitation, but in excess might lead to complete blocking of
reticular activation upon the cortex, with resulting disturbances in
awareness or attention (Lindsley, 1956). There is some evidence that
the reticular system can be influenced, not only by sensory and cortical
impulses but also by the cerebellum and the rhinencephalon (amygda-
loid nucleus). Iwata and Snider (1959) have reported that stimulation
of the cerebellum induced both an activation pattern in the cerebrum
and synchronized slow waves in the hippocampus. The limbic system
has afferent connections from the reticular formation and efferent connections with the posterior hypothalamus and other structures, including the cortex (Lindsley, 1957). Apparently, the limbic system is
sensitive to arousal by any sensory stimulus.

The regulatory functions of the hypothalamus have long been recognized. This neural center is said to translate messages from other parts
of the brain into visceromotor or endocrine impulses. One investigator
has referred to the hypothalamus as "now proved beyond doubt to be
the motor center from which impulses are sent to all parts of the autonomic nervous system" (Kennard, 1947). Other investigators (Brobeck, Wheatland, and Strominger, 1947) say:

> Consideration of data which suggest that disturbances in regulation of
> body temperature, spontaneous locomotor activity, food intake, and body
> weight can be produced by lesions of the hypothalamus led to the proposal
> of the hypothesis that the hypothalamus is the level of the central nervous
> system most intimately concerned with integration and control of rates of
> energy exchange in mammals (p. 65).

In line with this point of view is the fact that peripheral motor responses produced by stimulation of the cortex were usually intensified
by simultaneous stimulation of a certain area of the hypothalamus
(Murphy and Gellhorn, 1945). In other words, they occurred with
greater intensity when the hypothalamus was stimulated. Moreover,
stimulation of the hypothalamus may produce an alerting or arousal
reaction in the cortex.[2] Conversely, bilateral lesions in the hypothalamus of cats and monkeys produced extreme drowsiness (Harrison,
1940). In those animals which survived, this condition gradually wore

[2] Murphy and Gellhorn (1945), stimulating the hypothalamus by means of
inserted electrodes, reported that the excitatory effects on the cortex depended
on the ability of the stimulated point in the hypothalamus to produce sympathetic
discharge.

off, leaving the animals, however, much more tractable and "unemotional" than they had previously been—that is to say, their level of activation was lower. In fact, the general finding has been that a low level of overt activity in the animal follows the production of lesions in the posterior part of the hypothalamus (Brobeck, 1948).

Certain types of manipulation or stimulation of the hypothalamic region in man have been shown to produce effects upon the blood pressure, pulse rate, respiration, and other visceral functions, and to result in such phenomena as anxiety feelings, prolonged uncontrollable sobbing and, in many cases, manic excitement (Alpers, 1940). Congruent with these facts is the fact that R. W. Porter (1953) has demonstrated that, under the influence of stress, there is a marked increase in the electrical activity of the posterior hypothalamus.

There is evidence also that the hypothalamus plays an important part in the control of sleep, the lowest level of activation found in normal animals. Lesions and tumors in that area produce pathological drowsiness, while certain sedative drugs administered to animals have been found on post-mortem examination to be present in maximum concentration in that area (D. E. Cameron, 1941). The parts of the hypothalamus involved in the regulation of sleep have been found to be identical with those determining the autonomic balance (Nauta, 1946). Indeed, it has been suggested that the waking state may be merely one of the manifestations of activity of the sympathetic division of the autonomic nervous system (Nauta, 1946). Recent electroencephalographic studies have shown, however, that while destruction of the hypothalamus produces in the cortex of cats an EEG of the type found in sleep, this pattern could be changed to one of alertness if stimulation were sufficiently intense (Ingram, Knott, Wheatley, and Summers, 1951). It appears, therefore, that though the hypothalamus normally exerts an alerting effect upon the cortex, such as is involved in maintaining wakefulness, accessory structures also serve this purpose and may maintain wakefulness in the absence of the hypothalamus (Ingram et al., 1951).

It is not difficult to understand, in the light of these facts, how the hypothalamus came to be considered a center for the "emotions." Since the hypothalamus plays such a significant part in determining the level of activation of behavior, lesions of the hypothalamus prevented the occurrence of the highly energized modes of response usually found in the "excited emotions." The animal was therefore said to be unable to "experience emotions." Conversely, stimulation of the hypothalamus often produced responses which were more highly energized than those which usually occurred.[3] These responses were labeled "emotional" because of their regular occurrence in what are loosely defined as emotional states. It would appear, however, that the hypothalamus is more reasonably interpreted to be a center for the regulation of energy exchange than a center for "emotion" per se. This interpretation is in harmony with the suggestion of Masserman (1941) that the hypothalamus may possibly reinforce the motor manifestations of fear and rage, but there is little or no evidence for the position that it governs the motor responses themselves. The same objections may be offered to the later conclusions of Bard and Mountcastle (1948) that it was not so much the hypothalamus as the amygdala and the transitional cortex which produced differences in "emotional" responses.

Many studies, especially those employing the technique of electro-encephalography, have made it increasingly clear that the hypo-thalamus, the thalamus, and other parts of the subcortex are closely interconnected with the cortex, and that cortex and subcortex influence each other's activities so closely that there appears to be justification for the statement that "from some points of view, cortex and subcortex have to be treated as a single integrated organ" (Wright, 1948). Some of the neural circuits connecting these regions are excitatory (increas-ing activity), while others are suppressor (decreasing activity).

Factors which regulate the degree of activity in the excitatory cen-ters of the hypothalamus have been classified by Stellar (1954) into four groups: "(a) *inhibitory hypothalamic centers* which serve only to depress the activity of the excitatory centers, (b) *sensory stimuli* which control hypothalamic activity through the afferent impulses they can set up, (c) *the internal environment* which can influence the hypo-thalamus through its rich vascular supply and the cerebrospinal fluid, and (d) *cortical and thalamic centers* which can exert excitatory and inhibitory influences on the hypothalamus" (p. 6).

Indicating the closeness of the relationship between the cortex and the autonomic nervous system is the fact that in the areas of the cortex where there is somatic representation for a given body part, there ap-pears also to be autonomic representation for that part (Kennard,

---

[3] The influence on behavior of electrical stimulation of neural tissue versus de-struction of the same tissue seems to be somewhat more complicated than merely the production of opposite effects (Sheer, 1957). For example, electrical stimula-tion might induce blockage which would allow the release of an antagonistic sys-tem, thus conceivably affecting behavior in a way similar to that of tissue de-struction.

1947). For example, experimental disturbances of the cortical areas representing the face, lips, and mouth have caused salivation, gastric secretion, ulcer production, and peristaltic changes in the intestines— reactions presumably controlled by the autonomic system (Kennard, 1947). In fact, there appear to be anatomical and functional inter-relations of the autonomic nervous system and the central nervous system at many levels from the lowest to the highest.

It has been suggested by some that greater activity of the parasympathetic division of the autonomic nervous system is a major part of states of excitement (Kling, 1933); others have found evidence for simultaneous discharge over both sympathetic and parasympathetic branches during excitement, with the sympathetic predominating and masking the effects of the parasympathetic (Gellhorn, 1943); [4] and it has also been suggested that there is alternating action and reaction between the sympathetic and parasympathetic systems, so that extreme effects produced by one of the systems are counteracted by activity of the other system (Arnold, 1945). Darrow and Henry (1949) have suggested that parasympathetic effects often persist after the sympathetic activity has ceased.

Stimulation need not be intense, or of the so-called emotional variety, to produce either sympathetic or parasympathetic activity. R. C. Davis, Buchwald, and Frankmann (1955) found that the responses to simple auditory and tactual stimuli had many features usually considered to be sympathetic in origin, but also some characteristics usually regarded as signs of parasympathetic activity. They concluded that all the responses which they recorded "result from different combinations of the two divisions, with the dominance differing from site to site and from one stimulus to another."

Having started backward, in a sense, by describing the influence of cortical and subcortical centers upon each other and upon the motor fibers of the peripheral system, we would not have a complete account without specific consideration of afferent influences upon central functioning. These influences have already been mentioned in the statement that the classical sensory pathways, as they pass through the brain stem, give off collaterals which presumably set off discharges in the reticular formation. "Feed-back" effects from the contraction of skeletal muscles have long been recognized as a possible means of increasing the activity of higher nerve centers. It has been suggested that afferent

[4] A very useful reference, unfortunately not incorporated in this manuscript, is Gellhorn (1957).

collaterals from the viscera to the reticular system may also be important in producing and maintaining arousal of the cortex. Dell and Bonvallet (1956) state:

The nonspecific brain stem reticular system belongs to the visceral as well as to the somatic spheres of activity, it being affected by exteroceptive and interoceptive afferent impulses and its continuous tonic activity depending directly on crucial components of the milieu intérieur; at the same time it controls sensory receptors and motor effectors, as well as visceral regulatory efferents (p. 309).

Since increased activity in the muscles and viscera feeds back impulses into the reticular system, excitation of the cortex might be self-perpetuating and continuous were there not mechanisms for terminating it. Darrow (1950) has suggested in this connection the importance of subcortical pacemakers which serve to reduce cortical excitation and thus break the circular reaction. Similarly, others have advanced the hypothesis that the alpha rhythm may be the result of intrinsic rhythms of the cortex, "synchronized by the 'driving' effect of the central 'pacemaker' mechanism" (Aird and Gastaut, 1959). Differences in maturation were suggested as the explanation of the "slow" posterior waves found chiefly in youth.

Means have now been discovered whereby the cortex can control its own level of activation by controlling the activating mechanisms of the brain stem (Samuels, 1959).

Lairy and Dell (1957) have pointed out that we should conceive of the activity of the ascending reticular activating system, the descending facilitating reticular system, and the sympathetic reticular formation as being co-operatively controlled by the same factors from without and within, and that we should regard cortical electrical activity as situated in the composite of nervous activities and in the bodily functions as a continuous, non-specific activity which is on an equal level with muscular tone or sympathetic tone. They conclude that the cortical tone both reflects and is a test of the degree of activity in the brain stem structures which are responsible not only for the specific cortical activities (afferent, efferent, and intracortical) but also for the level of activity of the organism as a whole. An excellent review of those aspects of reticular function which appear to have the greatest behavioral relevance is to be found in an article by Samuels (1959).

Rapid advances are now being made in the study of the relationship between cortex and subcortex, and any interpretation of the details of their interrelations is likely soon to be outmoded. It seems probable, however, that further information will increase rather than decrease the emphasis placed upon the interrelations of the various parts of the brain and the peripheral nervous system in initiating and maintaining a state of arousal of the organism, as well as in terminating this condition in due time.[5]

CHEMICAL CONTROL OF ACTIVATION

Hormones

While in the higher animals the control of visceral, as well as somatic, functions is achieved primarily through the nervous system, hormones from the endocrine glands also play an important role in the regulation of behavior. There are reciprocal relationships between the nervous system and the endocrine system which are of basic importance in maintaining the functional equilibrium of the organism. One review concludes that "the endocrines are almost inextricably associated in function with the autonomic nervous system, the other major homeostatic regulator, . . ." (Brožek, 1958).

An example of neurohumoral relationships may be seen in the fact that activation of the cortex, initiated by neural impulses from the ascending reticular activating system, is said to be maintained by a subsequent humoral activation which also works, not directly on the cortex but through brain stem formations, on the ponto-mesencephalic activating system and then the cortex (Bonvallet, Dell, and Hiebel, 1954). By means of this humoral activation, cortical activity is said to be adjusted to the peripheral sympathetic activity of the moment. Increase in sympathetic tone (adrenalin, slight hypertension) is said to produce an EEG indistinguishable from that produced by an exteroceptive stimulus (Bonvallet, Dell, and Hiebel, 1954). Moderation of cortical activity may be achieved also, it appears, by chemical means as well as by subcortical and autonomic nervous system activity (Darrow, 1947).

The glands primarily concerned in the reciprocal relationships between the nervous system and the endocrine system are the adrenals,

[5] An important group of studies, not included in the present discussion, are studies by W. R. Hess, J. Olds, J. M. R. Delgado, N. E. Miller, and others, in which electrodes were implanted in the lower brain centers and observations were made, both of the effect of stimulation of certain areas of the brain upon behavior and of tendencies of animals to engage in self-stimulation of these areas. Since the studies and their ramifications have been numerous, any attempt to digest the findings and incorporate them in the present discussion would have delayed unduly the publication of this book. It is recognized, however, that since both the direction and the intensity of behavior were affected by certain of these experimental manipulations, the data are relevant to the topics under discussion.

the thyroid, and the pituitary (Kuntz, 1951). These glands play a well-known role in determining the degree of activation of the organism.

The adrenal glands have two parts, the adrenal medulla and the adrenal cortex, which differ in their functions. The pituitary gland also has two parts, the anterior pituitary and the posterior pituitary, which are functionally different. The adrenal medulla and the posterior pituitary have a direct secreto-motor innervation (Fulton, 1949). The anterior pituitary, on the other hand, is probably under the neurohumoral control of the hypothalamus (G. W. Harris, 1950; Hume and Wittenstein, 1950). The anterior pituitary gland in turn exerts a significant influence on the thyroid, the adrenal cortex, and the gonads through production of adrenotrophic, thyrotrophic, and gonadotrophic hormones—that is, the hormones which stimulate the adrenal glands, the thyroid gland, and the gonads. Adrenocorticotrophic hormone (ACTH) seems to have some influence upon the formation of acetylcholine (Wenger, Jones, F. N., and Jones, M. H., 1956), while an increase in the output of adrenalin from the adrenal medulla increases the reactivity of the adrenergic nerves (Kuntz, 1951).

The influence of endocrine secretions upon behavior, and especially upon the level of activation, has been demonstrated in many investigations and observed in many clinics. The fatigability of the hypothyroid individual and the restlessness and excess energy expenditure of the hyperthyroid individual are well known. So also is the lowered activity level of the animal whose gonads have been removed.

Adrenalin (from the adrenal medulla) has long been recognized as a hormone which has a marked influence upon energy mobilization, though its effects appear to be different in large and in small quantities, and to vary also with other factors. Small doses of adrenalin apparently increase the action of acetylcholine at spinal and at ganglionic synapses, while large doses decrease it (Bülbring and Burn, 1942; Wortis, 1949). It has been suggested that the depression of ganglionic transmission may be a protection against excessive sympathetic activity (Bülbring and Burn, 1942). In moderate doses, adrenalin is said to be a vasoconstrictor (McCleary, 1950). It is said to increase the electrical resistance of the skin and to diminish the GSR (McCleary, 1950).

Adrenalin is found in increased concentration in the blood, not only during the excited "emotions" as Cannon (1936) pointed out, but also as a result of even such mild stimulation as the muscular activity required in walking or in any kind of physical exercise (Kuntz, 1951). It participates in the regulation of blood pressure, the tonic state of the skeletal muscles, and the muscular capacity of the individual.

The adrenal medulla is innervated by the sympathetic nervous system, and it apparently facilitates the activity of most of the other end-organs stimulated by this system, exerting an effect similar to that of the sympathetic nervous system itself. There are, however, many contradictory reports as to the effects of adrenalin, some of them explainable no doubt by variations in dosage, and some perhaps by failure to distinguish between the immediate effects of the hormone and the organism's counterbalancing reaction to it (Arnold, 1945). It is of interest that Rothballer is said to have shown that epinephrin and norepinephrin have the same qualitative and quantitative actions in producing EEG arousal (Domino, 1957).

Secretions from the adrenal cortex, activated by the adrenocorticotrophic hormone from the pituitary gland, affect in important ways the cellular processes involved in the energy exchange of the organism. The activity of this gland, which has been the subject of many investigations, has been shown to be influenced by a wide variety of stress stimuli, including symbolic or "psychic" stimuli, and to play a significant role in the preparation of the organism to meet the stress situation. F. L. Engel (1953), summarizing the point of view of Ingle and of Sayers, comments that the adrenal seems to be involved in making energy available rapidly for a variety of defensive reactions. In fact, it has been said that the evidence reviewed by Sayers suggests that many, perhaps all, stimuli which act upon the sympathetic nervous system cause at the same time pituitary-adrenocortical activation (Cleghorn, 1953). Sayers (1950), after discussing the role of the adrenal cortex in homeostasis, comments that

. . . it is unlikely that the very numerous and diversified physiological functions of the cortical hormone are paralleled by as many different actions on intracellular biochemical processes. The law of parsimony necessitates the hope that these functions are the varied expressions of a ubiquitous single action, albeit complex, concerned with the mobilization of energy for cellular work, regardless of the type of cell involved or the nature of the work performed. On this point, however, there is practically no cogent evidence (pp. 243–244).

Chronic administration of large amounts of some adrenocortical steroids has been said to affect markedly the excitability of the central nervous system (Brožek, 1958), with one of the steroids elevating and another lowering the electroshock seizure threshold (Woodbury, Timiras, and Vernadakis, 1957).

The response of the body to endocrine secretions depends not only upon the hormones themselves but also upon the condition of the cells upon which the hormones act. This fact has been brought out particularly well in relation to the action of one of the cortical hormones (Sayers, 1950). The secretion of hormones in turn is influenced by vitamins (R. S. Harris and Thimann, 1947) and other environmental factors. Conditioning, for example, may influence the secretion of adrenocorticotrophic and gonadotrophic hormones (Graham, 1953). In many cases the activity and effects of one gland are influenced by two or three other glands located in different parts of the body (R. J. Williams, 1946). Reciprocal effects are exerted by the endocrine system and the nervous system, as may be seen in the interaction between the pituitary and the hypothalamus (Cleghorn, 1955) and in the hormonal feedback of autonomic nervous system discharge (R. L. Solomon and Wynne, 1954). We may conclude, then, that the response to any stimulus will depend upon continuous interactions between neural impulses and hormones (Mirsky, Miller, and Stein, 1953).

Drugs

Chemical intervention has been shown to affect the functioning of the nervous system. Depending upon the drug employed and upon the dosage, the administration of drugs may raise or may lower the level of activation, and, in the case of some drugs, may apparently exert differential effects upon different parts of the nervous system, thus producing differences in behavior other than differences in the degree of activation.[6] Drugs have multiple sites of action, with differing thresholds of susceptibility (Himwich, 1955).

An extensive study of some stimulant and some depressant drugs (caffeine, Benzedrine, Adrenalin, barbiturates, and morphine) showed that all stimulants tended to increase fast activity in the EEG while all depressants tended to increase slow activity in association with sleep and drowsiness (Gibbs and Maltby, 1943). The frequency shifts tended to be constant for a given class of drugs, while the voltage was variable.

Among the drugs which, at least in small concentration, appear to be stimulants, producing an increase in the level of activation, are caffeine, amphetamine, and LSD (lysergic acid diethylamide). Amphetamine, for example, facilitates the EEG arousal reaction (Himwich, 1955). It also raises the level of overt activity. Rats and monkeys, given amphetamine one hour prior to a test period, showed an increase of more than 100 per cent in the number of bar-pressing responses, as

[6] Gerard (1957) points out the fact that "a drug which depresses all neurones or synapses but acts more strongly on the inhibitory than the excitatory ones could evoke the same behavior changes as a drug which stimulates all units but favors the excitatory ones."

compared with those of a saline-control session (Brady, 1956). LSD-25 and mescaline produce desynchronization of the EEG and autonomic changes, chiefly sympathomimetic (Wikler, 1956). Sometimes they produce a slight increase in the alpha frequency. Low concentrations of LSD led, in the cat, to electrocortical facilitation of evoked auditory and visual responses to external stimuli (Purpura, 1956a). Higher concentrations depressed the auditory response but continued to facilitate the visual response. It was found also that, at drug concentrations which caused facilitation in specific afferent systems, an inhibitory effect was exerted on nonspecific thalamic and corticocortical systems (Purpura, 1956b). An explanation of the differential effect was suggested in terms of differences in the anatomical nature of the two different types of synapse in the systems.

Cholinergic drugs were reported, in the case of injected rabbits, to have their site of action at the mesodiencephalic level (Rinaldi and Himwich, 1955b), the function of the mesodiencephalic activating system being considered cholinergic in nature. Acetylcholine produced a sudden, diffuse, and transitory change in the EEG, which was identical with an alerting reaction, while atropine inhibited alerting responses and produced a sleep pattern (Rinaldi and Himwich, 1955a).

It is a well-known fact that the barbiturates induce relaxation and sleep. At least one important site of barbiturate action appears to be the mesencephalic reticular formation, which exerts an activating influence on the cortex (Shagass, 1954). Gastaut and his collaborators (H. Gastaut, Y. Gastaut, Roger, Corriol, and Naquet, 1951), in studies of the cortical excitability cycle, showed that barbiturates lengthen the recuperation time of neurones in the sensory cortex. Amphetamine, on the other hand, decreases the time of recuperation. Himwich (1958) states that the barbiturates in general act most strongly on the cerebral cortex and least on the most primitive parts of the brain.

The "tranquilizing" drugs, which exert their most potent actions on subcortical structures—midbrain reticular formation, hypothalamus, and components of the rhinencephalon (Himwich, 1958), have powerful effects on behavior, particularly the effect of reducing activity without loss of consciousness (Stellar, 1957). Reserpine, according to one review, may block afferent impulses to sympathetic centers in the diencephalon, and both reserpine and chlorpromazine can depress parts of the reticular activating system (Stellar, 1957). The consensus in regard to both reserpine and chlorpromazine is that they depress the hypothalamus (Himwich, 1955), an area which, it will be recalled, exerts neural control over basal metabolism, temperature, blood pressure, and the sleep-wakefulness cycle. In addition, these drugs change the hormonal balance since hypothalamic depression renders the anterior pituitary gland less susceptible to stimulation (Himwich, 1955). Rhesus monkeys in whom there had been established a conditioned response consisting of disruption of a stable lever-pressing pattern, crouching, trembling, etc., had higher concentrations of 17-hydroxycorticosteroids in the blood during the conditioned experimental sessions than during lever-pressing alone, and higher levels of steroid output during lever-pressing than that found in the course of normal diurnal variation (Mason and Brady, 1956). After one week of reserpine administration, the conditioned suppression of the lever-pressing response had virtually disappeared, corticosteroid levels showed no increase during the experimental sessions, and even the slight increase which usually occurred during lever-pressing without the conditioned stimulus failed to appear. Discontinuing the drug led to renewed suppression of lever-pressing and to an increase in corticosteroids during the experimental sessions, while readministration of reserpine again diminished these reactions, which, however, reappeared after withdrawal of the drug. (These findings are in contrast to those of another group of investigators who reported a marked increase in the adrenal corticoid secretion of dogs following reserpine administration, though for unknown reasons the effect did not appear until one-half hour to 3 hours after injection [Egdahl, Richards, and Hume, 1956]).

Reduction of activity as a result of reserpine administration was reported in a study by Brady in which, after 4 days of reserpine injection, there was a decrease of more than 50 per cent in the total number of lever-pressing responses occurring during a one-hour session (Brady, 1956). This result was obtained in spite of the fact that the drug interfered with the suppression of lever-pressing during the conditioning trials and led to the same rate of response during the conditioning trials as in the period between trials. The findings were replicated with several animals.

Both reserpine and chlorpromazine have been said to exert a depressant effect upon the central nervous system (F. M. Berger, 1960). In fact, they exert an effect upon the electroencephalogram similar to that of sleep, and they antagonize the cortical reaction produced by such drugs as amphetamine or by external stress stimuli (Bovet, 1959).

Chlorpromazine in small doses blocks the arousal response evoked by a pain-stimulus (Himwich, 1955). It also diminishes electrical activity in the skin and decreases involuntary muscular activity (M. Turner, Bérard, N. Turner, and Franco, 1956). Sweat-gland secretion and "electro-dermographic" changes evoked by adrenalin or by nociceptive stimuli were inhibited or abolished by chlorpromazine (Clerc, M. Turner, and Bérard, 1956). The temperature of the hand and leg was increased, while that of the cheek and arm was decreased.

Certain investigators (Lafon and Minvielle, 1960) state that the action of chlorpromazine is clearly different from that of reserpine and explain the difference as due to the fact that they act upon a different locus in the neural centers. They claim that chlorpromazine produces a considerable increase in sympathetic tonus and has much less marked parasympathetic effects, while reserpine lowers vagal tonus and decreases the excitability of the autonomic nervous system. Nevertheless, it has been reported that chlorpromazine, reserpine, and amytal, classified as tranquilizers or sedatives, decreased central sympathetic reactivity, inhibited conditioning of the galvanic skin response, and produced an increase in reaction time, while a stimulant (phenidylate) decreased the reaction time and facilitated conditioning (R. A. Schneider, 1960).

Bovet (1959) emphasizes the fact that there is similarity in the antagonisms between various groups of drugs in their action on the central nervous system and on the viscera stimulated by the autonomic nervous system.

Meprobamate, as compared with a placebo, consistently raised the level of galvanic skin resistance in patients in stress situations (J. G. Miller, 1960). It appears that the galvanic skin response is definitely affected by certain drugs (Kristofferson and Cormack, 1960).

CONCLUSIONS

It may be concluded that the level of activation of the organism has both a neural and a chemical basis. The chemical agents, while ordinarily endogenous, such as hormones, may on occasion be exogenous, such as drugs. Neural and chemical agents interact with each other and, while they may exert differential effects on different organs and systems, their effect is organismic in the sense that: (1) what is happening in one part of the organism affects what is happening in other parts, (2) the various part-reactions appear to be regulated in such a way as to maintain homeostatic balance, and (3) one of the end-results of this interaction is an over-all increase or decrease in the degree of activation of the organism, though not necessarily of each organ or system considered separately.

chapter 4
Variations in activation
with variations in the situation

INTRODUCTION

It is apparent that the degree of activation of the individual varies with the situation. This conclusion is supported, not only by general observation but also by empirical data from many sources (Duffy, 1951). If we inquire into the circumstances under which the degree of activation is high and those under which it is low, it becomes obvious that the answer must take into account (1) the total stimulating situation of the moment and (2) the nature and present condition of the individual responding.

The characteristics of the individual, which will be a determinant of the response, are themselves a result of his entire history of development up to the time of the recorded reaction. Both genetic background and previous experiences affect the response to the present stimulus. Moreover, temporary physiological states such as "drives," conditions of fatigue, or metabolic conditions produced by drugs are significant determinants of the response at a given moment. Under such circumstances, it is not altogether surprising that some have concluded that any adequate psychology must be an individual psychology (G. W. Allport, 1937; Snygg and Combs, 1949), for it is indeed true that the individual responds to the stimulus as he interprets it, in the light of his past experiences and present circumstances. This assertion finds, perhaps, wider acceptance if it is changed to read that an individual responds to a stimulus according to his drive-state and habit-strength (or cue-responses) in regard to the particular stimulus.

Though it appears that the degree of activation is that required by the situation, as interpreted by the individual, and within the limits of his capacity for response at the moment, it does not follow that no general principles of behavior can be discovered. There is considerable similarity in the anatomical structures and the physiological needs of different individuals. Within a given culture, there is considerable similarity in their learning experiences and social needs. It transpires, therefore, that most individuals of a given culture, when placed in a particular stimulating situation, will respond in a similar fashion, so that the mean or the modal response for a particular type of situation may, within limits, be predicted.

Situations appear to vary greatly in their energy demands, and hence in the degree to which they activate the individual. Standing requires more energy than reclining, and lying awake requires more energy than sleeping. Work requires more energy than rest; and work on more difficult tasks, or on those necessitating greater muscular activity, requires more energy than work on easy tasks or on those demanding less muscular exertion. Situations which present threats to the goal-achievement of the individual apparently release more energy than situations which present no such hazard. When the factor of physical exertion is held constant, it appears that there is a continuum in the activation of the individual as we progress from situations of relatively little difficulty or goal-significance to situations of greater difficulty or significance. This we have referred to previously as the continuum of energy mobilization (Duffy, 1941a, 1949, 1951), or the continuum of excitation (Duffy, 1934).

A given situation may produce greater or less activation in an individual if certain drugs affecting the level of activation (i.e., stimulants or sedatives) are administered. It may also produce greater or less (usually less) activation if the stimulus situation is repeated a number of times. This phenomenon is referred to as adaptation. Repetition of a situation is likely to modify the significance of the situation as perceived by the individual. For example, apprehension may diminish if "check-up by results" shows that nothing unpleasant or threatening is likely to occur. Activation may, on the contrary, increase if new and more significant aspects of the situation are observed upon repetition. R. C. Davis (1934) has found, for instance, a progressive increase in skin resistance upon successive repetitions of a simple auditory stimulus and a progressive decrease in skin resistance upon successive presentations of a piece of classical music. As an explanation of this finding he suggested that the classical music was so complex that, as it was repeated, new aspects of it undoubtedly were observed. It is also a well-known fact that the repetition of a certain stimulus situation affords an opportunity for mastering the techniques required for dealing with the situation; hence the situation may come to require less effort or to be regarded as less threatening. It would follow, then, that stress (defined as degree of activation by a stimulus when other relevant factors are held constant) does not depend upon the stimulus alone, but also upon the resources of the individual for dealing with the stimulus.

Presented below are a number of investigations in which concomitant variations have been found in the stimulus situation and in certain physiological measures employed in the study of activation. After reading these studies it is difficult to escape the conclusion that the degree of activation is in general finely adjusted to the demands of the situation, as interpreted by the individual, and within his capacity for response.

CHANGES IN TENSION OF THE SKELETAL MUSCLES WITH CHANGES IN THE STIMULUS SITUATION

There is a marked decrease in action potentials from the muscles, as recorded in the electromyogram (EMG), during the condition in which there would presumably be the lowest level of activation, that of sleep. Decreasing action potentials are indicative of greater muscular relaxation, since contraction of a muscle produces electrical activity in the muscle. Even in sleep, however, there is seldom complete absence of muscular activity. As is well known, sleep varies in depth. There is considerable evidence of correlation between the depth of sleep and the extent of action potentials in the muscles. As the individual goes to sleep, action potentials decrease progressively until he reaches the stage of deepest sleep, when he moves least and is least disturbed by noises. As he awakens, there is an increase in action potentials. In deaf mutes the decrease in action potentials during sleep is greater than in normal individuals, probably because deaf mutes are not disturbed by the sounds around them (Max, 1935). When the sleeping person is subjected to sensory stimulation or when a dream occurs, there is usually an increase in potentials (Max, 1935). Under these conditions, of course, the individual is releasing more energy than during undisturbed sleep.

R. C. Davis (1956a) concludes that there seems to be complete agreement that a response of any sort implies some skeletal-muscle activity. He says "if we compare doing something with doing nothing (or as near as we can come to the latter) there is a positive relation between muscular activity and the occurrence of any of the activities tested." Jacobson (1929) reported that mental work was almost impossible under an extreme degree of relaxation.

R. C. Davis, Buchwald, and Frankmann (1955) comment that "stimuli produce somatic responses even when there is no manifest movement. The body, it may be said, reflects external conditions with some sensitivity. Some of our stimuli were not unusually intense, yet even these elicited changes in the organism. As a person probably encounters similar brief stimuli many times a day, we may suppose that he is in a continuous and fluctuating state of somatic upheaval so long as he is awake" (pp. 64–65).

Stimuli of greater intensity produce more muscle tension than those of lesser intensity. For example, noises between 100 and 117 decibels were found to produce a degree of muscle tension nearly proportional to the decibal level (R. C. Davis, 1953). The increase in tension occurred at a greater rate within this range of stimulus intensities than it did within a lower range of intensities. Auditory stimuli near the threshold produced muscular activity whether or not the stimulus was reported to have been heard (R. C. Davis, 1950). The responses to unheard stimuli were smaller, however, than to those reported as heard; and, when the stimulus was heard, there was an increase in the size of the muscular response as the stimulus increased in intensity. In an earlier study (R. C. Davis, 1948), the effect of stimulus intensity on response was said to be "represented by a curvilinear function, steeper between 90 and 100 db than between 70 and 90 db." Since little evidence of curvilinearity was found in the later study, it was suggested that the curvilinearity probably lay between 90 and 100 decibels, or between 100 and 110 decibels, where it could not show because the points tested were too far apart.

Studies of a wide variety of activities have shown that, as they increase in difficulty, or as the "motivation" for their performance becomes greater, there is an increase in muscular tension. When such activities are interfered with by distractions or obstructions, there is also an increase in tension. When, on the other hand, the individual becomes habituated to a performance or a situation, and it thus becomes less difficult, demanding, or threatening for him, his muscular tension usually decreases. Only a few of the many studies in this area can be described.

Studies by Jacobson (1938), by Max (1937), and by others have shown that increased tension of the skeletal muscles is a regular ac-

companiment of "attention," "set," "imagining," and "thinking," as compared with resting states. Courts (1942b), in a review of studies of
muscle tension, concluded that most investigators had found an increase in tension during mental activity as compared with rest. In more
recent studies it has been shown that merely listening to material being
read produces an increase in tension in certain muscles (A. A. Smith,
Malmo, and Shagass, 1954; Wallerstein, 1954). Forehead EMG's increased slightly ($P = .02$) from the resting period to the "expectancy"
period, and increased further at the beginning of the story (Bartoshuk,
1956). The majority of the subjects had steeper EMG gradients (i.e.,
progressive rise in muscular tension) during the hearing of the story
which they rated as the most interesting ($P = .02$) (Bartoshuk, 1956).
Talking, as compared with listening, produced a significant increase in
tension, not only in the chin muscles but also in those of the forehead,
the neck, and both arms (A. A. Smith, Malmo, and Shagass, 1954).

R. C. Davis (1938) found that subjects working on a number-series
problem showed an increase in the action potentials from the muscles
of the arm and the neck as the problems increased in difficulty. This
increase occurred whether the subjects reported success or reported
failure in solving the problems; hence it could not be said to be due
to the frustration of failure. Other investigators have found that children attempting to solve mental arithmetic problems, prearranged into
five categories of difficulty, showed an increase in action potentials from
the arm muscles with each succeeding step of difficulty in the problems
except the final one (Shaw and Kline, 1947). There was a reliable
difference between the tension during rest and during work. Men
undergoing flight training were found to show more tension of the
muscles (grip pressure) during the solo stage of the training and during the maneuvers of take-off and landing (A. C. Williams, Jr., Macmillan, and Jenkins, 1947). Infants when hampered in their feeding
showed increased muscular tension (Halverson, 1938). Adults distracted by noises while they were carrying on an activity exerted
greater pressure upon the keys they had been instructed to press
(J. J. B. Morgan, 1916). Conversely, as a task becomes easier by virtue
of habituation, muscular tension has been found to decrease. This
phenomenon has been observed in several varieties of task and with
both adults and children (R. C. Davis, 1937; Duffy, 1932b). Clearly,
there is a positive relationship between the energy demands of the
task and the muscular tension of the individual.

In line with this conclusion is the proposal to use measurement of
muscular tension as an index of the energy demands of different occu-

pational tasks (R. C. Travis and Kennedy, 1949). With action currents recorded from electrodes placed just above each eyebrow, it was found, for example, that simple tracking produced a significantly higher tension level than reading, solving simple mathematical problems, and simulated lookout. For these three tasks the tension level was about the same.

Variations in tension during the same task have been used as measures of alertness (R. C. Travis and Kennedy, 1947, 1949; Kennedy and Travis, 1948). Muscle action potentials were found to decrease progressively as the subject became progressively less alert, if decreasing alertness is indicated by progressively longer simple reaction time and progressively less efficiency in performing the task. With appropriate stimulation, there was recovery of alertness, as indicated by a shorter reaction time and more accurate performance. Accompanying these changes in performance was an increase in muscle tension. The investigators believe they have the basis for an "alertness indicator" which, when the subject's electrical output reaches a specific minimal level, may give a warning signal (Kennedy and Travis, 1947).

Among the findings which support the contention that muscle tension varies with the significance and demands of the situation as interpreted by the individual are gradients in muscle tension found in Malmo's laboratory during many different types of activity. During a short-interval drawing task, a continuous increase in tension in the active arm was found as the subject approached the goal (A. A. Smith, 1953). Similar gradients were found in the arm during a size-discrimination test, and in the frontalis muscle while the subject was reclining and listening to a detective story or an essay being read (Wallerstein, 1954; A. A. Smith, Malmo, and Shagass, 1954). Data which relate the steepness of the gradient to "motivational" factors are, as suggested by Malmo (1954a), the following: (1) the fastest and most accurate subjects showed the steepest gradients, at least up to what may have been an optimal value of gradient slope (Bartoshuk, 1955b); (2) increased incentive produced steeper gradients (Surwillo, 1956); (3) increased difficulty of the task produced steeper gradients (Belanger, 1957); (4) task interruption left more residual tension in subjects with steeper gradients than in those with less steep gradients (A. A. Smith, 1953; Bartoshuk, 1955a).

Since gradients in muscle tension represent not merely an increase in tension of the muscles but a continuing, or progressive, increase, they present certain problems of interpretation. They are not new phenomena, having been observed earlier in point pressure and in grip pressure during various tasks (B. Johnson, 1928; Bills and Brown, 1929; McTeer, 1933; Telford and Swenson, 1942), as well as in the EMG, where they were described as "build-up" phenomena (R. C. Davis, 1937). Not all subjects show positive gradients (B. Johnson, 1928; Bartoshuk, 1956), and, under given experimental conditions, some muscles may show them while others fail to do so. For present purposes, however, it is sufficient to note that, on the average, an increase in muscle tension was found when the task was more difficult or the incentive was greater.

The relationship of muscle tension to motivational factors is suggested also by the report that "ego-oriented" subjects showed more muscle tension than "task-oriented" subjects when working on easy problems, and less tension than task-oriented subjects when working on difficult problems, where the ego-oriented subjects were said to "give up" (Reuder, 1951).

Opposite ends of the continuum of activation are seen in sleep and the startle response. Landis and Hunt (1939) have described the startle response as "an immediate reflex response to sudden intense stimulation which demands some out-of-the-ordinary treatment by the organism." On such an occasion the human subject shows a vigorous general flexion response: blinking of the eyes, head movement forward, contraction of the abdomen, forward movement of the trunk and shoulders, and movements of the arms, fingers, and legs (Landis and Hunt, 1939). In other words, there is a widespread and intense contraction of the musculature. The directional aspect of this response does not concern us at the moment. Our concern is rather with the increased intensity or level of activation of the behavior.

An extreme degree of activation is to be found also in conditions of frustration or other intense "emotional" responses. Frustration, it is agreed, is characterized by either the exertion of greater effort, with a consequent high degree of activation, or "giving up," with a consequent low degree of activation. The former type of response is readily observed to involve strong activation of the skeletal muscles as the individual attacks his barrier, himself, or some substitute object or individual; or, if he restrains overt activity, his muscles are nevertheless rigid—perhaps in preparation for the action which he does not take. The opposite type of response, "giving up," is on the other hand characterized by the low degree of activation appropriate for doing nothing and indeed noticing nothing. Totten, in studying the effect of "emotional" stimulation upon the metabolic rate, observed increased tension of the skeletal muscles whenever there was an increase in oxygen consumption (Totten, 1925).

Nursery school children showed an immediate increase in grip pressure upon the flashing of a light or the sounding of a horn (Duffy, 1930). Subjects with higher muscle tension scores tended to be rated higher on excitability, a term which was apparently equated by their nursery school teachers with instability and poor adjustment to the environment, in the second of two studies conducted by the author (Duffy, 1932a, 1930).

The psychotherapeutic progress of patients (during which the disturbing effects of certain stimuli would presumably be reduced) was found, throughout a series of psychiatric interviews, to be associated with a decrease in muscle tension (Malmo, 1954b). During a brief rest period following a TAT test, speech-muscle tension fell rapidly in both patient and examiner after the examiner had praised the subject's story. No such decrease in tension occurred after criticism (Malmo, Boag, and Smith, 1957).

Lundervold (1952) recorded, in his "labile" subjects, a considerable increase in muscular activity (needle electrodes) when the subjects were irritated or angry, and a decrease in activity when they became calmer.

There appears to be much evidence to support the conclusion that, when other factors are constant, the degree of muscle tension varies directly with the significance and the demands of the situation as interpreted by the individual, and that, with this variation in tension, is associated a corresponding variation in the degree of alertness or effort.

Either increases or decreases in muscle tension usually occur with repetition of a situation or a task. This finding is to be expected since repetition of a stimulus situation is likely to alter its degree of significance or its difficulty, and hence its energy demands. In general, a decrease in muscle tension during successive repetitions might be expected and has usually been found. Assuming, however, that with repetition an organism is likely to develop a more appropriate response, it may be surmised that an increase, rather than a decrease, of muscle tension would occur in situations in which repetition reveals greater complexity of the stimulus situation, or greater need for alertness, or unforeseen threats to goal achievement. Findings in harmony with this expectation have also been reported. In a few situations, according to the data now available, repetition appears not to alter the effect of the stimulus.

There seems to be rather general agreement that the level of muscle tension during rest periods decreases with repetition of the situation. This has been the report in a number of studies (Gelber, 1957; R. C. Davis, 1953).

The adaptation effect when the subject is listening to sounds apparently depends to some extent upon the intensity of the stimulation. Four repetitions of tones of three intensities (70, 90, and 120 decibels) led to the finding that the decrease of muscular response with repetition was greatest for the most intense stimulus and was relatively small for the other stimuli (R. C. Davis, Buchwald, and Frankmann, 1955). Since more intense stimulation produces greater muscular activity, it provides more opportunity for a decrease in muscle activity to occur during successive periods of stimulation. In one study, the subjects, when instructed to "do nothing" while a stimulus (white noise) was presented, showed progressive decreases in the muscular response to such an extent that the twelfth trial showed only a fraction of the increase in action potentials shown on the first four trials (R. C. Davis, 1953). When, however, subjects were listening for auditory stimuli close to the threshold, an increase in muscular tension with repetition was found (R. C. Davis, 1950). Perhaps under the latter circumstances the subjects were increasing their alertness or effort in an attempt to hear sounds which were barely audible.

Intense stimulation of a startling nature is, as might be expected, rather resistant to adaptation (Landis and Hunt, 1939). For example, when action potentials from the arms were recorded during the firing of 32 caliber blanks at intervals of two minutes, the initial muscular response (a-response) showed no significant adaptation for size, but did show significant adaptation for duration (R. C. Davis and Van Liere, 1949). It has been suggested that the "a-response" may be a part of the "startle response."

In the course of the performance of a task, muscle tension has been reported, as suggested, to increase, to decrease, or to show no change, depending apparently upon the requirements of the situation. Ghiselli (1936), for example, found that during the period when a visuo-motor task was being learned, pressure on the keys was maintained at a constant level, but that, during overlearning, there was a marked decrease in pressure as compared with the pressure during the learning period. Bills (1930), Stroud (1931), Duffy (1932a), and others have reported decreases in muscular tension with the repetition of a performance.

Subjects listening to the reading of a story and of a philosophical essay, who in general reported greater interest in the story on the first reading and in the essay on the second reading, showed reliably steeper EMG gradients in the frontalis muscle during the most, as compared with the least, interesting of three hearings of the material (Wallerstein, 1954).

Facts such as those mentioned above suggest that adaptation, like initial arousal, depends upon the complexity or difficulty of the task, the interest or "motivation" of the subject, and any other factors which may be related to the significance of the situation and the energy requirements for reaching the goal. Some apparent contradictions in findings have, however, been reported.

Variations in muscle tension, sometimes recorded as tremor, also show correspondence with the nature of the stimulus situation. Finger tremor, measured as the total distance the finger moved during each second, rose rapidly after a loud noise, decreased somewhat during mental multiplication, but rose above the resting level just before the answer was given (J. W. French, 1944). Work on more difficult arithmetic problems was apparently accompanied by more irregular finger pressures than was work on less difficult problems (Reymert and Speer, 1938–1939). Nervous movements, as measured by a time-sampling technique, were found to increase in children during stress (Olson, 1929).

Sainsbury (1955) recorded, during a psychiatric interview, the high amplitude muscle potentials accompanying movement and found that significantly more movements occurred during the stressful periods of the interview. This finding was checked in several ways. Using a tape recording of the interviews, the patients' remarks were grouped into topics. The topics rated as most disturbing (on the basis of case histories) were accompanied by significantly more movements. Four subjects were interviewed a second time, and it was found that the topics accompanied by most gestures in the first interview were accompanied by most gestures in the second interview also. An increase in heart rate, as well as in gestures, occurred during the stressful periods.

THE ELECTRICAL RESISTANCE OF THE SKIN

Variations in palmar resistance occur when there are changes in the stimulus situation or in the general organic condition of the individual. In sleep, where the level of activation usually reaches the lowest point it reaches under normal conditions, palmar skin resistance is very high. Going to sleep, however, does not represent a sharp break from a previous condition. Instead, there appears to be no particular moment at which sleep may be said to have been reached. As the individual becomes more and more drowsy and relaxed, the skin resistance rises. In one study where the subject was in a Morris chair turned away from the observer, it was possible, by watching the changes in electrical resistance, always to tell when drowsiness was coming over the subject (Kleitman, 1939). High skin resistance, then, does not occur at a particular moment when consciousness is lost, but instead it is characteristic of the general physiological condition which predisposes the individual toward sleep (Darrow and Freeman, 1934). As the person becomes more and more relaxed, the increase in resistance occurs at a slower rate. The degree of increase is related to some extent to the depth and duration of sleep, but it appears to be affected by other factors also (Kleitman, 1939). Interesting individual differences have been found. One observer reports that persons in whom sleep is accompanied by a great increase in skin resistance are persons who sleep soundly and are hard to awaken, while persons who show only a slight increase in resistance sleep lightly and are easily aroused (Richter, 1926).

Confirmation of these findings is seen in a study in which sleep was accompanied by a clear graphic record showing a rise in basal plantar resistance, while alertness was accompanied by a line of relatively low resistance, and relaxation and drowsiness were accompanied by gradually rising resistance with infrequent, large fluctuations, followed often by the high, stable resistance of sleep (E. Z. Levy, Thaler, and Ruff, 1958). Fitful sleep was shown by large drops in resistance which appeared on the otherwise high, stable line. When there were periods of arousal during sleep, there were sharp drops in resistance and the recovery was slow. Electronic monitoring of alertness seemed possible because the point of onset of sleep was closely approximated by the degree of ability to respond to stimuli (as, for example, light flashes), and the onset of awakening was confirmed by behavioral observation. Periods of work showed lower resistance than those of relaxation. Marked individual differences were found, e.g., the resistance of one individual when he was "relaxed" was higher than that of another when he was asleep.

As the individual awakens in the morning, skin resistance is relatively high; it drops during the day as he becomes more alert and active; and it rises again in the evening (Waller, 1919; Wechsler, 1925). Both sleep losses and fatigue from heavy muscular work may produce large increases in the resistance of the skin (A. H. Ryan and Ranseen, 1944). Some subjects, however, show a decrease, rather than an increase, in skin resistance as a result of the fatigue produced by prolonged exercise (Elbel and Ronkin, 1946).

Muscular work causes a decrease in skin resistance, and the level of resistance reached depends on the work load (A. H. Ryan and Ranseen, 1944). It is generally agreed that resistance is lower during work periods than during rest periods; that the presentation of a stimulus causes a drop in resistance; that very soon after the cessation of the stimulation, resistance begins to rise toward its former level; and that in general skin resistance is a very sensitive indicator of changes in the stimulus situation and the activity (overt or covert) of the subject.

Mental multiplication caused a drop in resistance (White, 1930), and attempts to solve mathematical problems caused a very great drop in resistance (Kuno, 1930). Skin resistance decreased while a subject waited to begin a task, dropped further while he was adding at top speed, and fell to a still lower level while he was adding under distraction (R. C. Davis, 1934). During problem-solving, the galvanic skin response occurred more frequently when the subjects reported difficulty or "predicament" than when they reported "ease" (Abel, 1930). Patients with anxiety, for whom a stimulus situation might be presumed to carry more significance or create more uneasiness than for normal subjects, developed galvanic skin responses for a partially reinforced nonsense syllable with a strikingly greater speed than did normal subjects (Welch and Kubis, 1947b; Schiff, Dougan, and Welch, 1949).

More difficult tasks, situations fraught with greater significance, or situations which the individual is unprepared to meet apparently cause greater decreases in skin resistance than easy tasks, situations which are less significant, or situations which the subject feels able to cope with.

The galvanic skin responses to words have been shown to vary with the meaningfulness and importance of the words. On the average, they were reported to be reliably greater for the very "meaningful, significant, and important" words than for the slightly meaningful, significant and important words. Words of "average" importance held an intermediate position in the size of the galvanic response they elicited (Bingham, 1943). Such differences in the galvanic response to different words have been the regular finding since the early study of Whately Smith (1922), in which the galvanic skin response was used as a measure of the "emotion" aroused by various words.

In one of the more interesting investigations of galvanic responses to words, Murray (1938) and his co-workers asked their subjects to write on a scale ranging from Yes 5 to No 5 the extent of their agreement or disagreement with each of a series of statements pertaining to provocative social questions. Four weeks later the galvanic skin responses of the subjects were recorded while they again rated verbally the same statements. This time, however, the experimenter announced before reading each statement the opinion of the majority of the group. It was found that responses in harmony with group opinion were accompanied by smaller galvanic responses than those at variance with the opinion of the group, and that "yes" responses were accompanied by a smaller galvanic response than "no" responses. From smallest to largest galvanic responses the order of the situations was as follows: (1) "yes" *with* group opinion, (2) "no" *with* group opinion, (3) "yes" *against* group opinion, (4) "no" *against* group opinion. Moreover, if indifference and absolute conviction are excluded, the size of the galvanic response varied proportionally with the degree of conviction asserted.

Prejudiced subjects, as measured by an attitude scale, have been shown to give larger galvanic skin responses to slides depicting Negroes than do unprejudiced persons (Westie and DeFleur, 1959).

So regular is the occurrence of a galvanic response when a so-called emotion-arousing stimulus is presented that at one time it was actually believed that the galvanic response might be specific to "emotional" conditions. Since the excited "emotions" always have as one of their characteristics a high degree of arousal, any physiological indicator of the degree of arousal would be expected to show a close association with such "emotional" states. For example, a Ferris wheel ride led to a statistically significant increase in palmar sweating (Laties, 1959). In this connection it may be noted that skin-resistance phenomena have been found useful in detecting the excited condition accompanying the telling of a lie (Ellson, Davis, Saltzman, and Burke, 1952), as well as the degree of arousal or excitement produced by various motion pictures. In a study of the effect of motion pictures upon children and adults, it was found that nine-year-old children showed large resistance changes when shown scenes of danger, or scenes so interpreted, while they showed little reaction to erotic scenes (Dysinger and Ruckmick, 1933). Sixteen-year-olds, on the other hand, gave a strong reaction to erotic scenes and responded less strongly than the children to scenes of danger. During a series of forty-two hours of psychotherapy, it was reported that the frequency of the patient's galvanic skin responses was inversely related to the judged permissiveness of the therapist (Dittes, 1957b). A number of studies have shown extreme sweat-gland activity during anxiety or stress (Darrow, 1936).

Finally, it has been shown that startle stimulation produces an immediate decrease in skin resistance (Landis and Hunt, 1939). Landis and Hunt (1939) state that "a sudden, loud sound is the best and most reliable stimulus for a drop in the electrical resistance of the skin." Moreover, they say in regard to the startle response in general, that the more intense the stimulus and the more unprepared the subject is to receive it, the more pronounced is the startle reaction. It appears that under such circumstances the individual would need to become more highly activated in order to meet what might prove to be an important emergency situation. If assessment of the situation (immediate perception) indicates that no danger is involved and no action is demanded, the skin resistance no doubt returns fairly quickly to its previous level, while, if action is demanded (as for example if the sudden, loud sound means the collapse of the building one is in), the degree of arousal no doubt remains high in order to make possible the vigorous action which must be taken.

The variation of skin conductance with variation in the task is shown rather strikingly in a study conducted some years ago by Oliver L. Lacey and the author. The investigators attempted, through the use of presumably exciting or relaxing stimulation, to raise or to lower the level of skin conductance, and to observe the effect of changes in conductance upon the performance of two tasks, the naming of colors as rapidly as possible, and the reporting of fluctuations of an ambiguous figure (Duffy, 1947). Though we were entirely successful in inducing at will higher or lower levels of conductance at the beginning of a task, we found that, within the short period of approximately two minutes required for the performance of each task, the conductance level moved so rapidly toward a level characteristic of the particular task that a significant difference was obtained between the conductance during color naming and that during the reporting of figure fluctuations, in spite of all our efforts to have the tasks performed at one time when the subject had a high level of conductance and at another time when the conductance was low.

Further evidence concerning the nature of skin-resistance phenomena is found in the studies of the adaptation of skin resistance in various situations. One of the most regularly reported findings is that repetition of a given stimulus causes a decrease in the amount of skin-resistance change (or GSR) produced by that stimulus. In other words, familiarity with a situation causes a decrease in the response to the situation. This decrease of the galvanic response (skin-resistance change) has been noted under repeated visual (J. M. Porter, 1938), auditory (Coombs, 1938), and electrical stimulation (Hovland and Riesen, 1940), under repeated collapsing of a chair (Blatz, 1925), and with the reshowing of motion pictures (Rasmus, 1936). It has been noted during psychotherapy, where embarrassing statements were more frequently accompanied by galvanic skin responses during the early, than during the later, hours of therapy (Dittes, 1957a). Many years ago Darrow (1936), in a review of the literature, concluded that there was an increase in skin resistance with drowsiness and sleep, a drop in resistance after sudden stimulation causing "startle," and a smaller drop in resistance when the stimulation was repeated.

Not only is there a decrease in the galvanic response, or the degree of change in skin resistance, produced by presentation of a stimulus if this stimulus is repeated a number of times during an experimental session, there is also evidence of a progressive decrease in the general level of palmar skin conductance over a period of three days when the individual is repeatedly subjected to the same auditory stimulation (Duffy and O. L. Lacey, 1946). In other words, adaptation to the situation occurs during a single experimental session and continues from session to session if the lapse of time between the sessions is not too great. The adaptation effect is greatest in the beginning and tends to level off. These findings, reported by Duffy and Lacey (1946), have been confirmed by Conklin (1951). DuToit (1956), on the other hand, reports contradictory findings, which are not in fact contradictory since he himself points out that his experimental situation was so designed as to allow almost complete adaptation before recording was begun, and the task being performed (the adding of numbers) had to be carried out at a more rapid rate in succeeding sessions.

It is apparent that decrease of response upon repetition of a situation is not the simple, direct outcome of repetition of the stimulus, as has been pointed out. If repetition of a situation permits the individual to feel more at ease in the situation or to perform the same task with less effort, or if it produces a continuous decrease in the significance of the situation, then a decrease in responsiveness, shown by a decrease in the GSR and an increase in the general level of skin resistance, is to be expected. If, however, new aspects of the stimulus may continue to be noted, with a consequent increase in the interest or significance of the situation, the response of the subject may not decrease in intensity but may actually increase. In line with this interpretation, another investigator found significant differences in the rate of adaptation of the galvanic skin response to three types of stimulation: a light, a buzzer, and a question used as an ideational stimulus (Kubis, 1948). Adaptation to the light occurred most quickly and adaptation to the question least quickly. Similarly, it was found that there was more adaptation in the skin resistance response to noise than in that to electric shock (Seward and Seward, 1935). Here the explanation would appear to be, not that new aspects of the situation might continue to present themselves, but that an electric shock has more continuing biological significance than a noise which is followed by no disturbing consequences.

The common factor which seems to be present in all situations where low skin resistance is found in a given individual is the factor of activity or readiness for activity, i.e., arousal of the organism. The common factor in all situations where high skin resistance is found appears to be relaxation or passivity. If this is the case, it is not surprising that psychologists have not been able to find a close correlation between skin resistance and any particular kind of mental activity or conscious state. If we assume that a decrease in resistance occurs (with certain limitations) whenever there is an increase in degree of activation, it is not surprising that such decreased resistance has been variously considered to be characteristic of "emotion," or "volition" and "conation," of a sudden check in the comprehension or solution of problems, and of states of alertness (Duffy and O. L. Lacey, 1946). All these conditions involve increased effort—i.e., a higher level of activation. In harmony with this interpretation also is the decrease in resistance which occurs with the presentation of a stimulus or the beginning of work, the progressive increase in resistance which occurs during rest periods, and the adaptation in skin resistance which occurs upon repeated presentation of the same stimulus situation—provided the stimulus pattern is not so complex that new aspects of it are perceived on successive repetitions.

In summary, it may be said that both the general level of skin resistance of the individual and the change in resistance known as the galvanic skin response appear to change in consistent fashion with changes in the degree of significance of the stimulus situation, or with the demands of the situation upon the individual.

THE ELECTROENCEPHALOGRAM (EEG)

Since the first report of human brain potentials, published by H. Berger (1929), there have been many studies of the pattern of electrical changes associated with various conditions of the subject, such as sleep, alertness, and "emotion," among others.

To the surprise of investigators, it appeared that the human brain, when the individual was at rest and was not being subjected to external stimulation, had an electrical beat or rhythm of its own. These brain rhythms, instead of being produced by specific stimulation, appeared to be spontaneous and "autonomous." In fact, they were diminished or abolished by certain types of sensory stimulation. The situation presented a paradox. Activity of the brain, in response to stimulation, seemed to decrease rather than to increase the electrical potentials from the brain. The suggested explanation was that potentials of sufficient size to be recorded from the surface of the scalp would have to come from a summation of discharges of individual neurones or be built up by synchronization of many individual components. Sensory stimulation, as well as other types of stimulation, presumably has a desynchronizing effect on groups of cells that are beating in unison. Hence under these conditions the large rhythmic waves disappear and are replaced by faster waves of smaller magnitude or by the loss of rhythm in the EEG.

Numerous studies have been made of brain potentials during the process of going to sleep. If an individual merely lies quiet for two hours or more there has been said to be a marked reduction in the frequency of the alpha waves (Loomis, Harvey, and Hobart, 1936). As he becomes more and more drowsy, the wave rate becomes slower and slower. When he falls asleep, the alpha rhythm drops out and slow waves of 4 to 5 per second appear, and, as the sleep becomes deeper, spindle-shaped waves appear and the slow waves increase in size and decrease in frequency (Lindsley, 1944). With still deeper sleep, the spindles become more prominent, until with very deep sleep they disappear. Simultaneously, the slow waves become increasingly large and slow (Lindsley, 1944). Varying depths of sleep, indicated by the duration or intensity of tones required to awaken a subject, are accompanied by decreases in the frequencies and increases in the amplitude of delta-type patterns (Simon and Emmons, 1956). It has been found that, when the alpha waves disappear, awareness of external stimulation is lost or is markedly decreased. Conversely, sounds or other disturbances during sleep, even though they do not awaken the sleeper, cause the alpha rhythm to reappear (Loomis, Harvey, and Hobart, 1936). During predominance of delta activity, the subjects did not respond to or recall material presented to them (Simon and Emmons, 1956). Dreams occur chiefly during the brain-wave records which characterize the lighter stages of sleep; they are seldom recalled if they occur during a period when the alpha waves have been absent for some time (Lindsley, 1944). As the individual awakens, alpha waves reappear, but they continue for some time to be of low voltage.

With the increase in the degree of excitation produced by the presentation of visual, auditory, tactual, gustatory or pain stimuli, the alpha waves become smaller or disappear entirely. This effect is especially noticeable in the area of the cortex serving the particular sense organ which is being stimulated. Under these conditions, low-potential, fast activity of the beta type is usually observed. But even without sensory stimulation, if the subject expects to receive such stimulation, the alpha waves will disappear. For example, if he opens his eyes in a dark room when he is expecting to see something (and probably is therefore alert), the alpha waves vanish. If he does not expect to see anything, they continue as before (Loomis, Harvey, and Hobart, 1936).[1]

Gastaut and Bert (1954) reported that, except in rare cases, the alpha rhythm, blocked by opening the eyes, reappeared partially after some 10 seconds, though with a lower amplitude and in brief bursts separated by long intervals of desynchronization. When a movie was shown to the subjects, alpha blocking again occurred, and subsequent bursts of alpha rhythm occurred more rarely and were of still lower amplitude and often of greatly increased frequency. When the movie was replaced by blank strips of equal luminosity, it was fairly common to observe a resynchronization of the alpha rhythm, which became well marked and continuous. The investigators concluded that variations in the alpha rhythm are not due merely to retinal stimulation by light. They reported that a large burst of alpha waves occurred with each relaxing of attention, as when, in the films, there were epi-

[1] Certain investigators are of the opinion that there are individual differences in alpha waves which may be related to the use or nonuse of visual imagery. Some subjects have almost no alpha waves even when the eyes are closed, some subjects have alpha waves whether their eyes are open or shut, and some have good alpha waves when the eyes are closed and show blocking of the waves when the eyes are opened (Golla, 1948). Individual differences in the ease of activation would appear, however, to be at least as plausible an explanation of these differences in alpha waves.

sodes arousing no special interest. Lindsley (1950) regards the alpha rhythm as "a manifestation of a resting state, physiologically, an inattentive, waking state, psychologically, and a relaxed and sensory free peripheral state."

Attention focused on a problem, even when there is no sensory stimulation, may block the alpha rhythm. It has been reported that working on problems in mental arithmetic or answering questions which involve mental effort blocks out alpha waves and in other ways modifies the EEG (Lindsley, 1944). During mental work, a predominance of fast beta waves has been found (Lindsley, 1944). Even silent reading has been said to increase the mean brain-wave frequency and to cause the distribution of frequencies to be skewed toward the high end (Knott, 1938). Mundy-Castle (1957) also has reported findings which support the view that blocking of the alpha rhythm occurs when the individual is alerted or attentive. He states, however, that attention, such as concentration during mental arithmetic, can occur without alpha blocking, thus suggesting that there is no one-to-one relationship between the two.

Some investigators have reported that difficult problems produce marked changes in the EEG, while simpler problems do not have this effect. Subjects working on multiplication problems were found to show an increase in the rate of the cortical rhythms which paralleled the extent of the mental effort demanded by the problems (Tyler, Goodman, and Rothman, 1947). Hadley (1941), however, who found a related increase in heart rate and in mean frequencies in the EEG during the solution of problems in mental arithmetic, found no relationship between the difficulty of the problems and either heart-rate changes or the EEG, in spite of the fact that he found variations in action potentials from the muscles which corresponded with problem difficulty.

Alpha blocking and beta augmentation have been reported during the acquisition of a conditioned galvanic skin response (GSR) (Motokawa and Huzimori, 1949). These EEG changes are, of course, identifiable with the activation pattern of Magoun and others.

An increase in the rate of cortical rhythms has also been found when the subjects were kept awake for long periods of time. This was attributed to the effort required to remain awake. When mental arithmetic problems were presented to the subjects after many hours of sleeplessness, the brain potentials showed irregular changes, which were interpreted to indicate a reduction in the capacity of the fatigued brain to further increase its rate of electrical activity (Tyler, Goodman, and Rothman, 1947).

Stimulation of the kind called "emotional" changes the character of the EEG in striking fashion. Darrow and his associates found that alpha waves decrease and beta waves increase after such stimulation (Darrow, Jost, Solomon, and Mergener, 1942). Others have reported that alpha waves were abolished, or practically abolished, by fright, embarrassment, or apprehension (Lindsley, 1944). "Startle" may block the alpha rhythm for 15 to 20 seconds, while beta waves are blocked only momentarily. Strong stimuli causing pain or excitement have been shown to produce the most marked inhibition of the alpha rhythm (Lindsley, 1944). Lindsley concludes that during emotional arousal two principal kinds of changes are seen in the EEG: (1) reduction or suppression of alpha rhythm and (2) increase in the amount of beta-like fast activity (Lindsley, 1950).[2] H. Berger (1933) had reported

[2] It is said that possibly in very young children "emotion" may produce an increase in the theta rhythm which is normal for the age (D. Hill, 1950). Where there is no organic brain disease, the theta rhythm is believed to be associated with neural immaturity, especially immaturity of the mechanisms linking the cortex with the thalamus and the hypothalamus (W. G. Walter, 1950b), or perhaps to represent a metabolic defect.

Darrow (1950) has observed on occasion an increase in alpha rhythm following "emotional" stimulation, and he accounts for the phenomenon as follows: Autonomic and other peripheral changes have a "feed-back" effect upon the central nervous system. Cortical excitation is usually characterized by low-voltage, fast activity in the EEG. This, as in anxiety, for example, seems to be circular or perseverative within the feltwork of the cortex. The alpha rhythm (the most prominent electrical pattern recorded from the outside of the skull in the waking state) apparently arises, on the other hand, from a pacemaker in the thalamus. Impulses from the thalamus are transmitted to the cortex and relayed back to the thalamus, setting up a reverberating circuit with a frequency of about 10 per second. This alpha rhythm disappears in sleep during presumed quiescence of the subcortical pacemaker, and it is reduced, on the other hand, by cortical excitation when the cortex is preoccupied with its own intrinsic activity. Alpha is apparently related likewise to activity of the hypothalamus, and to connected autonomic tone. Darrow suggests that exciting stimuli having both cortical and subcortical consequences might produce an EEG in which low-voltage, fast activity and alpha high-potential rhythmic activity would tend to cancel out each other. More often, he believes, the effects occur serially, cortical fast activity being followed by discharge of the autonomic system (GSR), and this in turn by subcortical effects upon the cortex (increased alpha or slower rhythmic activity) and termination of the excitation, as indicated by recovery in the galvanic skin response. He hypothesizes that in moderation these mechanisms regulate and terminate cortical excitation, but that in excess they may embarrass cortical function and even re-

earlier such a finding. Since that time the report has been confirmed by many other investigators. This "activation pattern" (reduction or elimination of synchronized alpha rhythms and induction of low-amplitude, fast activity) which appears to characterize "emotion" can be reproduced by electrical stimulation of the brain stem reticular formation (Lindsley, 1951). Conversely, destruction of these brain stem structures abolishes the activation pattern and leads to synchronized rhythmic discharges in the thalamus and cortex. The behavior which accompanies this EEG pattern is that of lethargy or somnolence as opposed to "emotional" excitement.

It appears that there is a relationship between the EEG pattern of response to stimulation and the basic pattern of electrical activity in the brain. For example, there is an inverse relationship between cortical excitability and the gross sum of the alpha rhythm—that is, when there is more alpha rhythm the cortex is less easily excited (Kennard and Willner, 1945).[3]

Fatigue has been found to reduce the alpha rhythm and to produce some of the random, slow waves which frequently occur in sleep. These disappear and the EEG tends to return to normal when caffeine (a stimulant) is taken (Lindsley, 1944).

Endocrine disturbances have a marked effect on the electroencephalogram. Removal of the adrenal glands slows the EEG, and injections of pregnenolone normalize it (Hoagland, 1950). Hypothyroidism is associated with low alpha frequencies, while hyperthyroidism is associated with abnormally high ones (Lindsley, 1944). The onset of menstruation has been said to be marked by movement of the cortical frequency spectrum toward the low end (9 out of 11 subjects), and two weeks before parturition most, but not all, of twenty pregnant

---

lease subcortical functions from cortical control. He reports data interpreted to indicate that, in brain-injured or emotionally unstable persons, there is a tendency for stimulation to increase the slow alpha-like or theta activity in the precentral parts of the brain, whereas in more stable persons "activation" and postcentral alpha "facilitation" are likely to be found (Darrow, 1953).

[3] Increased alpha rhythm may, according to Darrow (1950), be a means of eliminating the low-voltage fast activity of cortical cells and moderating or terminating excitation in the cortex. Thus he points out that "decrease of alpha rhythm may not only be a consequence of mental activity or tension, but a deficiency of alpha rhythm may be a factor permitting increase of tension." He maintains that the EEG is primarily a record of "facilitative and homeostatic regulatory processes which contribute to but which are not essential to integrative cerebral function." Some aspects of Darrow's homeostatic theory have been questioned by certain other investigators (D. Hill, 1950).

women showed a slowing of cortical activity (Heppenstall and Greville, 1950).

Hormones, stimulants, sedatives, and other chemical factors all affect
the EEG. Lindsley (1944) has pointed out: "The fact that temperature, blood-sugar level, acid-base balance, oxygen consumption, and
other physiological variables are known to produce variations in the
EEG is strong evidence that characteristics of the EEG are in part
controlled by metabolic factors" (p. 105).

Associated with changes in the EEG are changes in the general
degree of arousal of the organism. Alpha waves, it has been shown,
are most prominent during conditions of waking relaxation. As a person goes to sleep, they decrease and are replaced by increasingly large
and slow waves. As he awakens, the alpha waves reappear and increase
in size and frequency as he becomes more alert, until a degree of activation is reached which causes the alpha waves to disappear and be
replaced by low-potential, fast waves or, in the case of strong excitement, by desynchronized activity of low to moderate amplitude. In
other words, large, slow waves of a random, irregular pattern appear
to be characteristic of conditions of most complete relaxation (sleep),
while small, fast waves appear to be characteristic of alertness or a
moderate degree of effort, and desynchronized, fast activity characterizes strong excitement. Rhythmic patterns of intermediate frequency (alpha) occur between the two extremes.

These facts make plausible the contention of a German neurologist
—and of others—that fatigue (drowsiness) can be detected from the
EEG (L. Alexander, n.d.). The signs of fatigue in the EEG's of
aviators were choppiness and discontinuity of alpha waves and the
appearance of slow waves in the record. This neurologist invented a
signaling machine which, by recording brain potentials, could signal
whenever a man became inefficient either because of fatigue so severe
that it approached a condition of sleep, or because of oxygen deprivation. The device was set to signal all frequencies of brain potentials
lower than 8 per second and never to respond to frequencies above 8
per second. The signaling device could be installed in airplanes in
such a way as to inform the pilot whether any member of his crew
was falling asleep or becoming affected by oxygen deprivation, or
it could be used to set off an alarm system when the driver of an automobile was falling asleep.[4]

---

[4] The contention that fatigue can be detected by the presence in the EEG of
frequencies lower than those of the alpha rhythm does not appear to be negated
by the finding (Barnes and Brieger, 1946) that there was no loss of alpha rhythm

As is regularly the case with measures of the degree of activation, the EEG shows adaptation effects with repetition of the same stimulus situation. For example, many persons show few alpha waves during the first minutes of recording of the EEG, but, after they become more accustomed to the situation, alpha waves reappear (Loomis, Harvey, and Hobart, 1936). Auditory stimuli which block the alpha rhythm lose their effectiveness after a few repetitions, and persistent, unchanging stimulation with light flashes for a period of 10 to 15 seconds or longer usually results in a return of the alpha rhythm (Lindsley, 1944). Changes have been reported in the alpha index in the course of an hour's adding (Bujas and Petz, 1954). At first there was a rapid decrease in the index, but, toward the end of the work period, it began to rise slowly. Ford (1954b) however, found no adaptation effects in integrated frontal potentials when he compared the first and second halves of a period during which the subject was engaged in mental arithmetic. Adaptation effects (i.e., indicative of a lower degree of activation) have been observed upon repetition of a hypnotic suggestion or of a symptom-provoking life situation (Wolff, 1953). If, however, the situation acquires deeper significance as it is repeated, it has been said that no change may occur, or the change may be in the opposite direction. Darrow, Vieth, and Wilson (1957) have reported decreased blocking of the alpha rhythm when successive loud gong stimuli were presented at 10-second intervals. They concluded that any new stimulus requiring interpretation or readjustment produces blocking, but that, as the stimulus is evaluated and adjusted to, the blocking disappears. Familiarity with a situation, solution of a problem, or rendering an activity automatic were said to restore the alpha rhythm.

At this stage of our information, interpretations of the EEG must be made with some caution. Darrow believes brain potentials to be similar to "other preparatory and facilitative bodily changes which have been studied as indicators of psychological arousal and reaction" (Darrow, 1947). Jasper (1936) has shown that, in the normal human being and in the cat, states of extreme excitement are accompanied by

---

after the fatigue of an academic day. This finding may conceivably be explained by the fact that the fatigue was not great enough to approach a condition of sleep, or perhaps by the fact that the period with which the fatigue record was being compared was one in which the students were taking the test for the first time and were therefore tense and anxious, thus showing little alpha rhythm. Since a strong alpha rhythm does not appear except during conditions of relaxation, there may well have been little difference between the extent of the alpha rhythm during the two periods which were compared.

a loss of all rhythms in electric potentials. As the excitement grows less, small, rapid waves appear. As the organism relaxes moderately, the waves become more regular. With sleep, the rhythms become slower, and with deeper sleep, they become still slower and larger, and irregularities appear. Cortical rhythms, then, seem to vary in frequency and amplitude from the large, slow, irregular waves of sleep, through the faster, smaller, and well-synchronized waves of waking relaxation, through the very fast and small waves usually found during mental effort, to the loss of all rhythms in electric potentials which occurs in extreme excitement. A loss of rhythm of the potentials tends to occur in either very deep sleep or very extreme excitement. Perhaps in deep sleep there is too little activity of the brain to produce well-marked rhythms, while in extreme excitement there is activity of so many different parts of the brain that there is little synchronization. Where rhythms occur at all, their frequency appears in general to be lower in states of low activation than in states of high activation. Thus it appears that the electroencephalogram may, with the caution appropriate to our limited knowledge of its nature and correlates, be employed as an indicator of the general degree of activation.[5]

The activation pattern (reduction of alpha waves and increase of low-amplitude, fast activity) has been attributed by Lindsley (1951) to the reticular formation. This mechanism not only changes the cortical EEG but also increases somatic and autonomic activity. Experiments by Lindsley, Bowden, and Magoun have shown that, as more and more of the reticular formation of cats was eliminated, there were correlated changes in the electroencephalogram, from the initial activation pattern to one of increased synchronization (Lindsley, 1951). While Lindsley's discussion emphasizes the extremes of activation ("emotion" and sleep), there seems to be no good reason for not conceiving of a continuum of activation, and certainly, to the present author, no good reason for labeling one part of this continuum "emotion."[6]

OTHER MEASURES

Metabolic Rate

Total metabolic rate, like the other physiological measures which have been discussed, varies with differences in the situation. It is

[5] Among reviews of electroencephalographic studies are those by Ellingson (1956) and by Werre (1957).

[6] Lindsley (1952) apparently now conceives of a continuum similar to the one described by the author in an earlier publication (Duffy, 1951).

lowest during relaxed sleep and highest during extreme effort or excitement, showing gradations between these extremes which appear to correspond very roughly to the energy requirements of the moment. Intense mental effort has been reported to be accompanied by a slight increase in general metabolism (Benedict and Benedict, 1930; Altschule, 1953); oxygen consumption was found to be greater during the adding of numbers under conditions of noise than under conditions of quiet (Woodworth and Schlosberg, 1954); and "emotional" upset has been shown to elevate the metabolic rate in most, but not in all, instances (Altschule, 1953; DuBois, 1927). In a study of patients with mental disorders it was found that, without regard to the clinical classification of the disorder, higher rates of metabolism were associated with elated, overactive, overtalkative states, while lower rates of metabolism were associated with depressed, underactive, undertalkative states (G. W. Henry, 1929).

In rats, whose overt activity can be roughly measured by activity wheels, a striking correlation was found between metabolic rate and activity on the wheel over a two-week period ($r = .72 \pm .09$) (C. S. Hall, 1941).

Moreover, metabolic rate, like the other measures discussed, is affected by such factors as fatigue and adaptation. For example, three subjects who were kept working on mental multiplication problems for four consecutive twelve-hour days showed an increase in metabolic rate as the fatigue series progressed (Huxtable, White, and McCartor, 1945). Perhaps the increase was due to the extra effort required to perform the task as time went on—a phenomenon paralleled by the increase in the rate of brain potentials which occurred after prolonged lack of sleep.

Adaptation in metabolic rate may be noted in the common observation that basal-metabolism scores, as measured by oxygen consumption, are lower when the individual has had the measurement made on a number of previous occasions. It may be seen also in a study in which, during mental work, the oxygen consumption per problem solved decreased markedly in the last five days as compared with the first five days of the series (Rounds, Schubert, and Poffenberger, 1932). In other words, the metabolic cost per unit of output was lowered as the result of practice. It may be observed too in the finding that, by the seventh day of work, adding numbers under conditions of noise was no longer accompanied by greater oxygen consumption than adding under conditions of quiet (Woodworth and Schlosberg, 1954).

Respiration

Many investigators have reported a slowing of respiration during sleep, but this has not been the universal finding (Kleitman, 1939). Stresses of various kinds have been found to produce either increases or decreases in respiratory rate, with increases being more common (Altschule, 1953). "Emotional" upsets or other types of stress have been said to increase the respiratory rate in neurotic subjects (Altschule, 1953). In normal subjects also there are many reports of an increased rate of breathing during excitement. For example, during flight training it was found that the largest increases in the rate of respiration occurred during take-offs and landings (A. C. Williams, Jr., Macmillan, and Jenkins, 1947). In normal subjects, listening to music, steadily rising gradients of respiratory activity have been found (Ellis and Brighouse, 1952). Skaggs (1930) reported that, compared with the resting condition, respiratory rate was more rapid during anxious expectancy and after a shock or surprise. It has been said that, following startle stimulation, breathing is momentarily checked and then is greatly accelerated (Landis and Hunt, 1939). On the other hand, telling a lie was found in one study to slow the rate of breathing (Ellson, Davis, Saltzman, and Burke, 1952).

Muscular exercise is generally known to speed and deepen the breathing. Attention to a stimulus produces momentary inhibition of breathing. Auditory stimuli of a simple variety have been shown to produce slower, deeper breathing (R. C. Davis, Buchwald, and Frankmann, 1955), while mental multiplication has been reported to produce quicker and more shallow breathing (Skaggs, 1930).

Evidently, measures of breathing rate and amplitude would not prove to be among the best indicators of the general level of organismic arousal.

Cardiovascular Phenomena

Heart Action. Heart rate and blood pressure are also responsive to changes in the demands of the stimulus situation, a more rapid heart rate and a rise in blood pressure tending to follow increases in the intensity or the significance of stimulation. But the relationship of these measures to the general level of activation of the individual is complicated by the fact that an increase in heart rate and a rise in blood pressure tend to some extent to inhibit each other, or to show compensatory reactions directed toward the maintenance of homeostasis (Darrow, 1943; D. E. Cameron, 1941).

There are, nevertheless, a number of studies which show an increase in heart rate, or a rise in blood pressure, or both, when the individual becomes more highly activated. The pulse rate is higher when the individual stands than when he sits. It is increased by even such slight activity as counting to oneself (D. E. Cameron, 1941). Sudden attention to any stimulus is followed by a consistent increase in heart rate (Ford, 1953). Lying supine on a cot and performing arithmetical computations which required no speech or other body movements increased the electrical output of the heart and in the majority of subjects produced a more rapid beat (Ford, 1953). The correctness or incorrectness of the answers given bore no significant relationship to the increase in electric potentials. The result of cold-pressor stimulation was to increase both systolic and diastolic blood pressure, increase the heart rate, and decrease the finger pulse volume (B. T. Engel, 1959).

During flight training, the heart rate was greater during take-offs and landings than during other less difficult maneuvers (A. C. Williams, Jr., Macmillan, and Jenkins, 1947). During work on a clerical test, it was higher during work than during rest, and higher when the individual was working under distraction than when he was working under conditions of quiet—this in spite of the fact that there was no decrease in the efficiency of the performance under distraction (Bitterman and Soloway, 1946). During mirror-tracing, pulse rate was found to be a highly sensitive indicator of visuo-motor conflict (Brower, 1947). An invariable increase in pulse rate accompanied the taking of college examinations (Dodge, 1913), and sudden tilting in a chair led to an increase in both the pulse rate and the force of the heartbeat (Blatz, 1925). According to a review by Altschule (1953), "startle, anxiety, tension, and apprehension may increase cardiac output by two-thirds and occasionally by more."

Conversely, the heart rate is very much slower during sleep than during waking states, and slower during sleep at night than during daytime naps (Kleitman, 1939). However, uneasy sleep with exciting dreams may produce an increase in heart rate (Kleitman, 1939). Stimulation has in some instances produced a decrease, rather than an increase, in the rate of heartbeat. Auditory stimuli (70 to 120 decibels) led to an initial increase in pulse rate, followed in a few seconds by a decrease to a subnormal level (R. C. Davis, Buchwald, and Frankmann, 1955). A slowing of the heart was also reported during "neutral" questioning and during a shock threat, with a greater slowing occurring during lying than during nonlying (Ellson, Davis, Saltzman, and Burke, 1952). It is said that "at times and to a limited extent heart rate may decrease during effort, while the force of the beat increases." An explanation of some of these phenomena may perhaps be found in the statement that the effect of certain depressor reflexes is such as to make the heart rate tend to vary inversely with the blood pressure (R. C. Davis, Buchwald, and Frankmann, 1955).

Adaptation in heart rate has been found in a number of investigations. During arithmetical computation, the electrical output of the heart was smaller in the second half of the work period than it was in the first half (Ford, 1953). The slowing of the pulse which occurred under presentation of auditory stimuli decreased with repetition of the stimulation (R. C. Davis, Buchwald, and Frankmann, 1955). Moreover, under resting conditions, both before and after the presentation of conditioned auditory stimuli, there was a drift to a lower heart-rate level during each of two experimental sessions (Notterman, Schoenfeld, and Bersh, 1952).

It is of interest that the principles which hold for salivary and motor conditioning are applicable also to the heart rate. Dykman, Gantt, and Whitehorn (1956) report that: "HR is proportional to the intensity of the US; it is generalized to various signals in the early training trials; its differentiation develops gradually as a function of the number of trials; and the use of regular stimulus intervals produces a cardiac time reflex." Heart rate, however, decreased from one conditioning session to the next, in spite of the fact that the intensities of the reinforcing shocks were relatively constant.

Blood Pressure. Systolic blood pressure drops during sleep, and, in general, the greater the waking blood pressure the greater the fall during sleep (Kleitman, 1939). Most observers agree that the size of the blood-pressure drop is related to the depth of sleep (Kleitman, 1939). Conversely, blood pressure rises during noise of high intensity and short duration (Berrien, 1946), and also during startle stimulation. Mental concentration has been reported to produce either a rise or no significant change in arterial pressure (Altschule, 1953).

The increase in systolic blood pressure which occurs during "emotional" stress has been widely recognized for many years. During an experimental situation in which a wide variety of "emotional" stimuli were presented, high blood pressure was found to be present throughout the session (Landis and Gullette, 1925). A small rise in systolic pressure has been found during questioning, and a greater rise has been found during lying than during nonlying (Chappell, 1929; Ellson, Davis, Saltzman, and Burke, 1952). A number of investigators have found that an increase in blood pressure is produced by ideational stimuli or a disturbing nature, or by situations in which something of serious consequence is at stake (Darling, 1940). In fact, it has been said that "in the normal individual the most frequent response to a stimulus having an emotional meaning for the individual is a rise in blood pressure" (D. E. Cameron, 1941). It is not surprising, then, that in anxiety and panic states there is a general rise in the systolic and diastolic blood-pressure levels, though the most striking feature of the blood pressure under these conditions has been said to be, not its high level, but the fluctuation in the level (D. E. Cameron, 1941). Diastolic pressure appears to be somewhat less responsive than systolic pressure to changes in the stimulus situation (Altschule, 1953). In one experiment, it rose during questioning, but it failed to discriminate between lying and nonlying (Ellson, Davis, Saltzman, and Burke, 1952).

No adaptation effect in systolic blood pressure was found upon ten repetitions of a noise stimulus, though it was pointed out that experimental precision for this measure was poor (R. C. Davis, Buchwald, and Frankmann, 1955). Other investigators have reported a decrease in the systolic blood pressure rise both before and after a comprehensive examination on the second day as compared with the first day of the examination (C. H. Brown and Van Gelder, 1938).

Volume of Body Parts. A third circulatory measure which might presumably be used as an indicator of the level of activation is the volume of various parts of the body as this is affected by the distribution of the blood to these parts. The volume of any part of the body is, of course, increased by vasodilation and decreased by vasoconstriction.

Studies of the volume of the hands and feet have revealed circulatory changes which produce an increase in their volume during sleep and a decrease in their volume on awakening or on presentation of various types of stimulation (Kleitman, 1939).

An increase in the volume of the brain during sleep was also found in two subjects whose skulls had been trephined (Shepard, 1906, 1914). A stimulus which did not awaken the subjects nevertheless produced a transient decrease in brain volume. Stimulation during the waking state, however, led to the end result of a rise in brain volume and a fall in hand volume. Woodworth and Schlosberg (1954) suggest an explanation of this apparently paradoxical finding, and R. C. Davis and his collaborators have pointed out that a general vasoconstriction will have the effect of increasing the blood flow through the brain (R. C. Davis, Buchwald, and Frankmann, 1955).

Decreased volume of the finger was found as part of the response to a loud auditory stimulus, and the constriction was significantly greater for a stimulus of 120 decibels than for stimuli of 90 or 70 decibels (R. C. Davis, Buchwald, and Frankmann, 1955). Repetition of stimulation produced a nonsignificant decrease in the response. Volume of the chin area, on the other hand, increased as a result of stimulation in the case of most subjects. Some subjects, however, showed a consistent decrease in volume. These was no significant relationship to stimulus intensity. While the application of stimulation presumably produces a net constriction effect in the body as a whole, this effect is not found in each separate part of the body (R. C. Davis, Buchwald, and Frankmann, 1955). Many different types of stimuli, however, from those called emotional to those producing anticipation or concentration, have been reported by many investigators to result in vasoconstriction (Altschule, 1953). It is of interest that there has been confirmation of the finding of Binet and Courtier, in 1897, that strong pleasurable "emotions" produce peripheral vascular effects similar to those of unpleasant "emotions" (Altschule, 1953).

Temperature

Body temperature (e.g., oral or rectal) usually decreases when an individual lies down, especially if there is muscular fatigue and an inclination to relax (Kleitman, 1939). Less movement during sleep was found when the body temperature was lower (Kleitman, 1939). Caffeine in certain dosages produced both a rise in body temperature and an increase in body movements (Kleitman, 1939).

Skin temperature behaves differently from body temperature, reaching its greatest height in normal individuals at the time of deepest sleep and falling sharply at the time of awakening (Kleitman, 1939). Cooling of the hands and feet during "emotion" has frequently been found (Altschule, 1953), though a rise in the temperature of the palms was reported both for jumping electric sparks and for dynamometer squeezing (Baker and Taylor, 1954). Ax (1953) has reported that the temperature of the face, as well as of the hand, drops during strong "emotion." Other investigators appear, however, to have found a rise in face temperature under intense stimulation more often than a fall, though many drops in temperature have also been recorded (Helson and Quantius, 1934; Altschule, 1953). Helson and Quantius (1934) found that such stimuli as cold water, ice, loud sounds, a kiss, or the anticipation of an electric shock produced changes in face temperature in about 75 per cent of the recorded instances, and that these changes were rises in 133 cases and drops in 66 cases.

Finger temperature clearly drops during stimulation which alerts the organism. Hospitalized patients, while discussing traumatic aspects of their case histories, showed a drop in finger temperature with strikingly few exceptions (Mittelmann and Wolff, 1939). Less strong stimulation also produces a drop in the temperature of the fingers. This effect has been observed in normal subjects during a learning test, during a word-association test, upon interruption while reading, and upon the beginning of conversation when the subject had been relaxed (Flecker, 1951). Local vasoconstriction appears to be the major factor responsible for the decrease in skin temperature.

Groups of Measures

Dawson and Davis report that, when a subject pressed a key in response to a signal, muscular activity increased, sweat-gland action increased, breathing became faster and deeper, the heart slowed down, the blood vessels in the hand constricted, and the pulse pressure went up (R. C. Davis, 1957a). Davis expressed the opinion that all of these changes were initiated by the warning signal which, if it were sufficiently strong, would produce such responses even if no action were required of the subject. With action required, however, the total pattern of the responses would be stronger and, qualitatively, somewhat different.

In response to a rough tone of 98 decibels, subjects showed a decrease in skin resistance and finger volume (vasoconstriction) and an increase in skeletal-muscle tension, pressure pulse, breathing amplitude, breathing-cycle time, systolic blood pressure, and interpulse interval (R. C. Davis, Buchwald & Frankmann, 1955). The investigators noted that all these effects except two, breathing rate and heart rate, represent a greater amount of activity, and they suggest that the slowing of the breathing and the heart rate "may be compensatory action for the 'pressor' effects of the other variables." All the physiological measures showed effects in the same direction as that produced by the questions in a lie-detection experiment. Repeated noise stimulation led to less response in skin resistance, volume pulse, and interpulse interval, to little change in some of the other measures, and to a larger response in breathing amplitude.

R. C. Davis, Lundervold, and Miller (1957), in an experiment to be described more fully later, recorded a number of physiological measures in stimulus situations which included rest, tapping, and auditory and visual stimulation. They were able to describe both a general response pattern which their experimental conditions tended to produce and particular variations in the pattern which were produced by particular conditions. The general pattern consisted of "increased flexor and extensor activity, increased sweat-gland activity, increased heart rate, peripheral vasoconstriction (finger), and increased respiration rate and amplitude." They pointed out that, except for the vasoconstriction, this pattern was, on a small scale, that which accompanies exercise. All the experimental conditions tended to move the individual to some degree toward this pattern, maximum-rate tapping producing more of this effect than any other condition, and rest producing less of it.

Minimal stimulation (lying on a cot in a dark, soundproofed room for about forty minutes) produced increased muscular and circulatory activity and decreased respiration (R. C. Davis, 1959). It was suggested that this pattern may be characteristic of anticipation, and that the results of "sensory deprivation" may be explainable as due to increased sensitization.

Adaptation of autonomic responses is seen in an experiment in which continuous readings of skin resistance, heart rate, and respiration to serially presented stimuli rapidly diminished to a relatively constant level (Dykman, Reese, Galbrecht, and Thomasson, 1959). Skin resistance was found to behave more consistently and to show more reactivity.

SUMMARY

A review of studies of a number of physiological functions has demonstrated that measures of these functions show, in most instances, consistent variations with changes in the apparent demands of the stimulus situation. They show changes in one direction when demands increase, or stimulation is more intense, and changes in the opposite direction when demands decrease, or stimulation is less intense, the extent of the change being roughly proportional to the intensity or significance of the stimulation. These measures may therefore be regarded as indicators of the extent of arousal, or degree of activation, of the individual at the moment. It follows that, when other factors are constant, they may also be regarded as indicators of the degree of significance of the situation to the individual, or the impact upon the organism of the stimulation presented.

Variations in these measures appear to occur in a continuum, extending from deep sleep on the one hand to extreme degrees of excitement on the other hand. While the level of activation varies with such factors as hormones and drugs, which affect the susceptibility of the organism to stimulation, it varies also in striking fashion with variations in the stimulus situation.

chapter 5

The patterning of activation

INTRODUCTION

The activation of the individual shows patterning. The organism responds as a whole only in the sense that what goes on in any one part of the organism affects what goes on in any other part. It does not respond as a whole in the sense that every system is activated to an equal degree and at the same instant. On the contrary, the latencies of the various responses which contribute to the pattern of activation are different; the extent, and sometimes the direction, of the response of a given system such as the vascular system is different in different parts of the body; some responses (e.g., heart rate and blood pressure) may show compensatory relationships to each other; and, depending upon the circumstances and the individual, some organs or organ systems may be activated more highly than others. Nevertheless, it is apparent that it is the organism, rather than separate and independent systems, which is activated. The activation of one system bears a meaningful relationship to the activation of other systems, and the activation of the interrelated systems bears a meaningful relationship to the nature and degree of significance of the stimulating conditions. Moreover, the activation of the organism as a whole is measurable—if not with precision, at least with an approximation to accuracy.

Some of the respects in which patterning of response, rather than massive and undifferentiated activation is shown, are described below.

ADJUSTMENT OF THE RESPONSE TO THE PARTICULAR DEMANDS OF THE STIMULATING SITUATION

The response of the organism appears to be nicely adjusted to the demands of the specific stimulating situation, always of course within the limits of the ability of the organism as determined by capacity and experience. Examples of this nicety of adjustment of activation have been seen in variations in the degree of activation with relatively minor variations in the stimulus situation, and in the apparently appropriate increase or decrease in the degree of activation which has been shown to occur upon repetition of a stimulus situation.

Nicety of adjustment is shown, however, not only in finely graded degrees of activation but also in the locus of activation. A goal-oriented organism, with a particular stimulus to be attended to, or a particular task to be performed in order to reach its goal, not only releases energy in appropriate degree (within the limits of its ability), but also in appropriate places within the organism. An organism set to carry on one type of activity requires a different pattern of activation from an organism set to carry on another type of activity. When, however, instructions to the subject are the same, but the stimulus varies in intensity, the locus of the covert response is likely to remain the same while the degree of activation varies. It was found, for example, that presentation of auditory stimuli of varying degrees of intensity, with the subject instructed to make no response, led to little differentiation in the covert responses which were activated, but that the response systems (or physiological processes) were activated to different degrees, depending upon the intensity of the stimulation (R. C. Davis, Buchwald, and Frankmann, 1955).

The adjustment of the response to the demands of the stimulus situation has been shown most clearly in studies of the patterning of skeletal-muscle responses. When an overt response is to be made, tension tends to be focalized in the part of the body which will be most directly involved in making the response. For example, when a subject was asked to press a key in response to a tone, tension was highly localized in the muscles likely to be involved in the subsequent key pressing if only a simple reaction was required (R. C. Davis, 1952). If the subject was required to make a "choice response," tension was more widespread.

A group of headache-prone subjects showed increases in muscle tension in the forearm when in a situation judged by the experimenters to involve conflict over arm movement, and in the neck muscles in a situation judged to involve conflict over head movement (Malmo, Wallerstein, and Shagass, 1953). In another investigation, subjects working on arithmetical problems, with no movement of any kind permitted, showed considerable variation in the part of the body which was the locus of the greatest degree of tension (Ford, 1954a). Muscle tone, however, did not go up and down simultaneously all over the body.

On the other hand, it is not to be supposed that muscle tension is so highly localized that only the part of the body directly involved in a response is activated. It has long been known that activity in one part of the body affects activity in another part. For example, potentials recorded during the squeezing of a hand dynamometer revealed activity in the muscles of the arm, the hand, and the leg on the opposite side, the foot on the same side, and in the jaw, mouth, nose, ear, abdomen, chest, and neck (Shaw, 1938). Conversely, relaxation in one part of the body tends to be accompanied by relaxation in other parts of the body. Subjects instructed to relax the right arm during mental multiplication relaxed the muscles of other parts of the body as well (R. C. Davis, 1939).

The extent of "generalization" of muscle tension is influenced by a number of factors. Intense responses apparently produce more generalized tension than weaker responses (D. R. Meyer, 1953). The early stages in the learning of a performance appear to be characterized by more generalized tension than later stages, which show an increasing degree of localization of the tension in the muscle groups specifically involved in the performance of the task (Daniel, 1939; G. L. Freeman, 1931).

With adults it has been shown that muscular activity is consistently at a maximum in one part of the body and is present in other parts in decreasing amount, depending upon the distance of those parts from the focal point of the performing member (R. C. Davis, 1939). Children probably show more diffuse tension than adults, though this conclusion is based more upon general observation than upon direct experimental evidence. Finally, there are some data indicating individual differences in the extent to which muscular tension is generalized or localized. Such differences would be expected on the basis of known differences between individuals in the intensity of response to stimulation and the association of intensity of response with a tendency toward greater generalization of response.

Not only skeletal-muscle responses, but also autonomic responses, show patterning. Vasoconstriction in the extremities and vasodilation in the face is the most frequently reported response to stressful stimulation. Skin resistance of palmar and plantar areas has been said to differ from that in other areas of the body, both in the response to stimulation and, apparently, in the course of adaptation. While the palms show decreased conductance with successive periods of stimulation, the wrist has been reported to show either increased conductance or random fluctuation (Conklin, 1951).

MAINTENANCE OF HOMEOSTASIS AS A FACTOR IN THE PATTERNING OF RESPONSES

The processes involved in the maintenance of homeostasis apparently produce patterning of responses. For example, acceleration in heart rate and a rise in blood pressure are to some extent mutually inhibitory, a rise in blood pressure tending to slow the heart rate, and a rise in heart rate tending to inhibit a rise in blood pressure (D. E. Cameron, 1941). It has been suggested also that there is a homeostatic effect of blood-pressure rise on the EEG which is similar to the effects of blood pressure on pulse and on cerebral circulation (Darrow, Jost, Solomon, and Mergener, 1942). The reappearance of a strong alpha rhythm has been noted in certain instances following the termination of the galvanic skin response, and it has been proposed that this is a mechanism by which cortical excitation is moderated or terminated (Darrow, 1947).

Just as the organism carries on an exchange of water, oxygen, carbon, nitrogen, and other elements and compounds, so also does it carry on continuous thermodynamic exchanges, or continuous regulation of energy metabolism (Brobeck, 1948).

THE LAWFULNESS OF THE PATTERNING OF RESPONSES

One of the most extensive studies of the general patterning of responses has been conducted by R. C. Davis and his collaborators (R. C. Davis, Buchwald, and Frankmann, 1955). Presenting auditory stimuli of three different intensities (70, 90 and 120 decibels), and instructing the subjects to make no response, they simultaneously recorded a number of autonomic and skeletal-muscle changes in order to determine: (1) the latency of various responses, (2) the effect of differences in stimulus intensity, and (3) the effect of repetition of stimulation. They found that the various responses to the stimulation differed considerably in their latency. Changes appeared first in the skeletal muscles, next in skin resistance, then in a number of circulatory responses, and finally in breathing.[1] Increases in stimulus intensity produced an increase in the magnitude of the various responses without changing the patterning of response. Repetition of the stimulus decreased the magnitude of most of the responses, but at different rates, thus producing some change in patterning. Cutaneous stimuli produced a somewhat different pattern of response from auditory stimuli. On the other hand, considerable similarity was reported in the patterning of responses to auditory stimuli and those to interrogation during a lie-detection study.

Individual variation was not so great as to prevent the regular occurrence of the responses in the average subject under the conditions of the experiment. The investigators conclude that: "The results clearly show a lawfulness in somatic responses. The stimuli used regularly produce changes which show a certain variability but can by no means be called random" (R. C. Davis, Buchwald, and Frankmann, 1955).

R. C. Davis and his colleagues proceeded then to investigate the responses to some more complex stimulus situations: (1) viewing pictures and (2) paced key-pressing (R. C. Davis, Lundervold, and Miller, 1957; R. C. Davis and Buchwald, 1957). Considering these investigations in conjunction with the one mentioned above, we may note that four different stimuli (noise, cutaneous stimuli, mild exercise, and viewing pictures) produced in each instance an increase in palmar sweating and in muscle tension (R. C. Davis, 1957a). Davis remarks that "It looks as though any stimulus would produce an increase in sweat-gland and muscular activity. I do not recall having seen or heard of an opposite effect." It would be of interest to know whether the same consistency of response might not be found in the EEG, a measure not included in the investigations referred to. There are reasons for surmising that muscle tension, electrical resistance of the skin, and EEG phenomena may be more dependable as individual indicators of the general degree of activation than circulatory or respiratory phenomena (the other measures employed in the Davis studies).

Davis recognizes that "patterns of response" are not distinct entities which can be sharply separated from each other. He says: "All the

---

[1] This finding is in line with Golla's (1948) report that a subject will press the appropriate signal about one-tenth of a second after the presentation of a stimulus, but that no change in the electrical resistance of the skin occurs until two seconds after the stimulus is presented.

variables in the pattern are continuous, and it seems most likely that
the patterns would likewise merge into one another in a series of gradations if conditions were varied appropriately" (R. C. Davis, 1957a).
To let the facts of patterning obscure the significant concept of a continuum in the variation of physiological responses would be indeed a
mistake. We should be well-advised also, it seems, to continue the
search for a general factor in the various patterns—that is, a factor
such as the one described by the concept of the general level of activation—to avoid becoming lost in the particularities of the situation.

INDIVIDUAL DIFFERENCES IN THE PATTERNING OF RESPONSES

Within the general patterning of activation there are individual
variations. While individuals in general show an arousal pattern characterized by increased palmar conductance, increased muscle tension,
increased blood pressure or heart rate or both, as well as other changes
previously cited, there are differences between individuals, not only
in the extent of changes produced but also in the extent to which any
given organ or system participates in these changes. Thus, for one individual, heart rate may show a great increase and palmar conductance
only a small increase, while for another individual it may be palmar
conductance which shows the great increase, while heart rate is only
slightly affected. It appears that in one individual, one physiological
system may be most responsive to excitation, while in another individual it may be another system which shows this responsiveness. The
basis for these conclusions is to be found primarily in the experimental
investigations of John I. Lacey and his collaborators, and of R. B.
Malmo and his co-workers. D. E. Cameron (1941) pointed out, however, some years ago that it was not possible to use any one of the
physiological responses of emotion as an index of the activity of the
others. He said: "There are individuals in whom the blood pressure is
the major participant in the emotional reaction; in others it is the gastrointestinal tract."

In three studies, one of 12 pregnant women, one of 57 boys and 53
girls ranging in age from 6 to 18 years, and one of 85 male college
students, Lacey and his co-workers (J. I. Lacey, 1950; J. I. Lacey and
Van Lehn, 1952; J. I. Lacey, Bateman, and Van Lehn, 1953) have
found clear evidence of the existence of individual patterning in autonomic responses to stress. They measured palmar skin conductance,
heart rate, heart-rate variability, and blood pressure under several

different types of stimulation (cold pressor, mental arithmetic, word association, and hyperventilation). They found that, in a given stimulus situation, one individual might show his peak reactivity in, for example, palmar conductance, while another might show it in heart rate or in heart-rate variability. For one measure of autonomic reactivity, a given individual might be above the mean; for another, he might be at the mean; and, for still a third measure, he might be far below the mean. In one extreme case a subject was 3.6 sigma below the mean in pulse pressure, and 1.5 sigma above the mean in heart rate. In other words, there was a difference of 5.1 sigma between her peak response measure and her minimum response measure.

By means of retests in the same situation, it was shown that the patterns of autonomic response were not a matter of chance, though even upon immediate retest there was considerable variation in the pattern. (Reliability coefficients of pattern-index scores ranged from .43 to .78.) When measurements were made in four different types of situation, as listed above, it was shown that there was some tendency for an individual to respond with maximal activation in the same response system in each situation as he had in the others. Moreover, the systems not maximally activated tended to maintain their rank in the hierarchy of responsiveness, though all response systems showed considerable fluctuation from stress to stress in the degree of activation which separated one from the other.

Developmental changes in the patterns of autonomic responses were also shown (J. I. Lacey, 1949). When younger and older children were compared, it was found that the older children showed, under stress, relatively greater changes in palmar skin conductance and heart-rate variability, while the younger children showed relatively greater changes in blood pressure and in heart rate. Product-moment correlations between age and patterns of autonomic response showed significant correlations of age with patterns of palmar conductance, on the one hand, and systolic blood pressure, diastolic blood pressure, pulse pressure, and heart rate on the other hand. The correlation coefficients indicate that, with an increase in age (within the age limits employed), there is increasing responsiveness of palmar conductance as compared with the other measures. Age also showed a significant correlation with heart-rate variability on the one hand and with blood-pressure measurements and heart rate on the other, heart-rate variability becoming, as the child grew older, increasingly responsive as an indicator of stress. There was no significant relationship between age and the patterning among the blood-pressure measurements and heart rate. The evidence points, not to a decrease in the range of response as the child grows older, but rather to a reversal in the organs in which the greatest reactivity occurs.

In Lacey's studies only palmar conductance and cardiovascular responses were measured. So far as the cardiovascular responses are concerned, the well-established tendency of heart rate and blood pressure to show at a certain point an inverse relationship to each other would contribute to such findings as the one that an individual might be above the mean in one response and below the mean in another. Moreover, as Lacey has brought out clearly in his more recent publications (J. I. Lacey and B. C. Lacey, 1958a) there are notable differences between individuals in the extent to which they show consistency of response pattern. Some individuals show great consistency from one situation to another in the physiological measure which shows the peak response, and in the order of the other measures in the hierarchy of responsiveness. Other individuals show moderate consistency, and still other individuals show almost no consistency at all.[2]

Malmo and Shagass (1949b) have studied differential responsiveness in psychiatric patients with somatic complaints. They have reported that under the same pain stimulation (thermal), patients with headache or related complaints showed more skeletal-muscle tension than cardiovascular response, while patients with cardiovascular com-

[2] In a study reported at a meeting of the AAAS, M. A. Wenger (1955) challenged Lacey's hypothesis of "relative response specificity." Wenger, using four different types of stress during the same session, and recording skin resistance, heart rate, muscle potentials, respiration rate, pulse pressure, systolic and diastolic blood pressure, and other measures of physiological response, found no evidence of consistency of the measure which showed the maximum response, and no appreciable correlation between the response scores for one stressor and those for another. It appears that there are at least two factors which might contribute to the differences in findings of Lacey and Wenger: (1) Lacey allowed a recovery period of up to thirty minutes between stresses, while Wenger allowed only five minutes for recovery. It is questionable whether five minutes was sufficient time for recovery from the effects of the previous stress. (2) Wenger measured twelve physiological variables, while Lacey measured five (systolic and diastolic blood pressure, heart rate and heart-rate variability, and palmar conductance). Moreover, four of Lacey's five measures were rather closely related cardiovascular measures. It would appear likely that, the greater the number and the diversity of the physiological measures, the less would be the likelihood of finding the maximum response of the individual in the same measure on successive occasions. Experimentation as careful as Lacey's, but using a wider sampling of physiological measures, should throw further light on the question of response consistency. Within the limits of the measures he employed, Lacey has strong evidence for consistency, at least in some individuals.

plaints showed the reverse relationship between the two measures. These same investigators have found evidence in another study that the greater the skeletal-muscle response to painful stimulation, the less the rise in blood pressure (Malmo and Shagass, 1952).

R. C. Davis, Lundervold, and Miller (1957), using measures of skin resistance, muscle tension, and certain respiratory and circulatory changes, report a tendency, though not a strong one, for "the response variables to behave in a way specific to the individual."

Further evidence of individual patterning is found in a study in which administration under carefully controlled conditions of such autonomic drugs as epinephrin and Mecholyl led to the discovery of different physiological types, one reacting primarily to adrenergic stimulation and the other reacting primarily to cholinergic stimulation (Greenblatt, 1944).

The demonstration of individual patterning in physiological responses has, among others, the following implications: (1) Coefficients of correlation among individual indicators of activation can be expected in many instances to be relatively low. (2) A group of physiological measures, rather than a single measure, is likely to serve as the best indicator of the level of activiation. (3) It is possible, as suggested by Lacey, that the best measure to employ in comparing individuals with respect to the degree of arousal is the measure which for the individual shows the peak reactivity.

THE PATTERNING OF ACTIVATION IN VARIOUS "EMOTIONS"

Psychologists have long been interested in the possibility of discovering another type of patterning of physiological responses—a patterning which would correspond with specific "emotions." It has been supposed that the physiological responses in "fear," for example, might conceivably be characteristically different from those in "rage," and that these in turn might be different from those in some other "emotion." In general, the search for such differential responses has proved to be fruitless.

Ax, however, has reported that a comparison of the physiological effects produced by a "fear" stimulus and by a "rage" stimulus showed significant differences in seven of the fourteen measures employed (Ax, 1953). He found that "diastolic blood pressure rises, heart rate falls, number of rises in skin conductance, and muscle potential increases were greater for anger than for fear, whereas skin conductance increases, number of muscle potential increases and respiration rate increases were greater for fear than for anger" (Ax, 1953).

Since Ax used only a single "fear" stimulus and a single "rage" stimulus, he has not demonstrated that two or more dissimilar "fear" stimuli produce the same pattern of arousal, or that two or more dissimilar "anger" stimuli produce the same pattern of arousal. It seems probable that situations which might be classified as fear stimuli differ among themselves in many respects, and that situations which might be regarded as rage stimuli also differ among themselves in many respects, and that the responses of the organism, if measured with sufficient fineness and completeness, would reflect these differences. If this is true, it would appear to be futile to search for a universal pattern of "fear" or of "rage." Supporting this point of view is the finding of another investigator that, in the same stimulus situation (cold pressor test), different individuals showed so many different patterns of autonomic response that it was "impossible to assume that the subjects responded . . . with as many diverse emotional constellations as the varying patterns of response would suggest" (J. I. Lacey, Bateman, and Van Lehn, 1953). Indeed Ax himself reported that in his experiment the variance between subjects was significantly greater than that within subjects.

THE INTERRELATIONSHIPS OF MEASURES OF THE DEGREE OF ACTIVATION

Introduction

While the organism is not activated *en masse*, nevertheless activation in one part or system tends to be associated with activation in other parts or systems, so that the organism as a whole may be regarded as functioning at a relatively high or a relatively low level of activation. This is the common observation in regard to the arousal effects of what psychologists have called "motives" or "emotions." Were this not true, there would be no meaning to such statements as that the individual is excited or relaxed. Instead one would have to say, for example, that his muscular system was excited, but his cardiovascular system was relaxed. Though it is indeed true that one system may respond with a greater degree of excitation than another system, and that one part of a particular system may even on occasion respond in a direction opposite to that of other parts of the same system, yet, considered from an over-all point of view, there appears to be a predict-

able direction in which many of the systems of the organism will respond to more intense or more significant stimulation. In normal individuals, the type of response of each system will apparently be such
as to increase the general level of activation of the organism and make
it more ready for vigorous overt response, while at the same time maintaining internal equilibrium. Davis et al., finding the latency of the
skeletal-muscle response to be less than that of various autonomic responses, and finding also that the muscle response showed more rapid
extinction, remarked that "the autonomic responses cannot 'support'
one skeletal-muscle response of comparable type" (R. C. Davis, Buchwald, and Frankmann, 1955). It may be argued, however, that the
energy for the original muscular response was available in the muscles
themselves, and that the autonomic responses were a part of the preparation for possible prolonged action in the situation. The slower "recovery" of the autonomic responses may be related to their greater
latency.

J. I. Lacey (1950), while stressing the individual patterning of responses, nevertheless reported in one study that all individuals showed
an increase in both systolic and diastolic blood pressure and in palmar
conductance, and that ten of the twelve subjects showed moderate increases in heart rate and in heart-rate variability. He and his collaborators (J. I. Lacey, Bateman, and Van Lehn, 1953) conclude:

The autonomic nervous system does indeed respond to experimentally
imposed stress "as a whole" in the sense that all autonomically innervated
structures seem to be activated, usually in the direction of apparent sympathetic predominance. But it does not respond "as a whole" in the sense
that all autonomically innervated structures exhibit equal increments or
decrements of function (p. 9).

Under the circumstances thus far described, what should be the
expectation in regard to the correlation of the various measures of
activation which are commonly employed? Obviously, a perfect correlation is hardly to be expected. Differences in the latency of responses,
differences between individuals in the system which is maximally activated, and the fact that two processes, both of which are responsive
to changes in energy demands, may at a certain point begin to operate
in compensatory fashion, all would tend to reduce the size of coefficients of correlation. In addition, certain responses may reach their
physiological limit before that limit is reached by other responses with
which they are compared. Also, there appear to be differences between
measures in the degree of "generality" of the activation which they
reflect. For example, as G. L. Freeman (1948a) has pointed out, basal

metabolism reflects the activity of the entire organism, while muscular tension *recorded from one part of the body* [3] may reflect to a greater degree the activity of the local area from which the measurement is taken. While there may be usually, if not always, a fairly high correlation between local activity and general arousal, or the totality of local activity, the correlation is not perfect, and the absence of perfect correlation serves, of course, to reduce the coefficient of correlation between any two particular indicators of a general state of arousal. Finally, errors of measurement, which are always to be considered, may loom particularly large in this area of investigation. Physiological measurements are subject to many pitfalls of method and interpretation unsuspected by any but the most experienced investigators.

In the light of these facts, it is not surprising that coefficients of correlation between the various measures are in general positive but not high. A brief review of some of the studies in which simultaneous measurements were made of two or more of the functions affected by activation of the organism will provide a basis for considering further the problem of the measurement of activation.

Before reviewing these studies, however, it may be well to point out, as Malmo (1959) has done, that *intra*individual correlations among physiological measures, rather than *inter*individual correlations, provide the crucial data for a theory of activation. If, under changes in stimulus conditions, a number of physiological measures show a consistent increase or decrease in a significantly large percentage of individuals, we may conclude that these measures are indicative of the degree of activation of the individual, even though the extent of the change in one measure as compared with that in another is different in different individuals, thus reducing interindividual correlations. R. C. Davis (1957a) has already been quoted as saying that "It looks as though any stimulus would produce an increase in sweat-gland and muscular activity. I do not recall having seen or heard of an opposite effect." R. C. Davis, Lundervold, and Miller (1957), as will be shown later in this chapter, found a "general response pattern" to certain stimuli, which they described as consisting of increased muscle tension, increased sweat-gland activity, increased heart rate, and increased respiration rate and amplitude, accompanied by vasoconstriction in the finger. Except for the vasoconstriction, which in this instance they believed had a special explanation, they noted that this pattern was, on a small scale, that which accompanies exercise and which is also supposed to be present in "emergency reaction." The response variables were said

[3] Italics mine.

to behave with reasonable consistency from subject to subject under their experimental conditions.

Schnore (1959) has reported that, during visual tracking and mental arithmetic, in one instance under "low arousal" and in another instance under "high arousal" conditions, 56 per cent of his subjects (forty-three males) showed significant correlation among the various physiological measures which he employed. These were EMG (from right and left forearms and back of the neck), heart rate, systolic blood pressure, respiration, palmar conductance, skin temperature, and grip pressure. The measures which differentiated consistently between states of high arousal and those of low arousal, assumed on the basis of experimental conditions, were said to be heart rate, blood pressure, respiration rate, and right forearm muscle tension.

Dykman, Reese, Galbrecht, and Thomasson (1959), who measured skin resistance, heart rate, and respiration, found that, though an individual's reaction in one autonomic system was not an adequate basis for predicting his reaction in another, nevertheless their subjects tended to "maintain their group position in the three systems studied from one stimulus to the next" and that "the magnitude of reaction as judged by intraindividual data is correlated with the magnitude of reaction as judged by interindividual data."

It would appear, therefore, that we have, in intraindividual correlations of measures, a basis for a general concept of activation.

The Relationship between Muscle Tension and Other Measures

Muscle tension and the electrical resistance of the skin are without doubt related to each other. In fact, there is almost universal agreement that changes in skin resistance show consistent variation with changes in muscle tension, though the extent of the relationship between the two has not been clearly established (M. M. White, 1930; Wenger and Irwin, 1936).

In one study the parallel course followed by muscle tension and skin resistance was demonstrated by recording palmar resistance changes while the subjects pushed with their feet against lever arrangements attached to spring balance scales (Freeman and Simpson, 1938). The tension of the muscles varied from reclining relaxation, through pressures of 10, 20, and 40 pounds, to a pressure of 80 pounds. With each increment in muscular tension, a regular decrease in skin resistance was found. In fact, throughout the series of measurements there were only two reversals of this trend, both of which occurred in a subject who had college examinations on the day of the test. Action potentials recorded from the muscles used in pushing of the levers were related in similar fashion to skin resistance, though the relationship was not one-to-one.

There is also some evidence that muscle tension is positively related to the rate of respiration (Telford and Storlie, 1946) and to heart rate (Peters and Gantt, 1953; Hadley, 1941). A similar relationship to blood pressure was indicated by the finding that in lie-detector tests, voluntary muscular contraction could produce the blood-pressure changes which were regarded as characteristic of deception.

R. C. Davis, Buchwald, and Frankmann (1955) have reported, however, that muscle potentials from the arm failed to vary from one stimulus situation to another in a fashion corresponding to that of a group of cardiovascular measures which at the same time maintained consistent variation among themselves.[4] The cardiovascular measures included pressure pulse, pulse time, ballistocardiogram, volume pulse, finger volume, and chin volume. These measures showed considerably better than chance agreement in the extent of their response to each of six stimulus situations: heat, heat control, cold, pressure, prick, and tickle. For example, the stimulus situation which caused the greatest response in one of these cardiovascular measures tended to cause the greatest response in the other measures, and the stimulus situation which caused the least response in one measure tended to cause the least response in the other measures. In agreement with the cardiovascular measures were skin resistance, breathing cycle, and breathing amplitude. In terms of magnitude of effect, the six stimulus situations influenced these measures in similar ways and indeed, with the exception of finger volume, in a way similar to that of auditory stimulation.

Malmo and J. F. Davis (1956) have reported rather close relationships between autonomic activity and muscular activity when EMG's were recorded from the forehead, the right-forearm extensors, and the right-forearm flexors while the subject traced a circle viewed in the mirror. The autonomic measures recorded were respiration,

[4] It is conceivable that action potentials of the muscles recorded from only one part of the body would not be a sufficiently good indicator of general activation to correlate highly with cardiovascular measures which might be more closely related to the general level of activation. Cardiovascular measures appear, however, to have behaved less consistently than muscle tension in many reports of research. Perhaps they place a greater burden upon the investigator in regard to skill in recording and wisdom in treating the data. Or perhaps they are actually more erratic than certain other measures.

heart rate, and systolic blood pressure. Values of "gradient steepness," expressed as ratios, were computed for each of forty-three subjects, for eight trials. EMG gradients have been defined by a worker in the Malmo laboratory as "a progressive rise in muscle-tension, which begins with initiation of the task and continues to the end of the task" (Bartoshuk, 1955a). It may be assumed that autonomic gradients consist of similar increases in various autonomic functions. When trials 1–4 and 5–8 were treated as separate groups, extremely reliable gradients were found for right-forearm muscles, heart rate, and blood pressure. The gradients for respiration and forehead muscle tension were less reliable, but each of these measures showed a significant gradient in one of the two periods studied. More interesting for present purposes is the fact that a number of statistically reliable correlations in gradient steepness were found between skeletal muscles and two of the measures of autonomic functioning, heart rate, and blood pressure. In fact, the investigators comment that "higher r's were obtained between both autonomic measures and the skeletal-muscle values than were obtained by correlating the autonomic variables with each other." Trials 5–8 gave higher coefficients of correlation than trials 1–4. For the former, the product-moment correlation between extensor muscle and blood pressure was .55, and the coefficient of correlation between the flexor muscle and the heart rate was .47. A number of rather low coefficients of correlation between measures was also found. Forehead-muscle tension and respiration showed fewer significant coefficients of correlation than the other measures. Respiration correlated significantly once, however, with each of the other five variables.

It would appear that the "gradients" reported in this experiment and others to be mentioned later may occur only during tasks of relatively short duration, or during the first part of tasks of longer duration, or perhaps as an "end-spurt" in longer tasks. This view is supported by the fact that, in the experiment described, data from the fourth (last) traversal during each of the eight trials were omitted from the computation because they were said to show "an atypical downward dip." On a priori grounds, it does not seem probable that activation continues to increase throughout long tasks. Even during a short but demanding task (two-plate tapping) Buford Johnson (1928) reported that the grip pressure of only some of her subjects continued to increase. It appeared further that those subjects who showed a continuing increase in muscle tension after a certain initial period were the poorer performers.

The Relationship between the Electrical Resistance
of the Skin and Other Measures

The electrical resistance of the skin has shown varying degrees of relationship to measures of metabolic activity.

Golla (1921) contended that the work of Crile and his students had shown that, in all tissues, an increase in electrical conductivity was associated with an increase in their metabolic activity. The correspondence between metabolic activity and electrical resistance in particular tissues might well be expected to be closer than the correspondence between over-all metabolic rate and measures of electrical resistance. G. L. Freeman (1948a) refers to experiments by Freeman and Darrow which indicate that the organism shows different metabolic rates in its different parts, and that these are then composited in unknown ways in measures of general metabolism.

Simultaneous measurements of palmar skin resistance (converted into conductance) and insensible weight loss (a measure of metabolic rate) showed in some instances striking correspondence and in other instances discrepancies (Freeman and Darrow, 1935). Rank-order coefficients of correlation between the two measures ranged from .39 to .97, with a median coefficient of .70. The measurements were made while the subjects were active, not under "basal" conditions.

In a study of fifty subjects under basal conditions (followed in some cases by stimulation), simultaneous measurement of palmar skin resistance and metabolism (measured by oxygen consumption) showed uniformly low coefficients of correlation between the measures (Freeman and Giffin, 1939). However, high resistance was always associated to some extent with low oxygen consumption. The investigators noted that the palmar resistance measures were more stable on test-immediate-retest than the metabolic measures and also more reliable when measurements were made with several days intervening.

Darrow, Pathman, and Kronenberg (1946) reported that low palmar resistance was associated with increased metabolic rate or increased body temperature.

Using the Tarchanoff method to obtain electrical potentials from the forearm, Purdy, Johnson, and Sheard (1931) concluded that these potentials correlated rather closely with basal metabolic rate, if the metabolic rate was within the normal range. Higher basal metabolic rates were accompanied by lower differences of potentials and vice versa. To some extent, it was possible to predict metabolic rate from these potentials. On the other hand, in another study, no relationship

was found between metabolism and electromotive force (King, 1946)—
that is to say, the total electrical field of the organism did not appear
to be related to its total metabolism.

Various cardiovascular measures have been found to be related to
the electrical resistance of the skin. During rest and during exercise,
high palmar resistance was shown to be associated with low pulse rate
and vice versa (Elbel and Ronkin, 1946). When stimuli of a surprising
or startling nature were presented, heart action and skin resistance
showed a number of correlated changes, many of them statistically
significant (Lauer and Smith, 1932).

During a series of electric shocks, correlation coefficients between
the volume of the finger and the galvanic skin response ranged between .32 and .71 (Hovland and Riesen, 1940). While holding that
vasoconstriction and changes in the electrical resistance of the skin
were functions of common stimulating conditions, Darrow (1929)
concluded, on the basis of studies of those changes in the volume of the
extremities which could be attributed to vasomotor responses, that
there was no necessary relationship between vasoconstriction and the
galvanic skin response.

Body temperature also appears to be correlated to some extent with
skin resistance, a rise in temperature being associated with a decrease
in resistance and a fall in temperature with a rise in resistance (D. E.
Cameron, 1941). During sleep, skin resistance increases while body
temperature falls (Kleitman, 1939). In general, skin resistance during
waking hours undergoes a diurnal variation which follows closely the
diurnal variation in oral temperature (Waller, 1919).

The Relationship between the EEG and Other Measures

When the EEG has been studied in conjunction with a number of
measures of the functioning of the autonomic nervous system, it has
been found that the stimuli which produced the greatest effect on the
vegetative functions also produced the most marked blocking of the
alpha rhythm (Lindsley, 1944).

Simultaneous recording of the EEG, palmar skin-resistance change,
and the systolic blood pressure of "selected high alpha subjects"
showed that, after stimulation, beta potentials increased and alpha potentials tended to decrease (Darrow, Jost, Solomon, and Mergener,
1942). The palmar galvanic response was positively correlated with
the increase of beta rhythms ($r = .51$), and with the decrease of alpha
rhythms ($r = .50$), while blood pressure showed relatively small negative correlations with alpha and beta waves. It was suggested that

there might be a homeostatic effect of blood pressure on the EEG similar to the effects of blood pressure on pulse. Darrow (1947) later reported that stimulation during a state of waking relaxation frequently blocks the alpha rhythm, produces low-potential, fast activity (beta), and causes a palmar galvanic response. At the completion of the galvanic response, there was often an abrupt return of the alpha rhythm.

It has been shown that a generalized shift from low frequency to high frequency activity in the cortex is paralleled by sympathetic discharges, as indicated by arterial pressure and pupillary diameter (Bonvallet, Dell, and Hiebel, 1954). The spontaneous changes in blood pressure and in the frequency of the electrical activity of the cortex were completely parallel when the animal was curarized and at sensory rest. It is of interest that stimulation of the reticular formation has been said to produce the same effects (Bonvallet, Dell, and Hiebel, 1954).

Other studies also have shown relationships between the EEG and autonomic measures. For example, systolic blood pressure, heart rate, palmar conductance, palmar reaction to hyperventilation, and the extent of recovery from the effects of stimulation have been reported to be related to such aspects of the EEG as its frequency, its amplitude, and the pattern of the cortical rhythms (Henry and Darrow, 1947).

Rather low, positive coefficients of correlation were found between parietal-occipital potentials and palmar conductance ($r = .28 \pm .06$) and heart rate ($r = .33 \pm .06$) (Darrow, Pathman, and Kronenberg, 1946). Combining the measures of skin conductance and heart rate raised the correlation coefficient to $.48 \pm .05$. The subjects were 120 persons in the resting waking state. A later examination of the records of 400 subjects, confirmed the reported tendency for higher voltage and slower EEG's to accompany faster heart rates and accounted for some of the exceptions to the rule (Darrow and Henry, 1947).

Sherman and Jost (1945), using only a small number of subjects (20 emotionally disturbed children), and simultaneously recording the EEG and measures of heart rate, respiration, and changes in skin conductance, found that about one-third of the coefficients of correlation were reliable above the .05 level. There was a tendency for variability and extent of change in one of these physiological measures to correlate with variability and extent of change in a number of other physiological measures.

When comparing physiological measures, we sometimes note that a change in the same direction occurs in two or more measures which, however, show little correlation with each other. It was found, for example, that integrated electric potentials from both the frontal lobe and the heart increased during arithmetical calculations, but there was little or no direct correspondence between the two measures (Ford, 1954b).

While it is the frequency of the EEG which is the aspect of that measure most clearly related to other measures, amplitude also is of significance. It is reported that alpha amplitude and the level of palmar conductance is represented by an inverted U-shaped curve (Stennett, 1957b). During rest and during a tracking performance, low alpha amplitude was found to be associated with both relatively low and relatively high palmar conductance. This finding does not appear surprising since, with greater relaxation, approaching sleep, the alpha waves tend to disappear and, with greater stimulation, they also tend to disappear, being replaced in the former instance by theta or delta waves, and in the latter instance by beta waves. The investigator suggests that the nonlinear relationship between alpha amplitude and palmar conductance provides an explanation for the fact that, in many studies, the correlation between alpha amplitude and other physiological variables has been found to be low and negative. Such would be the finding, he points out, if most of the subjects in the experiment were, as in the present experiment, "in the region of the arousal continuum where a negative relationship obtains while a few were in the region where the relationship is positive."

Hadley (1941) has found relationships between the EEG and other measures which obtain during work, but not during rest. During mental multiplication, the frequency of electric potentials from the cortex was rather closely related to the heart rate ($r = .59 \pm .04$ or $.60 \pm .04$) and less closely related, in the same direction, to muscle-potential amplitude ($r = .23 \pm .05$ or $.17 \pm .05$). During rest, however, the electrical signs of activity of the cortex, of the heart, and of the muscles appeared to be unrelated to each other. While it is possible that the relationship between the various physiological measures indicative of the degree of activation is lower during rest than during work, failure to find correspondence between these measures during rest may conceivably be due to the fact that lower values of the measures obscured relationships which became apparent when the several values increased in magnitude.

Basal metabolic rate, the oxygen consumption of the brain, and the blood-sugar level have been reported to correlate well with the dominant frequency of the alpha rhythm (Lennox, Gibbs, and Gibbs, 1938). When thyroid was administered to normal subjects, there was a high positive correlation between the increase in the frequency of the alpha rhythm and the increase in basal metabolic rate (Lindsley and Rubenstein, 1937).

Brain potentials appear to be related also to body temperature. It has been shown that the frequency of both alpha and beta waves is increased by elevation of body temperature, and that there is a decrease in the electrical activity of the cortex upon cooling (Lindsley, 1944; Cameron, 1941).

Interrelationships of Other Measures

Other physiological measures also have shown interrelationships. In one study, in which measurements were repeated on several days under exceptionally well-controlled conditions, the following coefficients of correlation were reported: basal metabolic rate and pulse, .73 ± .14; basal metabolic rate and respiration, .75 ± .13; basal metabolic rate and systolic blood pressure, .49 ± .23; respiration and pulse, .66 ± .17; systolic blood pressure and pulse, .23 ± .29; and systolic blood pressure and respiration, .20 ± .29 (Herrington, 1942). All measurements were made while the subjects were resting.

Rather striking evidence has been offered for a relationship between oxygen consumption and cardiac output. Under both basal and non-basal conditions, and with varying methods of measurement, it was shown that for each 10 per cent increase in oxygen consumption there was an average increase of 7.07 per cent in cardiac output (H. R. Brown and Pearson, 1947). For forty-two human subjects the coefficient of correlation between the two measures was .55.

Certain other studies have shown, however, less close relationships between basal metabolism and cardiovascular measures (Omwake, Dexter, and Lewis, 1934), and no significant relationship between breathing changes and any of six variables comprising measures of heart rate and skin resistance (Lauer and Smith, 1932).

Low to moderate, but in most instances statistically significant, correlation ratios (eta) have been reported between skin temperature and pulse, and between skin temperature and skin resistance during rest periods and during stimulation (Baker and Taylor, 1954). As compared with reactions during the rest period, responses during two types of stimulation (display of jumping electric sparks and gripping of a dynamometer) showed significant increases in skin temperature, significant decreases in skin resistance, and significant increases in pulse.

Rank-difference coefficients of correlation during a cold pressor test have been reported as follows: heart rate and GSR, .59 (S.E. .11); heart rate and EMG, .46 (S.E. .14); GSR "index" and EMG, .60 (S.E. .11) (Ellingson, 1953).

Wenger (1943a) reported a number of coefficients of correlation between autonomic measures, most of them very low. In a field beset with so many difficulties of measurement and interpretation, negative findings cannot, however, be regarded as conclusive, especially when other investigators have frequently reported a closer relationship between the variables.

Interrelationships among Groups of Measures

Presented below are a number of studies in which several measures of activation have been simultaneously recorded, with the primary object of discovering patterns of relationship among the measures. Studies discussed in this section do not differ basically from some of those discussed in the preceding section.

A pioneer in showing the relationships among the physiological measures which are of particular interest here was Chester Darrow. In 1932 he constructed a polygraph designed to record simultaneously changes in skin resistance, blood pressure, and respiration (Darrow, 1932). In collaboration with Solomon, he studied the GSR and blood-pressure reactions in psychotic states (Darrow and Solomon, 1934), and in collaboration with Darling he formulated an hypothesis concerning measurement of the activity of the autonomic nervous system through simultaneous recording of skin resistance and blood pressure (Darling and Darrow, 1938).

Darling (1940) later investigated the relationship between a group of measures of skin conductance and a group of measures of blood pressure and found positive relationships within each of the groups and a negative relationship between the two groups. One measure, blood-pressure reactivity (the difference between blood-pressure readings on the first and second visits to the laboratory), however, showed a positive correlation ($r = .42$) with the skin-conductance measures and also a positive correlation ($r = .23$) with the blood-pressure measures. The interpretation suggested by the investigator was that, in the presence of higher blood-pressure levels, the smaller skin-conductance responses were due to excessive sympathetic nervous system tone, or adrenergic activity, in which there is an approach to the physiological limit of reactivity and there is little room for further response to specific stimuli. It was suggested that this view is supported by the fact that the presence of adrenalin in the blood may not only cause a rise in blood pressure but also inhibit sympathetic and parasympathetic mechanisms.

Wenger (1941, 1943b) and Jost and Sontag (1944) employed a group of weighted measures presumed to express the state of activity of the autonomic nervous system, and more particularly the dominance of sympathetic as compared with parasympathetic functions. The physiological measures employed were skin resistance, systolic and diastolic blood pressure, heart rate, salivation, respiration, and vasomotor persistence time. These various measures showed certain consistent relationships with each other, but the coefficients of correlation between the measures were in general low.

Wenger and his collaborators (Wenger, 1957; Wenger, B. P. Engel, and Clemens, 1957) later, in a more extensive investigation which included measures of skin resistance, muscle potentials, heart rate, heart-rate variability, systolic and diastolic blood pressure, respiration, temperature, salivation, and plethysmographic measures, concluded that it was probable that some individuals show an apparent dominance of the sympathetic branch of the autonomic nervous system in some functions and of the parasympathetic branch in other functions. The autonomic factor described in earlier studies was said to be similar in different populations, but to provide a description of less than one-third of each population (Wenger, 1957). The frequency of mixed patterns (i.e., lack of a consistent dominance of sympathetic or parasympathetic functions) was suggested as a major reason for the low coefficients of correlation obtained. Individual differences in patterns of response were therefore considered to be significant (Wenger, B. P. Engel, and Clemens, 1957). It was also pointed out that autonomic factor scores obtained under conditions of rest should not necessarily be expected to be related to autonomic reactivity under stimulation.

Three studies by R. C. Davis and his collaborators (R. C. Davis, Lundervold, and Miller, 1957; R. C. Davis and Buchwald, 1957; H. E. Dawson and Davis, 1957) show: (1) common features in the response to a wide variety of stimulating conditions, and (2) certain aspects of the response which appeared to be peculiar to the particular stimulating conditions. They tend to support the hypothesis presented here: (1) that any stimulus, or any performance, produces an increase in the general level of activation as compared with the activation when there is a minimum of stimulation or when no activity is required, and (2) the particular pattern of activation, in its details, is peculiar to the situation to which the individual is responding.

R. C. Davis, Lundervold, and Miller (1957), using a number of different experimental conditions [initial rest (1 minute); listening, without movement, to the clicks of a metronome; tapping with the left hand at a 10-per-minute rate (6 minutes); looking at certain lantern slides while tapping as above; tapping at a maximal rate (1 minute); tapping at a rate of 60 per minute (1 minute); and final rest (1 minute)], made continuous records of: (1) the skin-resistance level of the right palm, (2) the EMG of the flexor of the left forearm, (3) the EMG of the extensor of the left forearm, (4) volume pulse from the right finger tip, (5) pulse-cycle time, (6) finger volume, (7) chin volume, (8) breathing amplitude, and (9) breathing-cycle time. The extent of agreement between subjects in chin-volume change turned out to be negligible, so this measure was not considered in the treatment of the findings.

In examining the agreement of the various measures with each other, the action of each variable was ranked in such a way as to secure the greatest agreement among the variables. Computing the intercorrelations between the measures, the investigators found that all correlations were positive except three involving volume pulse. The mean correlation, however, was only .19. The agreement in the scores of the subjects for any given response variable was greater than the agreement obtained when all measures were included. The conclusions reached were as follows (R. C. Davis, Lundervold, and Miller, 1957, pp. 56–57):

1. The response variables, except for chin volume, behave with a reasonable consistency from S to S under the impact of our experimental conditions.

2. By favorable choice of ranking conventions it is possible to construct a table of ranks for conditions in which there is some agreement between the response variables.

3. The departures of response variables from the order so given are consistent from one individual to the next. Our experimental conditions produce patterns of response variables which are predictable regardless of the individual.

. . .

5. To some extent individual Ss have their own ranking of experimental condition, regardless of response variables.[5]

These general conclusions make it legitimate to describe the general response pattern which our experimental conditions tend to produce, and the particular response patterns which are evoked by particular conditions.

Describing this general response pattern, Davis et al. say that it "consists of increased flexor and extensor activity (i.e., greater muscle

---

[5] It would seem reasonable to suppose that this finding is due to the fact that, to some degree, different experimental conditions have different significance for different individuals.

tension), increased sweat-gland activity, increased heart rate, peripheral vasoconstriction (finger), and increased respiration rate and amplitude. Except for the vasoconstriction, this complex is, on a small scale, *the pattern which accompanies exercise*" [6] (Davis, Lundervold, and Miller, 1957). The investigators themselves comment that, except for vasoconstriction, which in this instance they believe may have a special explanation, the pattern is very similar to that supposed to *cause or* be present in "emergency reaction." Presumably, then, this is the *effect?*? general activation pattern which has been earlier hypothesized in this book. The investigators also report, after preparing a table in which the direction of response of each of the nine variables is indicated, that the "pattern is predominantly activating as compared with P pattern (responses measured while looking at certain pictures), which is predominantly depressing." It may be noted, however, that even the P pattern showed increased palmar sweating and EMG, and that the measures which were depressed were pulse rate, volume pulse, pressure pulse, finger volume, chin volume, respiration rate, and respiration amplitude, measures which in many investigations have shown less consistent relationships than the EMG, palmar sweating, and the EEG.

Ford (1957), using the data of Davis et al., computed the rho value when the rank order of each physiological measure was correlated with the averages of the ranks of the remaining seven reranked on the basis of the usual item-validity measure of selection. The reported correlation coefficient of each measure with the remaining seven was as follows: skin resistance, .80; EMG flexor, left hand, .71; EMG extensor, left hand, .43; pulse-cycle time (time between beats), .50; volume pulse, .69; finger volume (capillary), .69; breathing amplitude, .60; breathing-cycle time, .69. He suggests that the relatively low correlation of the EMG extensor with the other measures is accounted for by the fact that the extensor is an antagonist of the flexor, and that the relatively low correlation of the pulse-cycle time is due to the fact that the cardiac cycle is the reciprocal of heart rate. He further suggests that a better measure of cardiac energy is the integrated EKG, which is the product of both frequency and amplitude. Ford comments that combining breathing amplitude with breathing cycle probably gives a better measure of the demand for oxygen. Obtaining the product of breathing amplitude and breathing cycle, and correlating this measure with the remaining six measures, he found a rho of .99, which is a coefficient so high that it almost raises doubts. Ford's discussion, however, gives emphasis to one of the difficulties in physiological measurements of the sort with

[6] Italics mine.

which we are concerned: the difficulty of deciding precisely what should be measured and in what way the measurements should be combined.

A second study, by R. C. Davis and Buchwald (1957), also reveals responses, some of which are similar to those discussed above, and others of which are different. Since the stimuli were twelve pictures, the investigators call this the picture (or P) response. The following measures were obtained for twelve male subjects: galvanic skin response, number of GSR's, net change in the base level of resistance, volume pulse, pressure pulse, pulse time, finger volume, chin volume, bone pulse, breathing-cycle time, and breathing-cycle amplitude. The typical stimulus effect, or P response, was described as being "an increase in muscular tension, activation of palmar sweating, the production of a slow, large pulse, peripheral vasoconstriction, and inhibition of respiration in approximately that order of time." It is to be noted that, as in the experiment in which the subject engaged in such activities as listening, looking, and tapping, there was again an increase in muscular tension and palmar sweating, and the occurrence of peripheral vasoconstriction. Pulse and respiration, however, behaved differently. Seven out of eleven coefficients of correlation proved to be reliable when the correlation was between the rank in maximum change of each response variable and the rank of the sums of the ranks of the other response variables in all the situations. Reliability at the .05 level of confidence required a correlation coefficient of .52. Only one measure (pressure pulse) had a coefficient of correlation lower than .40. Perhaps a larger number of coefficients of correlation would have proved to be reliable if more than twelve subjects had been used. The investigators concluded that:

1. The responses to stimuli differ at least in degree, according to picture.
2. The response variables taken as a group show a significant agreement in their rating of the stimuli.

Justification for conceiving of a typical P or picture response would appear to be doubtful, and Davis does not actually make such a proposal. It seems probable that the response pattern would have differed in its details if different pictures had been substituted for the twelve which were used. In fact, it was reported that, as compared with a picture of a nude female, a picture of a starving man produced, not only less response, but a different kind of response (R. C. Davis, 1957a). There was an increase rather than a decrease of pressure pulse, and there was a reversed effect on the breathing measures. It seems reasonable to suppose that there would be a higher degree of activation, or greater energy expenditure, for any stimulus which is more intense or more significant than the stimulus situation employed in the comparison. It seems reasonable to suppose also that in many respects the response of the organism would be highly specific to the particular situation. If this should be the case, it would be as hopeless to look for characteristic patterns of response to particular classes of stimuli, such as pictures, as to look for physiological responses which characterize the particular "emotions." Conceivably, stimuli classified in some different—and functional—way, such as producing, or tending to produce, approach or withdrawal, might evoke certain characteristic patterns of covert responses beyond those of increased general activation. If such a relationship is to be found, it appears that the classification of stimuli must be functional, or goal-related, whatever the shudders produced in those who fear that teleology may be lurking behind the statement.

A third study, by H. E. Dawson and Davis (1957), also showed certain response characteristics common to the other two studies by Davis and his collaborators. When the subject pressed a key in response to a signal, muscular activity began shortly after the warning signal and, following the signal to respond, developed rapidly in both the acting muscles and remote parts. After the key was closed, the muscular activity began to decline. In the meantime, it was said that sweat-gland activity increased, breathing became faster and deeper, the heart slowed down, there was constriction of the blood vessels in the hand, and an increase in pulse pressure (R. C. Davis, 1957a). It may be noted that again there was increased muscular activity, increased activity of the sweat glands, and peripheral vasoconstriction. Heart rate and respiration did not behave in the same way in the three situations. Respiratory and circulatory measures, it has been pointed out, have shown great variation in a number of studies.

Conclusions

Both theoretical considerations and empirical data support the conception of some degree of "generality" in physiological responses and some degree of "particularity" with respect to the stimulus situation and the individual. All stimulating conditions result in some degree of activation of the organism, but one situation may differ from another, not only in the degree of activation it ordinarily produces but also in the locus of the maximum activation. It is suggested that both the degree and the patterning of the activation are nicely adjusted to the demands of the stimulating situation as perceived by the individual, within the limits of his capabilities at the moment. (These capabilities may, it would appear, be affected by numerous agents: drugs, nutrition, disorders of the endocrine system, and any other factors which may have either a temporary or lasting effect upon the nervous system.)

Measures of activation in one part or system of the organism are usually, but not always, found to be related in the expected direction to measures of activation in other parts or systems of the organism. Sometimes the relationships reported are relatively close, particularly in view of the rather appreciable errors of measurement which are to be expected. In other instances the relationships are negligible or even, occasionally, in the opposite direction. Negative relationships are often explainable as due to homeostatic regulation. The absence of closer positive relationships may be due in part to differences in the latency of responses, differences in the time at which the physiological limit of various responses is approached, and to differences between individuals in the system or systems maximally activated by stimulation.

Though it is too early to draw any final conclusions in the matter, it seems possible that such measures as blood pressure, heart rate, and respiration behave in a more variable fashion than skeletal muscle tension, skin resistance, and the EEG—or else that we are less successful in the procedures for measuring them. Assuming that measurements of the various processes are equally adequate, we are led to speculate as to the reasons for the apparently greater consistency of the three measures referred to above. Perhaps the EEG is relatively dependable because it reflects changes in the nerve centers which control behavior. Perhaps muscular tension is relatively dependable because it represents the end point of the response, since all action upon the environment requires muscular contraction. The apparent dependability of skin resistance is more difficult to explain, but it has been said that sweat-gland activity summates the action of both sympathetic and parasympathetic divisions of the autonomic nervous system (Darling and Darrow, 1938). Following this line of thinking, we may emphasize the compensatory reactions in certain other processes such as heart action and blood pressure, and we may consider the extent to which the internal economy is capable of sustaining delay or variability in various processes. On the other hand, it may be that measurement of the apparently more variable processes has not always followed the proper logic. Perhaps, as Ford (1957) suggests, heart rate should not be considered apart from the amplitude of the beat, or perhaps a measure combining heart action and blood pressure should be employed.

It is possible that there are somewhat different patterns, as well as degrees, of activation for broad categories of situations, such as those involving physical exertion, as compared with those in which, despite considerable internal arousal, there is little or no action upon the external environment. It is possible also that the pattern of activation found when an individual tends to approach, or seek more of, a situation will be found to be different from that when he tends to avoid, or seek less of, the situation. Conflict between these two tendencies may also conceivably be observed in the patterning of activation. Such statements represent only speculations since experiments have not been designed to test the hypotheses. Grouping of data in relation to functional categories rather than no grouping, or grouping according to traditional concepts, would seem to offer the greatest hope of progress.

The problem of the best way in which to measure the general level of activation is a difficult one. We are dealing with an autonomic nervous system which has the task both of maintaining the degree of arousal necessary for action upon the external environment, and of preserving relative constancy of the internal milieu; with a skeletal-muscle system set for differential response to different environmental demands; and with various organs and systems which show differences in the latency of their responses. Add to this the problems posed by individual differences in the organs or systems showing maximum activation under stimulation, and one might well despair of obtaining an adequate measure of the general level of activation. Nevertheless, the following conclusions stand out in striking fashion:

(1) *The effect of stimulation is to cause a greater degree of excitation in a wide variety of organs and systems.* As was shown in Chapter 4, the degree of activation varies with the intensity or degree of significance of the stimulation.

(2) Innumerable investigations in which only one type of arousal response has been measured (e.g., skin resistance, muscle tension, or EEG) have shown relationships of this one variable to stimulus conditions and to behavioral data which are consistent with the relationships found for other arousal responses.[7]

(3) The weight of the evidence appears to support a concept of

[7] See Chapter 4 for further support of this statement.

interrelationships among the physiological measures discussed, and not one of independence, except to a limited degree.

(4) It seems justifiable, therefore, to conceive of the level of activation of the organism as a whole and to attempt to measure it.

How this measurement may best be achieved remains at present a moot question. There are many physiological conditions which, measured separately, constitute reasonably adequate indicators of a general condition of arousal. Were this not true these measures would not have shown consistent relationships with stimulus conditions and, in general, agreement among themselves in the kind of relationship shown. On the other hand, the evidence does not suggest the conclusion that each of the several measures is itself a completely valid indicator of a general condition measured satisfactorily by any one of them.

It is probable that a combination of measures is more satisfactory than any measure taken singly. Problems arise, however, as to how the measures may best be combined. If it were possible to total, for events of short duration, "the energy consumption of all responses within a given period," this might, as Davis et al. have speculated (R. C. Davis, Buchwald, and Frankmann, 1955) provide the measure which has previously been proposed as desirable (Duffy, 1951). John Lacey and his collaborators (J. I. Lacey, Bateman, and Van Lehn, 1952) have suggested the possibility of measuring the autonomic reactivity of an individual by using the maximal t-score he makes on any one of a number of measures, and they have reported that this score correlates more highly with the Form-Color Index of the Rorschach Test than do any of the separate measures of autonomic reaction. Davis and his co-workers (R. C. Davis, Buchwald, and Frankmann, 1955), rather apologizing for such speculations, have mentioned the possibility of constructing "a multi-dimensional manifold for the response variables and by vector addition discovering the distance of a response from a certain point of origin."

It is evident that the measurement of activation presents many problems, and that further investigation will be required before the best means of measuring it can be determined. It would be unwise, however, to permit either the complexity of the problem or the inadequacy of our present information to obscure the fact that the level of activation is a basic aspect of behavior, which, even with the present imperfect means of measurement, shows significant relationships with stimulus situations and with other aspects of behavior. The general direction which should be taken in the measurement of activation is clearly apparent; it is only the details which remain to be worked out.

chapter 6

General conclusions

From the discussion in the preceding chapters the following conclusions are suggested:

1. All behavior is describable in terms of (*a*) its direction (approach or withdrawal) and (*b*) its intensity (internal arousal), though subheads of these basic categories are no doubt needed.

2. These descriptive categories, referring to functional and measurable behavior, might advantageously be substituted for the traditional descriptive categories of psychology, many of which cannot be defined operationally.

3. When the intensity of behavior, or the degree of activation of the organism, is the subject of investigation, it is observed that a large number of measures of autonomic functioning, of skeletal-muscle functioning, and of cortical functioning vary with considerable consistency *in one direction with increased stimulation* of the organism and *in the opposite direction with decreased stimulation* of the organism.

4. These changes are not specific to sleep, or to "emotion," or to any other particular condition. On the contrary, they may be found, not only during sleep on the one hand, and intense excitement on the other hand, but also during such intermediate conditions as waking relaxation, work on easy tasks, or work on more difficult tasks. They apparently vary in a continuum.

5. Changes in the level of activation may be produced by any type of stimulus, physical or symbolic. They may be brought about by drugs, by hormones, by the chemical products of fatigue, by simple sensory stimuli, or by complex situational stimuli, present, past, or anticipated.

6. Within the limits of his ability to do so, the individual appears to maintain a level of activation appropriate to the demands of the stimulus situation, as he interprets them.

7. There is a considerable degree of similarity in the interpretation of the same situation by different individuals; hence the *level of activation varies on the average with the situation.*

8. *There is patterning of activation.* The organism is not activated as an undifferentiated whole. Nevertheless, it is the organism, not relatively autonomous part-systems, which is activated. This is shown by the fact that measures of activation in one part of the organism are usually, but not always, related in the expected direction to measures of activation in other parts of the organism.

9. *The level of activation is measurable.* Measures of individual physiological processes which participate in the activation of the organism bear significant relationships to stimulus situations and, in general, to each other. Some type of summation of these measures should provide a more adequate indicator of the general level of activation than any individual measure. Such a composite measure would no doubt show closer relationships to stimulus situations and to measurable aspects of response. However, investigations based upon a single indicator of activation are in no sense meaningless. The consistent relationships which some of them have shown, both to stimulus situations and to other aspects of response, proclaim their relative adequacy as indicators of the average degree of activation of groups, if not as reliable measures of individual responsiveness.

10. The attempt of the organism to respond in adjustive fashion to its environment, and thus to reach its goals, appears to be responsible for changes in activation with repetition of the stimulus situation, and also for variations in the patterning of activation under certain conditions.

11. There is evidence that the organism, even when making no overt response, is in a constant state of flux with respect to both its general level of activation and the activation of its several parts.

12. The activation of the organism shows lawfulness in its variations. It is determined by known factors, physiological and psychological. It has, it would appear, predictable behavioral correlates, as will be suggested in succeeding chapters.

13. For certain forms of behavior, fluctuations in activation and the "recovery time" required for the return of a physiological measure to its level before the application of stimulation may prove to be of even more predictive value than the characteristic level of activation.

part II
THE EFFECTS
OF VARIATIONS
IN ACTIVATION

Introduction

Variations in the extent of energy release within the organism appear to be responsible for many significant variations in behavior. The general quality of an individual's performance is dependent not only upon his structural equipment in its present status, as produced by maturation and learning, but also upon the degree of activation at the moment the performance takes place. The same response mechanism of the same organism apparently functions in one way when the response occurs at a low level of activation and in another way when it occurs at a high level. Thus the same individual may, in similar situations, function at one time effectively and at another time ineffectively, depending upon the degree of activation.

Variations in behavior associated with variations in "motivation," and hence in the degree of activation, are commonplace to the psychologist.[1] Such variations may, however, be merely a special case of a broader principle that all variations in the level of activation, whatever their nature or the conditions of their occurrence, affect in theoretically predictable ways the characteristics of behavior. This principle, if established, would be of basic significance in psychology.

In the discussion which follows, the possibility will be suggested that variations in activation produced by a wide variety of agents (e.g., drugs, hormones, "emotional" stimulation, or changes in "motivation") and measured in a wide variety of forms (e.g., changes in muscle-action potentials, in skin resistance, etc.) show consistent effects upon behavior. The aspects of behavior which are conceivably

[1] A "motive" affects the direction as well as the degree of activation of behavior, but it is the effect upon the degree of activation of the organism with which we are concerned at the moment.

117

modified by variations in activation include sensory sensitivity, the speed of response, the vigor of response, the co-ordination of responses, and the general quality of performance.

In seeking an explanation of the presumed effects upon behavior of differences in the degree of activation, we are reminded of the statement that "the reaction to any stimulus, be it neurological or hormonal, is dependent upon the state of the cells, which in turn is determined by the continuous interactions between the effects of neural impulses and the effects of hormones" (Mirsky, Miller, and Stein, 1953). What occurs in one part of the organism affects, at least to some extent, what occurs in every other part of the organism. The functioning of the autonomic nervous system apparently affects the functioning of the cortex, other brain centers, and various other parts of the somatic nervous system, producing differences in the quality of responses and in the sensitivity of the organism to environmental influences. The functioning of the cerebral cortex affects the functioning of the autonomic nervous system. Moreover, the effect is circular. For example, by means of cortical activity, a given situation may be judged threatening (or to have a particular "cue-function") and the autonomic nervous system may therefore respond in such a way as to release more energy. The increased mobilization of energy may in turn affect the functioning of the cerebral cortex so that the individual may think or move more rapidly, and the co-ordination of his responses may be affected. Long-continued hyperactivity may lead to exhaustion of the ability to respond to stress by greater release of energy. Rest may produce recovery of this ability. In any case, what we are concerned with is a total condition of the organism, in which one aspect of its functioning is associated in predictable ways with other aspects of its functioning.

chapter 7
Sensory sensitivity and
the level of activation

One of the most basic aspects of behavior is the perception of the environment. The behavior of the organism is always a response to changes occurring either inside or outside the organism or, characteristically, in both places. The degree of sensitivity to stimulation is therefore of primary importance in the organism's adjustments to the environment. Evidence from many sources suggests the possibility that, at least up to a certain point, *sensory sensitivity is increased* (i.e., *faint stimuli are more easily perceived*) *when the level of activation is higher.*

There are few studies showing a clear-cut relationship between the measured level of activation and measured variations in sensory sensitivity. There are many studies yielding presumptive evidence of concomitant variation in these two aspects of the functioning of the organism. The history of the problem goes at least as far back as the middle of the nineteenth century. Ribot (1911) reported that Claude Bernard, in 1852, showed that "section of the great sympathetic in the neck" produced, along with increased temperature and muscular tonicity on that side, an increase in "sensibility." Electric current applied to the same nerve produced opposite effects. Féré (1900) suggested (despite the preconceptions which may be held by some) that the manifestations in the former case were, in general, those of the "sthenic," or excited, emotions, while those in the latter case were manifestations of the "asthenic" emotions. Féré's own work, directly or indirectly, lent support to the assumption that variations in what is here called the level of activation were accompanied by variations in sensitivity. It is said also that Breese, in 1899, found that increased muscular tensions, induced by having individuals press their arms tightly against their sides, resulted in increased visual acuity (Telford and Swenson, 1942).

POSSIBLE NEURAL BASES FOR THE EFFECT OF ACTIVATION UPON SENSORY SENSITIVITY

Before examining the presumptive evidence for a relationship between sensory sensitivity and the level of activation, it may be of interest to note the means by which such a relationship could be produced.

A possible mechanism for the lowering of sensory thresholds is suggested by an experiment in which it was found that strychnin acting on the thalamus of the rabbit lowered the visual threshold, so that a single afferent impulse became effective (Bartley, 1933). Piéron (1952) comments that this fact appears to indicate that "at the level of the thalamic relay the passage towards the cortex requires an iteration that the strychnin renders superfluous, by provoking from the start a repetitive burst of impulses by the last neurone of the afferent chain." Apparently, then, one of the ways in which changes in the level of activation may exert their influence is through their effect on the thalamic relay. It seems probable, however, that the influence may be exerted at any one of the several levels at which excitation occurs, from the periphery, where the stimulus acts upon a receptor, through the relay centers, to the terminal center. Piéron (1952) points out that a variation of central origin can influence various sensory functions. He suggests that this "implies the existence, partial at least, of a general process."

Neurological studies long ago showed increased electrical activity in one sensory system as the result of stimulation of another sensory system, though the means by which this might be produced were not as clear as at the present time. Gerard, Marshall, and Saul (1936), recording electrical activity in the cat's brain, found an increased rate of electrical responses to sound as a result of visual stimulation. They reported considerable interaction between neural impulses in separate elements of one sensory system or between those of separate systems, as, for example, optic and auditory. They stated that:

> In favorable locations, such as regions between the two colliculi or the two geniculate bodies, excitation of one sensory system increases the responses

to the constant stimulation of a second. Thus, regular watch ticks evoke larger, but otherwise unmodified, potential changes in the brain stem when the eyes are simultaneously exposed to light than when the subject is in the dark. Since the potential picture evoked in optic paths by light is distinct from that in the auditory paths, the explanation is clearly not a simple addition of active optic to active auditory structures. Rather, secondary auditory paths have somehow been facilitated so that more fibers are activated by a given discharge in the primary paths. . . . This interaction occurs where optic and auditory systems are in close anatomic relation, although presumably it does not involve the cross-passage of nerve impulses over synapses between them (Gerard, Marshall, and Saul, 1936, p. 705).

More recently, studies of the brain stem reticular formation and of the hypothalamus have indicated some of the means by which one sensory system may affect the functioning of another sensory system —or indeed the functioning of motor systems.[1] Sensory impulses apparently affect the level of activation of the organism, thus exerting a facilitating or an inhibiting effect upon the cortical reception of impulses from the sense organs.

It is known that the classical sensory pathways, in the course of their passage through the brain stem, give off collaterals which presumably set up recurrent discharges in the reticular formation and, by means of diffuse ascending paths, relay through subcortical centers to the cerebral cortex (Kaada, 1953; Lindsley, 1956).[2] The cortex is then activated, single cortical neurones firing at a greatly accelerated pace (Mountcastle, 1958). The activation produced by this unspecific sensory system has been shown to extend to the primary sensory areas, affecting their ability to react to the sensory impulses which they receive over direct cortical projection pathways (Jasper, Naquet, and King, 1955). In the absence of activation by this system, sensory impulses still reach the cortex, as indicated by evoked potentials, but presumably they do not result in discrimination. (Such, apparently,

[1] An increase in excitability of the motor cortex has been reported to follow a flash of light applied to the eyes (Wall, Rémond, and Dobson, 1953). It was suggested that, in the cat, the ventral division of the lateral geniculate was perhaps the most likely structure for transmitting the excitatory influence of the visual stimulus to the motor cortex in the way shown in this experiment. It was not necessary for either the primary visual receiving area of the cortex or the visual association area to be present in order to obtain the facilitating effect of visual stimulation on the motor cortex.

[2] Visceral, as well as somatic, afferents contribute collaterals to the reticular formation (Dell and Bonvallet, 1956). Moreover, to a certain extent, cells of the reticular formation are capable of activity independent of sensory input (Mountcastle, 1958).

is the situation when barbiturates are administered.) Adrian (1954) had earlier suggested that the reticular formation might be the decisive factor in the direction of attention since a signal reaching the cortex by the direct route, but reinforced by one from the reticular formation, might disrupt the cortical rhythm and secure a clear path, whereas a signal not thus reinforced might be unable to break through.

Demonstration of the facilitation of cortical response to sensory stimuli by means of stimulation of subcortical areas is seen also in an investigation reported by Gellhorn, Koella, and Ballin (1955). Recording action potentials from the cerebral cortex of nine anesthetized cats, they found that hypothalamic stimulation facilitated the response of the cortex to optic and acoustic stimuli. The facilitation was shown, among others, in the following ways: (1) optic or acoustic stimuli near the threshold produced a cortical response more often when the hypothalamus was stimulated than it did under control conditions; (2) subthreshold stimuli might become effective, especially in experiments involving strychninization of the projection area; (3) multiple discharges might occur under combined sensory and hypothalamic stimulation, when they did not occur under either by itself. Acoustic and hypothalamic stimuli applied at the same time produced their greatest excitatory effect on the auditory projection area, but they produced more excitation in the visual projection area than was produced by either form of stimulation presented alone. Since hypothalamic stimulation produces excitation of the whole cortex, it was assumed that such summation processes would occur in other cortical projection areas also, though it had not been determined to what extent the interaction takes place at the thalamic level and at the cortical level (Gellhorn et al., 1955). It is of special interest for our purposes to note that an increase in cortical convulsive response to optic stimuli, such as occurs when these stimuli are accompanied by hypothalamic stimulation, occurs in the absence of hypothalamic stimulation if the intensity of the optic stimuli is increased sufficiently. Thus an effect which would be produced by increased intensity of stimulation can be produced with less intense stimulation if the hypothalamus is stimulated.

Without experimental stimulation of the hypothalamus, mild nociceptive stimuli have been found to interact with acoustic or optic stimuli to produce increased reactivity in the respective projection area, as shown by evoked potentials (Gellhorn, Koella, and Ballin, 1954). The investigators concluded that nociceptive impulses acted on the cerebral cortex as a whole by way of the hypothalamic-cortical system.

In human subjects with electrodes over the occipital and temporal regions, the response to a click was apparently facilitated when a photic stimulus was added (Torres and Marshall, 1953). Presenting sound stimulation immediately before light stimulation produced a greater reduction in the alpha wave, and for a considerably longer period, than the presentation of light stimulation alone (Popov, 1955). Moreover, it was reported that visual afterimages were more numerous and more intense.

It has been shown in another way that sensory stimulation has great influence upon the general level of activity of the brain, and hence presumably upon sensory modalities other than the particular one being stimulated. Granit (1955) refers to an experiment by Chang in which he recorded the response to light from the lateral geniculate body of cats and found that, in the dark, the response to a slowly repeated electric shock applied to the optic nerve was small, but that, when the light was allowed to shine for some time, it gradually increased in size, and to a considerable degree. The effect was also noted in the striate area and was observed to spread to the auditory area, thus showing that the general level of activity of the brain was greatly influenced by the discharge through the optic nerve. Granit suggests that spontaneous firing from sense organs, now established as a fact, makes the sense organs one of the brain's more important "energizers." He believes the effect is exerted through the unspecific pathways previously referred to.

While potentials of the sort recorded from cortical projection areas do not necessarily indicate the presence of conscious sensations since they can be found during anesthesia, it has been suggested that the minimal requirement for sensations and perceptions is the interaction of hypothalamic and sensory discharges (Gellhorn, Koella, and Ballin, 1955). It is obvious, however, that the organism would be at the mercy of a bombardment of sensory impulses if some screening of impulses were not possible. Several investigators have suggested an excitability cycle in the cortex and perhaps also in the thalamus, making possible two levels of screening of incoming sensory impulses and, by working either in harmony or to the exclusion of each other, determining selective awareness (Lindsley, 1956).

It seems likely that too much, as well as too little, arousal may interfere with the reception of sensory impulses. Bruner (1957) points to psychophysical experiments as showing on the whole that "too alert an observer pays a price in a raising of sensory thresholds, and that a certain amount of relaxation in the observer yields the lowest thresholds." Lindsley (1956) also has suggested that neural interaction in moderation might lead to facilitation, while in excess it might lead to blocking of reticular activation upon the cortex, with resulting disturbances of awareness and attention. It may be hypothesized, then, that the relationship between sensory sensitivity and the degree of activation is curvilinear rather than linear, though most experimental work apparently has been concerned with the ascending part of the curve.

INTERSENSORY PHENOMENA

The neurological findings discussed above are in harmony with behavioral reports of intersensory effects, or the effect upon one sense modality of stimulation of another. In most instances it has been found that stimulation of one sense will increase the sensitivity of another sense. Under certain conditions, however, a decrease, rather than an increase, in the sensitivity of the other sense has been observed. Gilbert (1941), in a survey of studies in this field, suggests that a stimulus of moderate intensity momentarily increases the sensitivity of another sense modality, while a very intense stimulus momentarily reduces sensitivity in another modality. After an interval of about five-tenths of a second, however, the effect is reversed and the sensitivity of the other sense modality is increased. In either case the explanation is based upon the assumption that excitation of a receptor does not remain strictly localized but irradiates to some extent throughout the entire nervous system, affecting other responses by affecting the excitatory state of various conductor mechanisms (Gilbert, 1941). T. A. Ryan (1940), in his review of the interrelations of the sensory systems in perception, also concludes that there is an interplay between the sensory systems of the organism, although he states that the exact nature of the influence of one modality upon another is not clear. There is some evidence of accompanying changes in muscle tonus and in endocrine secretions (Gilbert, 1941). In fact, it has been said that stimulation of any afferent nerve brings about sympathetic excitation (Barron, 1947).

With prolonged stimulation, some stimuli tend to raise sensory thresholds and others to lower them, depending, it was reported, upon the quality of the stimulus, e.g., whether it was "bright" or "dark" (Gilbert, 1941). This difference in effect may be a result, not of the sensory stimulation as such but of variations in "cue-function," with consequent differences in the level of activation.

It has been found also that stimulation of one sense modality may affect not merely the sensitivity to the intensity of stimulation in another sense modality, but also the discrimination of stimuli within that modality (Gilbert, 1941). As Gilbert suggests, the change in discrimination appears to be a secondary result of the change in sensitivity to intensity of stimulation. It thus appears possible that various intersensory effects may be explainable in terms of differences in excitation. Perhaps any excitation tends to increase to some extent the level of activation of the organism. This increase in the level of activation, if not excessive, may produce a lowering of sensory thresholds. Perhaps under certain conditions, as for example when the stimulus is very intense, there is momentary interference with attention to data from other sense organs in favor of maximum attention to data from the strongly stimulated organ, while, after a very brief interval, impressions from the other sense organs experience the stimulating effect of the general increase in excitation. An explanation of this sort is in line with the suggestion (Gilbert, 1941) that sensory facilitation may be produced by a mechanism of nervous interaction similar to that underlying the bilateral knee-jerk.

Among the studies in which stimulation of one sense modality has apparently increased the sensitivity of another modality are a study by Jacobson (1912) in which his subjects reported that an odor seemed more intense when presented along with a sound; a study by Cason (1936) in which a sound was judged to be more intense when it was accompanied by a light, and a light was judged to be more intense when it was accompanied by a sound; a study by Harry M. Johnson (1920) in which, with the subject wearing ground-glass lenses, tactual form discrimination was found to be reliably better (by 2 per cent) in light than in darkness; a series of experiments by Kravkov and by Hartmann; and a number of studies reported in journals in the Soviet Union.[3]

Kravkov (1930) found that simultaneous auditory stimulation increased the ability to distinguish as separate figures two small black squares on a white ground, but decreased the ability to distinguish white squares on a black ground. The explanation of this finding was suggested by a later study in which he found that both auditory and olfactory stimulation increased accuracy in judging the width of a black stripe on a white ground but decreased accuracy in judging the width of a white stripe on a black ground (Kravkov, 1933). With

[3] Kravkov's studies were conducted in the Soviet Union but were published in many instances in foreign journals.

auxiliary stimulation the width of the white stripe was overestimated. This effect was ascribed to irradiation of the visual response, due perhaps to lowering of the threshold for neighboring excitations. Both types of findings would therefore be in harmony with the conclusion that auxiliary stimulation (which would presumably increase the degree of excitation, or the general level of activation of the organism) lowers sensory thresholds.

Hartmann (1933), unlike Kravkov, found that auxiliary stimulation produced greater accuracy in judging both black-on-white and white-on-black. It has been suggested that differences in temporal relationships may explain the difference in the results (Gilbert, 1941).

In another experiment Hartmann (1934) found that tonal discrimination was about 3 per cent finer under bright illumination than under conditions of dimness or darkness.[4] There was some indication that persons whose normal performance was relatively poor were the ones who showed greatest improvement under illumination. Perhaps these were subjects who ordinarily functioned at too low a level of activation. It is of interest to note that Hartmann's subjects claimed that they felt more alive and awake under the light.

Research on sensory interaction has received considerable attention in the Soviet Union. Ivan London (1954), in an excellent review of this work, points out that, while many of the studies are open to methodological criticism, and while Western investigators have often been unable to replicate the findings, the mass of data collected and the consistency of the findings command attention.

All sense modalities are said to undergo modification of response when another sense modality is appropriately stimulated. The modification of response may be either an increase or a decrease in sensitivity. It appears that most, but not all, of the phenomena reported in these studies are explainable within the framework of activation theory if account is taken of such factors as the differing effects of strong and of weak stimulation; of arousing stimuli, such as stimulation of cold receptors, and of relaxing stimuli, such as stimulation of warmth receptors; of the strength of the primary stimulation and the condition of the sense organ (e.g., light-adapted or dark-adapted) at the time of the accessory stimulation; and, according to the Soviet investigators, of the antagonistic relationship between blue-green re-

---

[4] Having the subject give his responses orally in complete darkness, on the contrary, gave an unreliable difference in favor of the dark condition. It has been suggested that this result may have been due to the fact that oral reporting provides more auxiliary stimulation than reporting by pressing a key.

ceptors and orange-red receptors.[5] In predicting the effects of accessory stimulation upon visual discrimination, it is said that factors to be considered include irradiation effects and the degree of figure-ground contrast in the primary stimulation. The time at which measurement is made is also important since lowered sensitivity may be followed by supernormal sensitivity and heightened sensitivity by subnormal sensitivity.

Most interesting for the purpose of the present discussion is the fact that experimental effects are said to vary with the general physiological condition of the individual, and to be explainable in large part in terms of the functioning of the autonomic nervous system. In "various hypodynamic states" the usual effects of accessory stimulation are said to appear more sharply. Moreover, the antagonistic relationship reported to exist between blue-green and orange-red color sensitivity is explained as due to "inversely related ionic concentrations," which in turn are believed to be accounted for by the fact that the autonomic nervous system is brought into play, with sympathetic and parasympathetic divisions exerting opposed influences. It was found that some accessory stimuli quickened the pulse; others slowed it. The effect upon color sensitivity was said to correspond with the pulse action.

Chapanis, Rouse, and Schachter (1949) were unable to replicate Russian findings in regard to the effect of intersensory stimulation on dark adaptation. They suggest that random fluctuations in threshold, magnified by the form of expression, may possibly have been misinterpreted as real effects. As these investigators point out, research on the facilitation or inhibition of functioning in one sense modality, as a result of stimulation of another sense modality, has had a long and controversial history. Among the non-Russian studies of intersensory phenomena, in addition to those cited earlier in this chapter, are a study in which differential brightness sensitivity was reported to be increased following excitation of the vestibular mechanism (Di Giorgio, 1940) and one in which the effects of auditory stimulation on visual sensitivity were said to be either facilitatory or inhibitory, depending upon whether the simultaneous stimulus occupied the ground in the "perceptual figure-ground" relationship or was "attributively strong enough to become the figure" (Thorne, 1934). Findings by Matthews and Luczak (1944) in regard to the effect of exercise upon dark adaptation are opposed to those of Rose and Schmidt (1947). The former investigators reported a favorable effect, while the latter found no

---

[5] The statement of the relationship of the findings to activation theory is that of the present writer, not that of the reviewer.

effect, either from exercise or from stimulation of the taste receptors. Data from intersensory studies, together with neurological data, might be said on the whole to lend plausibility to the hypothesis that a relationship exists between the level of activation and sensitivity to sensory stimulation. It seems probable, however, that the relationship is not a simple linear one.

CONDITIONS CORRELATED WITH VARIATIONS IN SENSORY SENSITIVITY

Sensory thresholds apparently do not vary in random fashion (Verplanck, Collier, and Cotton, 1952; M. Wertheimer, 1953). It has been reported that reliable changes in thresholds of different modalities are slightly correlated; [6] that successive threshold measurements are not independent; and that in some instances thresholds can be observed to undergo cyclical drifts (M. Wertheimer, 1953). Analysis of variance, applied to visual and auditory thresholds, showed that the day-by-subject interaction contributed significantly more to the total variance than did the error term. Since the day of the measurement did not contribute significantly to the total variance, it was apparent that the drift in measurements was not due to such factors as the weather, the condition of the apparatus, or other variables independent of the subject that might be associated with the day on which the measurement was made. It would appear that something within the subject, that changed with time, was the factor primarily responsible for changes in threshold measurements. Wertheimer's suggestion that the basic factor might be the metabolic condition of the individual is in line with evidence from a number of sources.

Diminished sensory acuity has been found in conditions of thyroid deficiency (Lerman, 1941), and it has been said that sensory thresholds vary with the menstrual cycle (Herren, 1933). In one study, in which the number of subjects was only four, but the findings consistent for all subjects, it was reported that the period in which the concentration of follicular hormone is usually highest was a period in which there was a lowered threshold for two-point touch and pain

---

[6] In a study published later but conducted earlier, M. Wertheimer (1955a) reports little evidence of correlation between auditory and visual thresholds. In a private communication, he states that the correlation seems to be of the order of .2. Such a low degree of correlation suggests that variations in the general level of activation may account for only a small part of the variance in sensory thresholds.

discrimination and for tactile sensitivity (Herren, 1933). Conversely, during the period when the concentration of follicular hormone is usually lowest, these sensory thresholds were highest. The tests were made within 5 days before the onset of menses, within 3 days following the end of menstruation, and on a day 2 weeks after the first day of the last menstrual period. That these are periods of variation in the concentration of the follicular hormone has been shown by a biological assay on two hundred women undertaken by another investigator (Frank, 1929). It was found that the hormone builds up from a low level to a peak in the 7 days preceding menses and that, with the first day of menstruation, there is a sudden fall in this level. Another slight increase in the hormone was reported about the seventeenth day of the intermenstrual period. The threshold measurements described above apparently varied in corresponding fashion. Moreover, other investigators have reported that there is typically "a burst of motor and mental activity just before the onset of menstruation" (Altmann, Knowles, and Bull, 1941), which suggests that this may be a period when the level of activation is higher. A secondary high-activity period was found during the ovulation phase of the cycle.

A study of the resting EEG of ten women, from the time of ovulation to the day before menstruation, showed a drop during this period, in the amount of 8-to-10-per-second activity in the EEG which was significant at the .01 level (Lamb, Ulett, Masters, and Robinson, 1953). The trend was for the greatest amount of alpha activity to occur with ovulation and the smallest amount to occur premenstrually. Just before menstruation the peak alpha frequency shifted from 10 to 11. A control group of eleven men of comparable age, with EEG's recorded at four intervals over a 3-week period, showed only a progressive increase in the amount of alpha, due no doubt to increased relaxation as a result of greater familiarity with the recording procedure. Electroencephalographic variations associated with the menstrual cycle have been reported also by other investigators (Dusser de Barenne and Gibbs, 1942).

It is of interest to note that there are studies indicating that many women exhibit monthly rhythms in temperature, blood pressure, and metabolism (Tinklepaugh and Mitchell, 1939). It thus appears that increases in the follicular hormone may be associated with a higher level of activation and an increase of sensory sensitivity.

Changes in metabolic condition produced by drugs or by anoxia have also been found asociated with changes in threshold measurements. A 40 per cent increase in color sensitivity (reddish-orange and green) has been reported after the administration of 100 milligrams of caffeine, a stimulant (Kravkov, 1939). Another stimulant, Benzedrine, eliminated the decrement in visual discrimination which occurred as a result of a prolonged, monotonous test session (Mackworth, 1947). Lysergic acid diethylamide (LSD-25), on the other hand, raised the absolute visual threshold, apparently not as a result of the production of hallucinations (Carlson, 1958). Since this drug has frequently been reported to increase tension and restlessness, and often to produce hallucinations similar to those found in certain psychotic conditions, it should presumably be classified as a stimulant. It appears possible that it produced a level of activation too high for good sensory functioning. This interpretation is made plausible by the fact that neurotic and psychotic patients (most of whom, it can be argued, have an elevated level of activation) show an elevated absolute visual threshold (Granger, 1954). While Granger explains the effect of LSD as due possibly to differential inhibition of activity in synapses of nonspecific cortical neurones, as suggested by Purpura (1956b), he notes that the elevation of visual thresholds in the pigeon, following relatively larger doses of LSD than those used in man (Blough, 1957), was probably due to subcortical effects. He notes further that high doses of LSD have been found to decrease synaptic transmission at the lateral geniculate nucleus and, to a lesser degree, at the retina (Evarts, Landau, Freygang, and Marshall, 1955), while Purpura (1956a) reported facilitation of the primary cortical response to photic stimulation of the eye with doses of LSD comparable to those used in man.

There is some evidence that depressant drugs raise sensory thresholds. A review of the literature (De Somer, 1950) indicates that small doses of alcohol raise visual and pain thresholds. Sedatives or anticonvulsants administered to neuropathic patients (10 Ss) apparently produced higher temporal acuity thresholds for various sense modalities than were found in a nonmedicated group of neuropaths (12 Ss) (Ax and Colley, 1955).

Anoxia has been reported to affect both visual and auditory functioning. Brightness discrimination becomes increasingly impaired at higher altitudes (Nims, 1948). At an altitude of 15,000 feet there is in addition a statistically significant slowing of the alpha rhythm of the EEG. It has been found that auditory sensitivity is reduced when the inspired oxygen is about one-half normal concentration at sea level (Gellhorn and Spiesman, 1935; McFarland, 1937; Tonndorf, 1953).

Various types of visual discrimination which apparently depend upon threshold properties appear to be affected by metabolic factors. One of the best known of these is flicker-fusion, or the rate of presentation of successive light stimuli at which the sensation of flickering disappears. The slower the rate of presentation at which this occurs, the less is the sensitivity to flicker. Critical fusion-frequency may be considered a measure of visual "temporal acuity" (Geldard, 1953). The point at which fusion of discrete sensory stimuli occurs may be measured for other senses also.

In hypothyroidism, flicker-fusion frequency is usually below normal limits (Enzer, Simonson, and Blankstein, 1941), while in hyperthyroidism there is an increase in the rate of presentation at which fusion takes place (Simonson and Brožek, 1952).

During anoxia, parallelism has been found between the degree of change in critical flicker-fusion frequency and cortical potentials. (Gellhorn and Hailman, 1944). Benzedrine and Dexedrine are said to have improved the perception of visual flicker and also the auditory acuity range when these had been impaired by exposure to simulated altitudes of 18,000 feet (Adler, Burkhardt, Ivy, and Atkinson, 1950). The effect was accomplished without supplemental oxygen, and it was frequently accompanied by sleep disturbance for a period of 6 to 12 hours after administration of the drugs. Other agents said to increase sensitivity to flicker are strychnin, lysergic acid, thyroxin, and adrenalin (Landis, 1954). Barbiturates, on the other hand, are said to lower flicker-fusion frequency (Landis, 1954).

When critical fusion-frequency was measured hourly over a 10-day period, it was found to show a more or less constant pattern of diurnal variation, unique for each individual, and related in some subjects to fluctuations in body temperature (Landis and Hamwi, 1954). Other investigators also have shown variations in critical fusion-frequency with the time of day (Schmidtke, 1951; Grandjean, Egli, Diday, Bloch, and Gfeller, 1953) and with the work output and the distribution of rest periods (Grandjean et al., 1953). The effect of work apparently depends upon the type and conditions of work (Simonson and Brožek, 1952). Two hours of mental arithmetic produced decreases in the fusion-frequencies of both visual flicker and auditory flutter (S. W. Davis, 1955).

In studies of the difference between the appearance and disappearance thresholds for flicker, Motokawa and his collaborators are said to have found the measure to yield different values in normal rested states and in states of fatigue (Gebhard, 1953). The measure was also affected by oxygen deficiency. One of the investigators compared oxygen consumption and thresholds of electrical flicker while the subjects were engaged in various forms of physical exercise. He is said to have reported that the data ran parallel to each other with remarkably small discrepancies.

Thresholds for apparent movement were found to be shifted when they were taken before and after various experimental conditions (a 2-minute inspection of visual stimuli, auditory stimulation, pacing up and down, and solving mental arithmetic problems) (Brenner, 1953). Brenner makes the point, wholly in line with the hypothesis presented here, that changes in the perception of apparent movement are produced by such diverse factors that they must be due to more general conditions than "short circuits" or satiation in the visual area of the brain.

Temporal acuity thresholds for four types of stimulation (visual, auditory, tactual, and electrical) showed an average correlation coefficient of .60 between the modalities for 21 psychopathic patients, though, for a neuropathic group of 22 the average coefficient was only .24 (Ax and Colley, 1955).

Groups of subjects rated high in anxiety showed less sensitivity to flicker than groups rated low in anxiety (Goldstone, 1955). If it may be assumed that states of anxiety are states in which the level of activation is exceptionally high, this finding would tend to support the notion of a curvilinear, rather than a linear, relationship between sensory sensitivity and the level of activation. Low anxiety subjects, while presumably having a lower degree of activation than the high anxiety subjects, all except two of whom were psychiatric patients, need not be presumed to have had a level of activation at the other extreme of the scale. It is possible, however, that poor discrimination was related, not to the level of activation, but to other factors associated with psychoneurosis.

The size of figural aftereffects, or the effects of prolonged figural stimulation on subsequent perceptual responses, has been suggested by Michael and Nancy Wertheimer (1954) to be related to various metabolic factors. In an investigation of this hypothesis, kinesthetic and visual figural aftereffects were shown to be correlated and to "tend to fluctuate together within an individual in time" (M. Wertheimer, 1955b). Basal metabolic rate showed a curvilinear relationship to kinesthetic figural aftereffect. Those subjects whose metabolic rates were closest to normal had the largest aftereffects, while those whose basal metabolic rates were either very high or very low had smaller aftereffects. Subjects with thyroid uptake of radioactive iodine in the normal range showed a significantly greater visual figural aftereffect than those above or below the normal range, though the kinesthetic figural aftereffect failed to show a significant relationship to this measure. Thus there is some evidence that sensory functioning is affected by the metabolic condition of the individual.[7] Again, such evidence as is available suggests the possibility of a curvilinear relationship between sensory sensitivity and the level of activation, though the evidence is by no means clear-cut.

It has been generally recognized that the auditory threshold, as well as the thresholds for other forms of sensory stimulation, rises during sleep (Kleitman, 1939). The curves representing the auditory threshold during the onset of sleep are strikingly similar for different human subjects and for dogs (Kleitman, 1939). Of greater interest is the fact that engaging in activity, or being subjected to stress, has been found to lower certain thresholds. For example, performing mental tasks has been shown to lower the auditory threshold, the effect being greatest when the subjects were working hardest (L. E. Travis, 1926). Recognition scores for a figure or a word have been found to be higher for subjects tested immediately after pushing for 20 seconds on a push-board than for subjects tested after relaxation (Krus, Wapner, and Werner, 1958). Human visual acuity at twilight was reported to be increased by cold-pressor-induced hypertension and oxygen inhalation and to be reduced by amyl nitrite hypotension and rebreathing (Callaway and Thompson, 1953).

Chapman and Jones (1944), investigating variations in cutaneous and visceral pain sensitivity, reported some variation in the thresholds of some of their subjects as a result of "nervous tension" or "mental fatigue" after an 8-hour study period, and the time of day of the measurement.

It has been shown in an initial experiment that there is a statistically significant, but low, relationship between blood pressure and enhancement in the brightness of a test circle (Diamond, 1960). With higher blood pressure, regarded as an indicator of the amount of reticular activation, there was greater enhancement in brightness.

One of the more clear-cut demonstrations of the relationship between the level of activation and sensory threshold is found in an investiga-

[7] It has been shown that drugs which decreased metabolic rate produced a significant decrease in perceptual modifiability (M. Wertheimer, H. Levin, and N. Wertheimer, 1955). Those which increased metabolic rate did not, however, have a significant effect.

tion by R. C. Davis (1950). Davis measured, by means of action potentials, the subject's muscular tension (right arm and both jaws) during the .3 second prior to the presentation of auditory stimuli close to the threshold. A rough measure of the individual's auditory threshold was secured by taking a mean of the strongest stimulus not heard and the weakest stimulus heard. When means of the tension measures were converted into log values and correlated with the threshold measure, he found a significant correlation (an r of —.38 and a corrected ϵ of .60). An individual's auditory threshold was thus shown to depend in part on the logarithm of his prestimulus tension. When the threshold was correlated with the log of the maximum tension level reached during the 0.9 to 1.8 seconds after the stimulus onset, an r of —.50 was found. Higher tension levels were shown to be associated with lower auditory thresholds.

Pain thresholds have been the subject of a number of investigations. In one of the earliest studies in this field, subjects were trained in techniques of relaxation, and were then given standard electric shocks under the two conditions of (1) ordinary rest and (2) extreme relaxation (M. Miller, 1926). Under extreme relaxation, the subjects almost without exception reported the shock as less painful, less disagreeable, or apparently weaker. Confirming the subjective report was the fact that, under extreme relaxation, arm movement in response to the shock occurred less frequently and, when it did occur, was of smaller extent than during ordinary rest. These differences in arm movement under the two conditions were found to be statistically significant. Freeman (1933) later confirmed the finding that a withdrawal movement is of smaller extent under relaxation than under tension by simultaneously measuring tension in the quadriceps muscles and the extent of the finger withdrawal movement in response to an electric shock. Jacobson (1929) claimed that, when a patient with wire electrodes under the skin showed complete local muscular relaxation, no pain was reported, but that with the appearance of even slight action potentials from the muscles, pain was reported by the subject.

Wolff and Wolf (1948) found that the degree of pressure required to produce pain varied with the contractile state of the stomach. Using glass rods to stretch the stomach, they reported that, when the contractile state of the stomach was average, 100 grams of pressure per square centimeter was required to produce pain. When the stomach wall was strongly contracted, a pressure of 50 grams produced pain, while, when the stomach was relatively relaxed, 150 grams was required.

In recent studies of pain a distinction has been proposed between the threshold for the perception of pain and the threshold of reaction to pain. A survey of investigations in this field maintains that there is convincing evidence of the uniformity of the cutaneous pain-perception threshold "in so far as it relates to definitely instructed subjects who are able to maintain a detached objective attitude" (K. R. L. Hall, 1953). Lanier (1943), on the other hand, using electric current as a stimulus, has found the variability in the pain-perception threshold to be almost fifty times as great as that reported by certain other investigators who used thermal stimulation. He concludes that the pain threshold of an individual may vary considerably from day to day, some subjects showing much more stability of threshold than others.

Clark and Bindra (1956), using electrical, mechanical, and thermal stimulation, found high intercorrelations of reports of pain. They attributed the finding to attitudinal variables independent of the type of stimulation. The results could as well be attributed to individual differences in constitutional factors, such as the characteristic level of activation. The fact that in 95 out of 102 cases it was possible for Clausen, Urdal, and Gjesvik (1955) to determine the pain threshold on the basis of a record of galvanic skin resistance suggests a physiological basis for threshold differences. They found that the pain threshold as determined by skin resistance was not significantly different from that determined by verbal report when, on three consecutive days, twelve subjects had their skin resistance recorded simultaneously with the determination of the pain threshold by the Wolff-Hardy-Goodell technique. (Attitudes, of course, also affect skin resistance.)

In Hall's survey of studies of cutaneous pain (K. R. L. Hall, 1953), elevation of the pain threshold was reported when the subjects breathed mixtures of 5 per cent and of 7.5 per cent carbon dioxide. Hypoxia (similar to anoxia, but with less reduction of oxygen tension) was found to affect pain sensations much less than other sensations. Emotional upset, on the other hand, was said to lead to lowered thresholds for perception of, and withdrawal from, pain and to overestimation of the intensity of pain (Chapman and Jones, 1944). There was a fair correlation between sensitivity to esophageal discomfort and sensitivity to auditory discomfort. Epinephrin, however, had no effect on these thresholds.

Judgment of the size of a distant object has been found to be changed by immersion of the foot in ice water or the inhalation of amyl nitrate (Callaway and Thompson, 1953). Under these conditions the far object is judged to be relatively larger in comparison with a near object. It is somewhat difficult to be certain of the process by which this effect is produced, though the experimenters present some evidence to support their contention that the phenomenon is not due to local ophthalmic effects or to decreased attention. They favor the hypothesis that it is due to a narrowed awareness with a reduction of reaction to distance cues. If this is the case, the finding would serve as an example of decreased perceptual efficiency under a higher level of activation. Such an interpretation would be in line with the finding that paratrooper training, with the stress which it imposes, decreased the ability to discriminate the presence and location of openings in circles flashed on a screen (Korchin and Basowitz, 1954). It has also been reported that the threshold in dark adaptation is raised by heavy exercise (Wendland, 1948). The latter finding, however, may be due to relative anoxia produced by the exercise.

Later it was shown that monkeys with electrodes implanted in their brains demonstrated better tachistoscopic perception when the brain stem at the level of the mesencephalon was stimulated (Fuster, 1958). As compared with controls, they gave a higher percentage of correct responses and shorter reaction times. When, however, the stimulation was of an intensity higher than the threshold for eliciting certain motor effects, sensory discrimination was adversely affected. This was shown in both a smaller number of correct responses at all durations of exposure and in longer reaction times. The brain areas which, when mildly stimulated, improved tachistoscopic discrimination were those shown by other investigators to produce electroencephalographic and behavioral arousal. Certainly, this investigation tends to support the hypothesis advanced in this chapter, an hypothesis advanced in manuscript form long before experimental evidence gave it its present credence.

CONCLUSIONS

Data from various studies show that sensory thresholds measured for the same individual at different times show considerable variability, and that this variation is not random. Sensory sensitivity is apparently affected by hormones, by drugs, by anoxia, by exercise, by stress, and by other factors. Stimulation of one sense modality apparently affects the functioning of another sense modality. Such findings emphasize the organismic character of response and lend themselves to interpretation within the framework of activation theory.

The level of activation, if it affects sensory thresholds, is only one of many factors determining sensory sensitivity. That its influence should be relatively small compared with the sum total of other factors is to be expected. It may, however, account for some of the reported variability in threshold measurements made on the same individual at different times.

An embarrassment in reaching conclusions in regard to the relationship between activation and sensory thresholds is the fact that negative findings are difficult if not impossible to obtain from most of the data now available, since it is assumed that changes in the degree of activation may produce either an increase or a decrease in sensory sensitivity, depending on the level of activation at which the change occurs and the extent of the change. Moreover, it is apparent that variations other than changes in the level of activation can also produce changes in sensory sensitivity.

A crucial test of the hypothesized relationship between activation and sensory sensitivity would apparently require: (1) careful control of all factors other than organismic arousal which might affect sensory sensitivity, and (2) systematic variation of organismic arousal over a wide range of values, with concomitant testing of sensory functioning. Such an experiment would offer formidable difficulties since, if the degree of activation affects sensory sensitivity, the effect may be small and difficult to measure, while the degree of organismic arousal itself is by no means easy to determine or to vary at will. Manipulation of the level of activation might be attained through the use of drugs in varied dosage if it can be shown that side effects of the drugs do not modify the functions measured. Normally occurring diurnal variations in activation might be utilized, though this would no doubt limit the range of activation open to investigation. Changes in activation might be produced by the administration of hormones or by the manipulation of stimulating situations or activities. If the effects produced by a given level of activation were the same regardless of the means by which the activation had been brought about, a basis would exist for concluding that the level of activation was in itself a determinant of sensory sensitivity, however minor a determinant it might prove to be. Individual differences in the effect of a particular degree of activation may exist, and it may prove to be necessary to determine individual curves representing the relationship between activation and sensory sensitivity. It seems likely, nevertheless, that some communality of effect would be found.

On the basis of present evidence, most of which was accumulated for other purposes, it might be hypothesized that there is indeed some degree of relationship between the level of organismic arousal and sensitivity to sensory stimulation. It seems probable that the relationship is curvilinear—i.e., that sensory sensitivity is somewhat less when there is either a very low or a very high level of activation, and that an intermediate degree of activation is most facilitative to sensory functioning. Too low a degree of arousal may fail to provide the cortex with sufficient stimulation from the reticular activating system, while too high a degree of arousal may lead to what Lindsley (1956) has referred to as "blocking of reticular activation upon the cortex," or it may interfere with the hypothesized coding of sensory impulses, or provide the basis for succumbing to distractions. In any case, a curvilinear rather than a linear relationship seems probable. In fact, Fuster's (1958) experiment referred to above, seems to meet most of the conditions required and to indicate that there is indeed a curvilinear relationship between activation and sensory functioning.

If it is assumed that a relationship is established between activation and sensory sensitivity, the question may be raised as to whether this relationship is due to factors referred to as set or attention, or whether it is due to changes in the functioning of the sensory cortex or the neural avenues through which the cortex receives impulses. While, in the intact human being, it would be difficult to conceive of a situation in which the two could be separated, neurological studies of the cat brain have shown differences in potentials in sensory areas when hypothalamic stimulation occurred at the same time as sensory stimulation, and also in a given projection area when stimulation of the sensory avenue serving that area was accompanied by other sensory stimulation. These facts make plausible the hypothesis that sensory sensitivity may be increased or decreased by changes in organismic arousal which exert their effect on sensory projection areas as well as on other parts of the brain.

chapter 8

Activation and performance

On theoretical, as well as empirical, grounds there is reason to suppose that differences in activation may affect, not only sensory responses, but also various aspects of motor responses and the general quality of performance. Before studies of the activation of lower brain centers showed the means by which differences in arousal might affect behavior, there appeared to be behavioral evidence that differences in excitation in the various systems of the body were associated with differences in the performance of various tasks (Duffy, 1932b; Freeman, 1933; R. C. Davis, 1937). Though most of the studies were concerned with the correlates of differences in muscle tension, at least some of the formulations of the problem suggested that a more general excitation was conceived (Duffy, 1934, 1941a). The plausibility of these conceptions has been increased by the discovery of neural means through which the phenomena could be produced. Lindsley (1956), for example, points out in a review of physiological psychology that the reticular activating system may play a significant role in perception and learning "by focussing attention and by controlling the elaboration of sensory messages which have arrived at primary cortical reviewing zones, over direct cortical projection pathways." In other words, he suggests that the degree of alertness or arousal may affect both sensory and motor responses. He quotes Sperry as having said that the ultimate end of all brain excitation is to aid in the regulation of motor coordination, and that "the entire output of our thinking machine consists of nothing but patterns of motor coordination." Animal studies are said to have emphasized the importance of the limbic system for "motivation" and learning. He reviews a study which showed that lesions in the dorsomedial nuclei of the thalamus produced, among other things, impaired performance on discrimination and learning problems.

Any given performance is controlled by neural centers and is carried out through activity of the muscles. Affecting and reflecting the activity of neural centers are various autonomic responses (cardiac, vascular, respiratory, sudoral, and others). These autonomic responses are also related in varying degrees to skeletal-muscle response. Although the various systems of the organism are not activated to the same degree at the same time, it has been argued that the interrelationships between the systems is such that it is meaningful to conceive of the degree of activation of the organism as a whole and not merely the activation of separate systems. At the same time, the patterning of the activation—especially that at the terminal point, the muscles—is of primary importance in determining the effect of the activation upon performance. Such a conclusion is represented in R. C. Davis' (1956a) statement that the problem he is dealing with is not the effect of muscular tension upon performance but "the question of how responses which are going on at the same time will affect each other." The patterning of the muscular tension apparently affects the outcome no less than the degree of the muscle activity.

The volume of data bearing on the topic of the present chapter is too great for even cursory review. Where the degree of activation affects the general quality of performance, as it usually does to at least some degree, such questions as the following arise: (1) What aspects of performance does it affect, and in what manner? (2) Is the relationship between activation and performance linear or curvilinear? (3) Does activation produced by diverse means have the same general effect? (4) What is the relationship between activation, practice, and efficiency? (5) Are there individual differences in the effect of a given degree of activation upon performance?

Questions such as these cannot be answered with finality at the present time, but an increasing volume of data bearing upon these points is being accumulated. The time does not seem distant when the findings may have widespread application in industry, in military operations, and even in assessing the performance of the individual on aptitude and achievement tests. If it is indeed true that the same response mechanism, of the same individual, at a given level of practice, may function with varying degrees of effectiveness, depending upon the degree of activation at which the response occurs, this fact is of the greatest importance in many different contexts. A few of the numerous studies dealing with the problem will be reviewed below. Some of the simpler aspects of performance will be considered first.

REACTION TIME

The relationship between reaction time and other variables is an old problem in psychology. Many years ago it was shown, by work in Störring's laboratory, that unpleasant sensations (produced by strong vinegar or salt solutions) usually decreased the reaction time for finger contractions (Woodworth, 1914); and M. Miller (1926), and later Freeman (1933), reported that relaxation increased the reaction time to electric shock. It had been shown by another investigator that the reaction time to simultaneously presented sound and shock stimuli was shorter than that to either of them presented alone (Todd, 1912). Teichner's (1954) review of studies of reaction time supports the conclusion that shorter reaction times are obtained when more than one sense modality is simultaneously stimulated than when stimulation is applied to only one. Conceivably, the increase in the number of stimuli raises the level of activation and thereby shortens the reaction time.

A relationship between reaction time and the level of activation is also suggested by the fact that Kleitman (1939) found a diurnal curve in reaction time, with a progressive decrease during the morning and early afternoon, and a rise in the late afternoon and evening. This variation in reaction time was related to the diurnal curve for body temperature, which suggests that it is related to the degree of activation. In fact, Kleitman reached the conclusion that there probably is no diurnal reaction time curve independent of the body temperature, and that whenever the temperature changes, that change is accompanied by a change in the opposite direction in reaction time. His data were treated in two different ways to bring out this relationship, which appeared for both simple and choice reactions. No very adequate analysis of the statistical data is, however, presented.

Other findings also make plausible the hypothesis that reaction time varies with variations in activation. Like sensory sensitivity, reaction time varies somewhat in the same individual from day to day (Woodworth and Schlosberg, 1954); there is usually a positive correlation between visual and auditory reaction time (Teichner, 1954); and different members of the body appear to show a fairly high correlation in their speed of response (Woodworth and Schlosberg, 1954).

Stimuli which are known to affect activation have frequently been reported to affect reaction time, though the findings are not without ambiguity and evidence of this sort is at best merely suggestive. Among such factors are drugs, anoxia, exercise, nutrition, fatigue,[1] and factors

[1] It is recognized that the term "fatigue" is used in many different senses. No doubt a distinction should be made between "simple fatigue," or a condition of

affecting motivation (Teichner, 1954; Woodworth and Schlosberg, 1954).

Alcohol dosage and simple reaction time have been found to show a highly significant positive correlation, although the actual difference in reaction time was small (Carpenter, 1959). Results with caffeine were not as clear-cut, though the data suggested, but did not prove, that a small reduction in reaction time occurred when there was high-intensity stimulation and a high alcohol dosage—that is, when the potential for improvement was greatest (Carpenter, 1959). Earlier studies had reported, in one instance, that coffee drinking increased reaction time (Gilliland and Nelson, 1939) and, in another instance, that no effect was produced (Thornton, Holck, and Smith, 1939).

Amytal, chlorpromazine, and reserpine, classified as sedatives, prolonged reaction time (R. A. Schneider, 1960) while a stimulant, phenidylate, shortened reaction time (R. A. Schneider, 1960). The results were significant at about the .08 level of confidence.

Meprobamate, at dosages of 800 milligrams, gave indications of slowing reaction time on a driving test and reduced galvanic skin resistance during stress (J. G. Miller and Uhr, 1960).

One brief review of some of these studies points out that Benzedrine produces a slight but reliable shortening of the complex reaction time to a visual stimulus but exerts little effect on the reaction time to auditory stimuli; that small doses of morphine or of alcohol first shorten and then lengthen reaction time; and that a 30 per cent saturation of carbon monoxide increases visual reaction time (Abramson, Jarvik, and Hirsch, 1955). At dosages of 0 to 100 milligrams, LSD-25, presumably a stimulant, significantly increases the time required to name colors, with larger doses producing longer reaction times (Abramson, Jarvik, and Hirsch, 1955). Manual reaction time tests, on the contrary, were not ordinarily impaired, though the reaction time to sound was significantly increased with a dosage of 100 milligrams as compared with a zero dosage. The intensity and duration of stimulation, as well as the size of dosage of the drug, have also been shown to affect reaction time (Teichner, 1954), perhaps, it may be suggested, through affecting activation.

More direct studies of the relationship between reaction time and

---

low activation following a period of exertion, and "nervous fatigue," which may be a compensatory condition of high activation. "Fatigue" should presumably not be used to refer to a condition of low "motivation" which makes a person disinclined to work even though there is no evidence of exhaustion from previous exertion.

indicators of the level of activation in various systems are studies in which measures of reaction time have been made simultaneously with, or in close succession to, physiological measurements.

G. L. Freeman (1933) reported that reaction time was shorter when muscle tension was greater. R. C. Davis (1940) found that a greater increase in tension in the responding arm during the interval between stimuli was associated with a shorter reaction time to the second stimulus. He also reported that "An increase in overall muscular activity will shorten the time (latency plus recruitment) of subsequent responses . . ." (R. C. Davis, 1956b). Patton (1957) found that increasing the tension of the right arm by means of a flexion movement of the left wrist shortened the discrimination reaction time of the right arm. The introduction of an extraneous noise was shown to increase muscle-action potentials and decrease reaction time (Fink, 1956). The coefficient of correlation between the magnitude of the muscle-action potential in the forearm and the latency of the overt response was —.97. A continuous noise, however, was reported to increase the level of muscular tension and slow the response time for a discriminant movement (R. C. Davis, 1956c, 1956d).

Meyer (1953) has claimed that there is no relationship between the speed of reaction and tension in the muscles not involved in the response, but R. S. Daniel (1949) has claimed that Meyer's data would not warrant this conclusion (Teichner, 1954). Moreover, Henderson (1952) reported a relationship between the reaction time of one arm and action potentials taken from the other arm.

Lundervold (1950) found that individuals who showed action potentials of the muscles when an electrode was inserted had, on the average, a shorter reaction time than those who did not. He suggested that the former might make better fighter pilots and the latter better bomber pilots.

A series of studies by Travis and Kennedy have demonstrated a progressive increase in reaction time as action potentials from the brow muscles became progressively fewer. This relationship was found for reaction time to occasional visual and auditory stimuli, both during a simulated lookout task and during a tracking task in which the subject operated a hand control in such a way as to follow the movements of a target (R. C. Travis and Kennedy, 1947, 1949; Kennedy and Travis, 1948). The same association of low tension in the brow muscles with long reaction times was found in another task which involved merely pressing a key, and in which the signal was a combined light and buzzer (R. C. Travis and Kennedy, 1947). Thus it appears that the tension variation with which concomitant variation in reaction time is found need not be in a part of the body intimately involved in performance of the task.

It should be noted that in the studies of Travis and Kennedy the subjects started from a "normal" or moderate level of muscle tension and proceeded to lower levels of tension, and in Davis' studies, also, the tension levels investigated were within the middle range, with perhaps the exception of the tension produced by a continuous noise. There is some evidence which suggests that very high levels of tension may decrease the speed of reaction.

In his studies of reaction time, Judd (1905) many years ago observed that sudden reactions of antagonistic muscles in some cases increased, and in other cases decreased, the speed of reaction. He pointed out that antagonistic actions of the sudden type are clearly cases of excessive effort, and that where this excessive effort was properly directed it was favorable to speed. Where, on the contrary, it was misapplied, it interfered with speed. An excessive effort did not, therefore, always result in shorter reactions. While gradual antagonistic movements were favorable to rapid reactions, and might be regarded as indications of normal concentrated preparation, the sudden antagonistic reactions were too excessive, and they constituted sources of irregularity.

In a study with six subjects, Freeman and Kendall (1940) reported that reaction time was reduced by a prior tension-producing movement. They suggested, however, that "too much tension will immobilize a muscle just as too much stretch of a rubber band will make it unresponsive to stimulation."

Both reaction time and muscle tension show practice effects. Typically, reaction time decreases and so also does muscle tension, thus producing a situation in which more rapid reaction time is associated with a lower degree of muscle tension. Henderson (1952), for example, found that, over a period of 6 days with 100 trials per day, reaction time declined steadily, while muscle tension in the non-responding arm declined for the first 4 days and showed a statistically insignificant rise for the last 2 days. Lower muscle tension was therefore associated with more rapid reaction time. Assuming that reaction time decreases with practice and, with less certainty, that muscle tension also decreases, the question of concern here is whether, *at a given level of practice*, reaction time shows consistent variations with variations in muscular tension. Most studies apparently indicate that this is the case.

There would presumably be little objection to the conclusion that muscle tension, and particularly that in the responding arm, is related to the speed of reaction. More skepticism may well greet the suggestion that the extent, or the pattern, of activation in other systems is also related to reaction time. Evidence of such a relationship is, however, suggested by some of the studies described below, but not by all of them.

Many early studies gave chiefly negative evidence in regard to a relationship between alpha blocking time and motor reaction time (Ellingson, 1956). Since the two have similar latencies and may be set off by the same stimulus, it was surprising to find so little support for the hypothesis of a relationship between them.

The evidence was not all negative, however. When visual reaction times were measured as the subject was (1) resting with alpha waves, (2) resting without alpha waves, and (3) alerted with alpha blockade, the reaction times during the alerted condition averaged 220 milliseconds as compared with an average of 273 milliseconds during resting conditions (Lansing, Schwartz, and Lindsley, 1956). EEG activation thus appeared to be related to reaction time.

Lansing (1957) later found no consistent relationships between reaction time and the frequency or amplitude of the alpha rhythms in the occipital and motor areas. The mean reaction time of individual subjects, however, showed a definite correlation with their alpha blocking time.

In 1959, Lansing, Schwartz, and Lindsley (1959) again reported a relationship between EEG activation and reaction time. Under alerted conditions, reaction times averaged 225 milliseconds, while under non-alerted conditions they averaged 280 milliseconds, a difference which was significant at better than the .01 level. When a buzzer preceded the visual signal for reaction (alerted condition), there was almost complete identity between the curve for reaction time and the curve for alpha blocking (percentage of trials for each foreperiod interval in which blocking was complete). In the nonalerted condition, when no warning buzzer preceded the visual signal for reaction, no difference in reaction time was found between periods showing good alpha waves, poor alpha waves, and no alpha waves. No explanation for the latter finding was offered.

Callaway and Yeager (1960) have demonstrated, at a reliable level of confidence, a relationship between visual reaction time and the alpha phase at the time of stimulation. This was done through sampling reaction times at various phases of the alpha cycle, finding the phase with the slowest reaction times and measuring a number of reaction times to stimuli at this phase and at a control phase.

A high degree of resting skin-resistance activity—i.e., "spontaneous" changes in skin resistance—and of cardiac activity were found to be significantly associated with a short reaction time in the last ten "training" trials for reaction time, and to be nonsignificantly related in the same direction during other groups of trials (J. I. Lacey and B. C. Lacey, 1958b). The level of resting skin resistance and of heart rate were nonsignificantly related to reaction time (in the same direction) in these various groups of trials.

Certain studies by G. L. Freeman and others, though the data are fragmentary, have lent support to the opinion that there may be a curvilinear relationship between activation and reaction time. Freeman (1940b) measured the skin resistance and reaction time of twenty subjects under two conditions: (1) the subject set his own standard of performance, and (2) the standard of performance was set one P.E. higher than the subject's average for the first condition, and failures in reaching the raised standard were called to his attention. Under the second condition, skin resistance was slightly lower than under the first condition, and reaction times were somewhat longer. When the change in skin resistance under the two conditions was correlated with the change in reaction time, Freeman concluded that "those who exerted the greatest effort (reactivity) showed the least improvement and often did worse under supernormal conditions." The coefficient of correlation was —.41.

Skin resistance and reaction time, measured simultaneously on a single subject at various hours of the day for 105 trials over a number of days, gave an inverted U-shaped curve when plotted on a graph (Freeman, 1940b). The shortest reaction times occurred when there was a moderate degree of skin resistance.

A check on Freeman's findings was made by a student of Schlosberg who secured on herself one hundred sets of twenty simple reaction times together with measures of skin resistance at various hours of the day (Schlosberg, 1954). Again the inverted U-shaped curve was found. Schlosberg and Kling (1959) later questioned the reliability of this study and failed in their efforts to replicate the results.

Freeman and Hovland (1934) reported that Waller, Wechsler, and Regelsberger had agreed in finding diurnal changes in "bodily resistance and polarization capacity of the skin." While the diurnal curve apparently depended on the individual and on circumstances, there was, typically, high resistance in the morning, a drop in resistance at mid-day, and then a gradual increase in resistance which became most noticeable toward evening. Bodily temperature, it was noted, follows a similar course.

If there is a relationship between reaction time and the level of skin resistance, certainly this relationship has not been clearly established.

The effect of drugs on reaction time has been the subject of a number of investigations (Teichner, 1954). Since the outcome is no doubt determined by many factors, such as size of dosage, habituation, the level of activation at which the drug is administered, and others, no attempt will be made to draw any general conclusions. Small doses of meprobamate (800 milligrams), for example, were found to produce no effect on reaction times, while large doses (1600 milligrams) produced significant decrements (Kornetsky, 1958).

Hormones also apparently affect reaction time. Both hypothyroid and hyperthyroid patients were found to have slower visual and auditory reaction times than control groups of patients or of normal subjects (Stern, 1959). Thyroid therapy produced significant changes in the direction of the reaction times obtained from the normal control subjects.

SPEED OF MOVEMENT AND THE SPEED OF COMPLETING A TASK

Reaction time and the speed of completing a task are somewhat different functions. Carrying out a task requires many complex coordinations, and hence would not be expected to correlate very highly with simple reaction time. The less complex the movements involved and the narrower the field of attention required for adequate performance, the more highly might speed of movement be expected to correlate with speed of reaction time. One review reports, for example, that there is no relationship between reaction time and card sorting, pursuit rotor performance, or discrimination reaction time, and little or no relationship with a tapping test (Teichner, 1954). Moreover, various tasks differ in their requirements to such an extent that speed in one task may show little relationship to speed in another task.[2] In fact, little co-variation between scores has been reported between a number of "speed" tests, as well as between tests purporting to measure other aspects of voluntary motor performance, such as strength, co-

[2] Brožek and Taylor (1954) suggest, for example, that "in speed of small repetitive movements (e.g., tapping) the limiting factor appears to be the refractory period of the motor centers, while the speed of single ballistic movements reflects the force developed during isotonic contraction and the speed of simple reaction time is principally a measure of the delay at the central sensori-motor synapses" (p. 607).

ordination and endurance (Brožek and Taylor, 1954). In general, the motor tests showed a low but positive correlation with each other.

Concomitant variations have been found in the speed of various performances and indicators of the level of activation or conditions presumed to produce changes in activation. For example, the maximum frequency of finger movements, which has been shown to bear a close relationship to the frequency of impulses in the motor centers, is diminished in fatigue and in conditions characterized by a decreased metabolic rate and diagnosed as primary or secondary hypothyroidism (Enzer, Simonson, and Blankstein, 1941). Conversely, an increase in the rate of finger oscillation has been reported to occur when the electrical resistance of the skin became lower (Freeman, 1940b), and also when there was an increase in muscle tension (Freeman, 1933). Similarly, "emotionally reactive" rats, defined by the Hall criterion of open-field defecation, had a higher speed of swimming under water in an adapted Y-shaped discrimination apparatus (Broadhurst, 1957).

Caffeine produced an increase in the speed of tapping (Golla, 1944), increased the rate of running of hunger-motivated rats (N. E. Miller and Miles, 1935), and speeded up the response of a conditioned reflex (Skinner and Heron, 1937). In small doses it increased, and in large doses decreased, the speed of typewriting, while in all doses used it increased the speed of association (color naming and opposites) (Hollingworth, 1912). It thus appears that large doses of caffeine may decrease the speed of complex motor co-ordinations, while facilitating certain associative processes. Dexedrine Sulfate has also been reported to increase the scores of normal subjects on an association test (Welch, Diethelm, and Long, 1946). Chlorpromazine affected the speed of tapping in a direction opposite to that of dextro-amphetamine sulfate (Lehmann and Csank, 1957). Benzedrine, as well as caffeine, not only increased the mean rate of responding in the case of a conditioned response, but also restored the rate of responding to its former level when administered after several days of extinction (Skinner and Heron, 1937). These investigators suggest that "any factor which increases the rate of energy output should result in an increase in the rate of responding."

Tentative findings have shown an association between the electrical output from a subject's muscles (degree of muscle tension) and the length of time required for assembling units in a simple assembly task (R. C. Travis and Kennedy, 1949). An increase in the speed of addition, but a decrease in accuracy, has been reported to accompany increases in muscle tension under "supermaximal effort" (Freeman,

1933). The threat of failure has been said to produce an increase in both speed and errors on a digit-symbol test (Lazarus and Eriksen, 1952). No physiological measurements were made in the latter investigation.

Freeman (1938) reported that, in eleven out of fifteen individual curves for speed of finger oscillation, there was an increase in the number of finger oscillations per minute as the tension load was increased, until a certain point was reached, after which there was a decrease in speed of movement. Using relaxation, "normal" tension, and induced tension, he also reported that there was decreased accuracy of discrimination during both relaxation and hypertension (Freeman, 1933). Discrimination reaction time, however, was shorter under tension. The statistical treatment of the findings would, by present standards, be considered inadequate.

Malmo and Davis (1956) reported that "autonomic gradients [3] (especially blood pressure)" were significantly related to the speed of mirror drawing, with steeper gradients being associated with shorter performance time. The physiological measures recorded were heart rate, blood pressure, respiration, and EMG's from the forehead and from the flexor and extensor muscles of the right arm. The measures showing a reliable correlation with the speed of performance were blood pressure, heart rate, and the EMG from the extensor muscles. It was said that Bartoshuk's (1955b) study of muscle-potential gradients suggested an optimum value of gradient slope, beyond which performance did not benefit from further increase, and might be slightly impaired by what he called "excessive motivation."

A rather high correlation was found between the frequency of the alpha rhythm and the speed of writing where there was a normal EEG and normal mechanisms of writing, but little correlation when there were abnormal EEG's or "abnormal motor mechanisms of writing." The subjects were psychiatric patients (Denier, van der Gon, and van Hinte, 1959).

Speed on a battery of "psychotechnical" tests was reported to be associated with certain characteristics of the electroencephalogram (Rémond and Lesèvre, 1957). Subjects with a slow, widely distributed, and not easily disturbed alpha rhythm were said to perform slowly on the tests. Slowness of performance was found also in hyperexcitable subjects with a basic rhythm that tended toward desynchronization and marked reactivity. The slowness of the latter group was regarded

[3] A "gradient" in a measure is a progressive increase in the measure from the beginning to the end of the period of measurement.

as due to "emotional instability" since, in their method of expressing themselves, they often showed speed and impulsiveness. Subjects with a "normally modulated and reactive" alpha rhythm showed more speed and better "psychomotor control." Two causes of slowness were therefore suggested. The first was a lack of responsiveness, and the second was hyperexcitability, which, it was thought, made the subjects too vulnerable to stimulation and led either to anxious inhibition or to impulsiveness. It is of interest that, as the investigators pointed out, the responses which correlated with the EEG were of a very elementary nature. No relationship was found between the more complex psychological processes and any particular characteristic of the EEG or the general type of the EEG. Auditory reaction time was more discriminative than keeping a pointer on a circle, which measured a certain motor rapidity but permitted the subject to work at his own speed without disturbance by any signals. While no correlation was found between the frequency of the alpha rhythm and the speed of certain "psychic processes," there was a bimodal distribution of the psychotechnical tests when the subjects were grouped according to the frequency of the alpha rhythm.

Mundy-Castle (1957) has reported a significant correlation of .61 between alpha frequency and a battery of "psychological, speed, and tempo tests." Among the individual tests showing significant coefficients of correlation with alpha frequency were speed of tapping ($r = .403$), tapping at preferred rate ($r = .381$), rapidity of walking ($r = .332$), and speed of drawing circles around identical groups of letters ($r = .318$).

Studies of manic and of depressed patients, who presumably differ in the level of activation, suggest a relationship between these psychiatric conditions and the speed of response (D. E. Cameron, 1945). In depressed patients the reaction time was prolonged, and ocular movements, speed of concept formation, and the fluctuations of an ambiguous figure were slower. The latter function has been said to vary with the degree of the depression.

In manic patients the findings are less clear-cut. A slowing down has, however, been reported for these patients also in reaction time, speed of ocular movements, speed of concept formation, and fluctuations of an ambiguous figure (D. E. Cameron, 1945). Such findings are in harmony with the suggested curvilinear relationship between certain functions and the level of activation. It has been suggested that manic patients, while showing in general a facilitation of response, are so overresponsive to all aspects of the environment that distraction of attention slows up any given response which is being measured. On the other hand, psychiatric patients have been found to show facilitation of associative activity during elation (Welch, Diethelm, and Long, 1946). Distractibility seemed to be ruled out, and the patients did significantly better than normal subjects in memorizing a list of fifteen nonsense syllables.

Variations in activation, if they do indeed affect the speed of response, would be only one of a number of factors influencing this aspect of behavior. While extremely low or extremely high degrees of activation may have a decided effect upon speed, it is possible that variations within the middle range may have their influence overshadowed by the influence of other factors. Again a curvilinear relationship is suggested between activation and an aspect of behavior. It is questionable, however, whether there exists a unitary aspect of behavior which can be called "speed."

THE INTENSITY OR EXTENT OF RESPONSE

The Extent of Motor Responses

Intensity of response may be measured through measurement of either the extent or the force of a movement. A greater extent of movement was found by Golla (1921) during the state of "effort." He measured the triceps-jerk and the knee-jerk during rest and during effort and found that the latter condition increased the magnitude, as well as the velocity, of these reflexes. During effort he found heightened general bodily activity. He had expected that inhibition of general activity might occur since inhibition of general activity might conceivably increase the readiness to respond to a specific stimulus.

That increased muscular activity in one part of the body tends to be accompanied by increased activity in other parts of the body is illustrated by the well-known fact that the extent of the knee-jerk may be increased by clenching the fist. In line with this fact is the report that there is a systematic increase in the amplitude of the knee-jerk with increases in the force exerted on a hand dynamometer (Courts, 1939). The correlation of the extent of the knee-jerk with the general level of activation is shown also by the fact that the knee-jerk is smaller in sleep (Tuttle, 1924) and is less active on first awakening in the morning than later in the day (Kennard, 1947). Congruent with these findings is the report of Jacobson that decrease of the knee-jerk tended to be prevented by anything which seemed to have a stimulating effect. Such an effect was produced by exciting conversation, by noises, by disturbances by the investigator, and by vigorous voluntary movement (Jacobson, 1928).

Correlation between the extent of movement and the level of muscle tension of the individual is demonstrated by the fact, previously mentioned, that the extent of arm movement (M. Miller, 1926) or of finger movement (Freeman, 1933) in response to a standard electric shock has been shown to be greater under conditions of tension than under conditions of relaxation. Tense individuals also show a greater extent of movement in the patterned muscular reactions known as the startle response (Landis and Hunt, 1939).

Changes in the extent of movement have been found to accompany changes in endocrine conditions known to produce variations in the degree of activation. For example, in one dog, removal of the thyroid gland greatly reduced the height to which the forepaw was raised in a conditioned withdrawal response, while administration of thyroid extract tended to restore the normal extent of movement (Anderson, 1941). In other dogs the magnitude of this motor response was found to be greatly increased during the lactating period (Anderson, 1941). At the height of the period its average extent was 124 millimeters, compared with an average of 37 millimeters during the last month of pregnancy, and 27 millimeters after nursing had ceased. It is known that at the time of nursing there are marked changes in the endocrine secretions of the animal.

Responses of the duct glands also appear to be affected by the level of activation. In a conditioned-response experiment with dogs as subjects, the quantity of flow of saliva was shown to vary with natural changes in the physiological state of the animals or with experimental alteration of endocrine conditions (Anderson, 1941). The changes in the condition of the animals appeared to involve changes in the level of activation, and the changes in the quantity of salivation may be regarded as changes in the extent of the response. It was found that salivary response was increased during the lactating period and during estrus. At the height of estrus one animal who showed no conditioned salivation when not in heat not only had a copious flow of saliva, but also a vigorous head movement. The investigator states:

The increase in the salivary conditioned response is no doubt associated with the generally heightened excitability and increased neuro-muscular activity of the bitch when the mating period is at its height. This heightened nervous irritability is probably closely associated wth the underlying physiological glandular changes which presumably take place at the time, namely an acceleration in the secretory activity of the pituitary, the gonads and the thyroid. The effect upon the salivary conditioned response is strikingly similar to that seen when a hypothyroid dog is fed thyroid extract (Anderson, 1941, p. 662).

The conditioned secretion of the salivary gland has also been shown to vary with variations in other conditions which imply a change in the degree of activation. For example, the response was shown to be stronger in dogs immediately after the animals had pulled a cart containing a heavy weight than after they had pulled a lighter weight (Bykow, Alexandroff, Wirjikowski, and Riel, 1927). Increasing the weight continued to strengthen the salivary response until a certain point was reached, after which the relationship was reversed. It appears uncertain whether this reversal of relationship should be attributed to fatigue or whether we have here another instance of the suggested curvilinear relationship between the level of activation and response.

Administration of a drug (prostigmine) restored the conditioned avoidance response to electric shock in a dog who had for many trials failed to respond to the signal (W. T. James and Ginsburg, 1949). The withdrawal response after administration of the drug not only occurred regularly for a number of trials but was much more intense than the response elicited by the electric shock itself before the injection of the drug. There was an accompanying increase in heart rate and respiratory rate. In another less phlegmatic dog the percentage of responses did not increase but there was an increase in general activity.

Administration of 0.1 milligram of adrenalin to dogs produced an increase in the intensity of the conditioned response, while a larger dose produced an inhibitory effect (Pribytkova, 1936). Similarly, other investigators found in one dog a slight increase in the magnitude of the conditioned salivary response during mild dosage, a noticeable increase during stronger dosage, and a decrease to a point below the normal level during very strong dosage (Anderson, 1941).

In spite of the fact that these investigations of the behavioral effects of drugs or of changes in endocrine secretions were carried out on a small number of subjects, and the statistical treatment of the findings was by present standards inadequate, the findings fit into a broader pattern which has apparently been established by other investigators.

The Force of Movement

The force of muscular responses under various degrees of activation has been less frequently investigated than the extent of these responses. However, experiments concerned with the "dynamogenic" effect of this or that sensory stimulation may perhaps be interpreted as demonstrating that increased energy mobilization frequently increases the force of response, for the sensory stimulation may well have exerted its effect through increasing the degree of activation of the organism. In Störring's laboratory, for example, it was shown that the force of contraction of finger muscles, measured by a spring ergograph, was, in 65 per cent of the cases, increased by the application of such stimuli as strong vinegar or a strong salt solution (Woodworth, 1914).

Féré (1900) pointed out many years ago that both intellectual effort and stimulation of the muscle sense increase the "dynamometrique" force of muscular contractions. He cited the instance of exercise of the foot producing this effect in the corresponding hand. His studies, however, were qualitative and incomplete.

In a somewhat more recent experiment, which is widely known, J. J. B. Morgan (1916) showed that typewriter keys were pressed with reliably greater force during noisy periods than during quiet periods, and pointed out that the change in pressure appeared to be indicative of the tension under which the subject was working. Where increased key-pressure was found, the speed of response was also greater. Incidentally, breathing ratios increased under these conditions.

Frustration has been cited in various experiments as producing greater force of action (Marzocco, 1955). Frustrated rats pressed the bar of the Skinner box harder and faster, and chimpanzees pressed the nozzle harder when drinking water was turned off.

Further suggestion that an increase in the degree of activation produces an increase in the force of movement is to be found in the report that the administration of the stimulant, caffeine, causes an increase in the strength or force of the hand-grip (Golla, 1944).

Of interest also are data on the intensity of motor responses produced by stimulation of a cortical point. Such stimulation evoked responses of increasing intensity as the state of the animal changed from that of sleep to that of moderate activity (Delgado, 1952). Strong activity, however, appeared to decrease cortical excitability or to block pathways, thus abolishing the motor effects of electrical stimulation. Again, we have an instance of a relationship approximating that of the inverted U-shaped curve.

Clinical Observations of the Extent and Force of Movements During Excitement and During Depression

Clinical observations are in harmony with the findings of experimental studies in reporting an increase in the extent and force of motor responses during excitement (i.e., a condition of high energy level). Thalbitzer (1926) many years ago described what he called "active productive mania" in the following terms:

Beside the highly exalted mood, the strongly marked feeling of pleasure, mania is characterized by an increased impulse toward movement; the movements of the maniac are livelier, quicker and also more frequent and stronger than those of the normal human being, all this being the expression of the increased activity of his psycho-motor centres. This applies also to his speech; the maniac talks incessantly, and this gives scope to his greatly increased intellectual productivity which, together with an alert and very easily distracted attention, forms the third main symptom of his disease, intellectual over-activity (p. 47).

Bagby (1928), in his discussion of disorders of personality, defined manic-depressive psychosis as a disturbance of activity level. He says:

During the period of excitement, or *high activity level,* the patient shows curious symptoms. Thoughts are expressed in loud tones and with remarkable rapidity, there being an almost constant flow of somewhat incoherent expressions. Conduct is similarly affected, for excessive energy is expended in behavior, and there is a production of random movements of wide range. Distractibility is prominent. And, finally, fatigue does not seem to develop in the normal way, sleep being induced very slowly. The depressed phase, or *period of low activity level,* gradually replaces the condition of excitement and finally becomes quite the reverse of it. Behavior and thinking are retarded to an extreme degree. There is but little production of spontaneous movements, and responses to questions and requests are made slowly and often incompletely (pp. 15–16).

More recently D. E. Cameron (1945) has pointed out that both the manic excitements and the anxiety states are conditions in which overactivity is prominent, though in the anxiety states the overactivity is continually curbed by inhibitory processes.

General observation suggests that the highly activated individual usually shows more vigor in his motor responses than the relaxed individual. He may often be observed to walk with a heavier tread, to press harder on his pencil, and to speak more loudly or in a higher pitch. In some instances, however, it appears that inhibitory processes may be so dominant that he actually walks and speaks more softly than the average individual. In any case, he appears likely to go to one extreme or the other in the expression of force in his activities. The foregoing statements, it will be recognized, represent, not established facts, but hypotheses which are subject to verification.

THE GENERAL QUALITY OF PERFORMANCE

Any discussion of the relationship between activation and performance must recognize the fact that, in this area, there are many unsettled questions and, at the present stage of information, legitimate differences of opinion in regard to certain basic principles. While some psychologists favor an organismic approach to the problem (taking into account, however, the effect of differences in the activation of different systems and of the patterning of activation in a particular system) other psychologists favor a strict stimulus-response approach and prefer to consider, not general activity level, but the specific effect of one response system upon another (R. C. Davis, 1956a). The present discussion has an organismic orientation but recognizes the fact that excitation is not equal in all parts of the organism, and that differences in the locus of maximum excitation, especially in the muscles which are the terminal point of activity, produce differences in the effect upon performance. Actually, the two points of view are not as far apart as the emphasis placed upon them by their exponents would suggest. R. C. Davis (1956a), for example, while emphasizing the study of specific response systems, imparts some degree of "generality" to his discussion by the statement:

Although muscular activities are to be the basis for evaluating response similarity, there is no implication that combination effects are solely determined by muscular activities. Such effects may have no single locale. We may regard the muscular actions as convenient signs of the excitation of response systems of which they are the terminal points and also, typically, the source of feed-back loops (p. 4).

Even though this present account focuses on the effect of differences in the general level of activation, recognition is given to the necessity of limiting any general statement about the effect of various levels of activation by including the phrase "other factors being equal." It remains for further research to determine what the factors are which must remain equal, though some of them have already been identified and others have been suggested.

It seems worthwhile to consider the findings of some of the studies in this area, even though reports are in many instances contradictory. The value of the suggestions in such a survey (incomplete though it must be) will be apparent.

Many years ago Féré (1900) elaborated the position that what goes on in one part of the organism affects in many ways what goes on in any other part of the organism. He said: "These observations taken together indicate to us that a cerebral center, each time it enters into action, provokes by a process as yet undetermined, an excitation of the entire organism; although it is said that the brain thinks, it is the entire being which enters into activity." [4] Experimental support of this statement has been provided by the work of Jacobson, Max, and others who have shown the participation of skeletal-muscle activity in the processes of imagining, remembering, thinking, and dreaming.

Féré (1900) also maintained the converse of the proposition stated above. He argued: "If psychic activity shows an influence on the energy of voluntary movement, voluntary movement can also have an influence on psychic activity." [5] In support of his argument he cited the fact that lying in bed is not conducive to mental work and that a psychopathic patient can make himself tipsy through the exercise of speech. Finally, he pointed out the fact that activity in one group of muscles may augment the activity in other groups of muscles. For example, exercise of the foot may increase the force of muscular contractions in the hands. He (Féré, 1900) quotes Bain as having said:

Rapid movements . . . produce a kind of mechanical excitement. An organ, however small it may be, when it moves rapidly tends to set to its pace all the other organs of movement. In a rapid walk, and more still in running, the mind is excited, the gestures and the speech are accelerated, and the face shows an unusual tension (p. 25). [6]

G. L. Freeman (1948a) has suggested that, through the blood stream and the nerves, the effect of heightened metabolic activity or energy release in one tissue is conveyed to other tissues. For example, activity in a muscle sets up proprioceptive stimulation which causes excitation in the brain, and this excitation in the brain stimulates some other muscle, gland, or nerve tissue to increased activity. In other words, reactivity in peripheral muscle tissue both reflects and helps to determine reactivity of central neural tissue. Bills (1927) had previously pointed out that it is thought that, when the sensory-neuromuscular system is already active, the threshold is thereby lowered to subsequent neural excitation and discharge.

More recent experiments have shown that prolonged exposure to a low level of stimulation, produced by having the subject lie on a bed with various sensory avenues cut off or interfered with, produced a statistically significant loss in the ability to solve simple problems

[4] Translation mine.
[5] Translation mine.
[6] Translation mine.

(Hebb, 1955a). The subject complained that he could not concentrate. After leaving the cubicle, he showed a disturbance of motor control and a significant decrease in score on the same kind of intelligence tests he took before his isolation for 24 hours. Heron (1957) has reported that, with prolonged exposure to a monotonous environment, thinking was impaired, visual perception was disturbed, and "childish emotional responses" appeared. Evidently, an organismic effect was produced.

R. C. Davis (1959), in an attempt to discover what physiological changes occur under monotonous stimulation, found that after 40 minutes of reduced stimulation, the experimental group, as compared with the control group, showed increased muscular and circulatory activity and decreased respiration, a pattern which he thought might be characteristic of "anticipation." He suggests an hypothesis of increased sensitization to explain the results of "sensory deprivation." This would appear to be an organismic-type hypothesis.

Leuba (1955) has outlined a concept of optimal stimulation, a condition which he believes all organisms seek, and has suggested its relationship to learning. He says:

> A stimulus impinging upon fresh sense organs and initiating nerve impulses in fibers possibly sensitized by a hormone or a drug, may have far more stimulating effects than similar stimuli impinging upon fatigued sense organs or when a depressant drug is circulating in the blood stream. It is conceivable, as we have seen, that a stimulus which at one time was part of a reinforcing state of affairs might at another time be part of an over-stimulating state. It is only as that stimulus is seen in its entire context that a generalization may be possible. The suggested principle of optimal stimulation emerges from the total situation; and its existence may be overlooked by those occupied in studying the reactions of organisms to specific stimuli (pp. 31–32).

The Optimal Level of Activation

For performances of many kinds, there appears to be an optimal level of activation at which the performance reaches its greatest excellence. It seems that the individual's level of activation may be either too low or too high for producing the best quality of work of which he is capable. This hypothesis was suggested (Duffy, 1932b) in relation to muscular tension (conceived to be indicative of degree of excitation) and later (Duffy, 1941a, 1957) in relation to activation in general, as indicated by a number of physiological measures. It has been proposed by Lindsley (1952) in relation to the EEG.

When activation is too low, as for example in drowsiness or extreme relaxation, it might be expected that the individual would lack alertness. He might fail to respond to cues, or his response might lack force and speed. When, on the other hand, his level of activation is too high, there might be excessive impulsion to action and reduction of what Easterbrook (1959) has called "the range of cue utilization." The nature of the task appears to be an important determinant of the effect upon performance of a high degree of activation; so also perhaps are other factors, such as the stage of practice and the inhibitory ability of the individual. It seems likely that there is an optimal level of activation for the performance of a given task at a given stage of practice, which may vary somewhat with the individual and with other aspects of the total stituation. If such is the case, the curve expressing the relationship between the degree of activation and the quality of performance would be an inverted U-shaped curve, in which increases in activation would be associated with an increase in the quality of performance up to a certain point, after which further increases in activation would be associated with increasingly inferior performance. Perhaps, if this curve were extended far enough, a point would be reached at which disruption of all organized activity would occur.

Direct evidence in support of the U-shaped curve is fairly meager. Indirect evidence is more abundant. In many studies, changes in activation, or in conditions presumed to produce a change in activation, have been found associated with changes in performance, but seldom has activation been varied systematically from a very low to a very high degree and observation made of corresponding changes in performance.

In an early study of the relationship between performance and activation of the muscular system, Stauffacher (1937) had his subjects memorize nonsense syllables under four different degrees of muscle tension: (1) no induced tension, (2) one-fourth of a subject's maximum pull on a dynamometer, (3) one-half of a subject's maximum pull, and (4) three-fourths of his maximum pull. He found that, while a certain amount of induced muscular tension would facilitate learning, a degree of tension which was smaller or greater than the facilitative degree, would produce little or no improvement in learning. The effect of induced tension varied somewhat with different subjects. Poor learners appeared to benefit from induced tension, whereas good learners did not. It was suggested that good performers might already be working at a higher tonus level than poor performers, and that therefore the increments in tension might cause their tension level to go higher than the level which would be most facilitative of performance.

F. A. Courts (1939) corroborated the finding that the degree of muscular tension could be either too low or too high for optimal performance, both for memorizing nonsense syllables and also for the early stages of learning to manipulate the Koerth pursuit-rotor. He found, however, only slight and statistically insignificant differences between the effect of increased tension upon good memorizers and poor memorizers.

The expectation that there would be an optimal degree of muscular tension for learning was not borne out, however, in an experiment in which two discrimination tasks were learned under three different degrees of induced muscle tension (McFann, 1952). No significant difference in learning was found.

Shaw (1956) reported evidence for the inverted U-shaped curve when the relationship represented was that between induced muscular tension and the perception span for digits, or the number of digits reproduced after tachistoscopic presentation. The optimal tension varied as a function of the task difficulty. One-fourth of the maximum dynamometer pull improved performance on digit series of all lengths. A greater pull than this improved the performance on the longer, more difficult series more than that on the shorter, easier series, but there was an inverted U-shaped curve representing the effect of induced tension on all series and for both good and poor performers, good performers being optimally facilitated by a less strong pull. The experiment was replicated two months later with the same subjects.

Shore (1958), using three groups of subjects scoring low, medium, and high on the Taylor Manifest Anxiety Scale, and inducing muscular tension through a pull on a dynamometer, found that an increase in induced tension up to an optimum improved the recognition of briefly exposed nonaffective stimuli for all three groups, thus yielding a U-shaped curve. The optimum tension was found to be higher for the high-anxiety group, perhaps, it may be suggested, because they were more accustomed to handling a high degree of activation.

D. R. Meyer (1953) found that, in almost all the studies using induced muscular tension, performance was at first facilitated, reached an optimum, and then showed a decline. He concluded that the optimal level of muscular tension was a function of the nature and difficulty of the task and of the type of muscular condition induced.

The relationship between induced tension and performance, Courts (1942b) suggests, can be explained in ways which do not necessitate the assumption of an increase in the general level of activation. It will, therefore, be of interest to determine whether other presumed indicators of the degree of activation show a relationship to performance similar to that of muscular tension.

Support for the inverted U-shaped curve between arousal and performance is seen by Stennett (1957a) in a study in which he recorded palmar conductance and EMG's during an auditory tracking task. When he controlled the effects of learning on performance scores and partialed out the interaction effect of the order of presentation of the experimental conditions, both the palmar conductance scores and the EMG response from four different muscle groups were significantly related to performance in the way hypothesized.

A suggestion that the relationship between certain aspects of the EEG and performance in flying may be represented by the U-shaped curve is found in the report that the flying ability of pilots tended to be best if the alpha energy peak was about 10.5 cycles per second (Thorner, Gibbs, and Gibbs, 1942), and by the conclusion of H. Gastaut (1957) that the best pilot was usually the one with the most "normal" EEG. Gastaut's conclusion was based upon a study of 309 cadet pilots made by Picard, Navarranne, Laboureur, Grousset, and Jest (1957).

An inverted U-shaped curve was also found by Belanger and Feldman to represent the relationship between the Skinner box performance of rats and the number of hours of water deprivation (Malmo, 1959). Hours of water deprivation were closely related, in linear fashion, to the heart rate, so it may be said that, after 48 hours of water deprivation, an increase in heart rate was accompanied by a decrease in bar pressing. Up to that point, an increase in heart rate had been accompanied by increased frequency of bar pressing.

Studies which may conceivably be interpreted to offer indirect support to the conception of an optimal level of activation include one in which the degree of anxiety of subjects, as measured by the Taylor anxiety scale, showed a significant curvilinear relationship to the time required to learn a human stylus maze (Matarazzo, Ulett, and Saslow, 1955). Subjects across the whole range of anxiety level were employed. Individuals in the middle range of anxiety were significantly superior to those at both the high and the low ends of the scale, though the degree of anxiety accounted for only 10 per cent of the variance shown in time scores. When, however, the criterion of learning was the number of trials required, a rectilinear relationship with anxiety scores appeared. No significant curvilinear relationship was found between anxiety and digit-symbol learning, though the performance of the groups in the middle range of anxiety was significantly superior to that of subjects in the low anxiety group (Matarazzo and Phillips, 1955). Two unpublished studies from the Iowa laboratory, on the other hand, suggest a curvilinear relationship between anxiety scores and total amount of conditioning, with a greater difference occurring between the highly anxious subjects and those at the median than between subjects at the median and those with low anxiety scores (Spence and Taylor, 1953).

An inverted U-shaped curve represents the relationship between performance and strength of incentive found in a number of studies (Courts, 1942b). In an early study by Yerkes and Dodson (1908), fewer errors in learning were found when an electric shock administered was of medium intensity than when it was weaker or stronger. The optimum motivation for learning decreased with increases in the difficulty of the task. More recently it has been shown that rats deprived of food for 12 hours showed greater conditioning strength in the Skinner box than rats deprived of food for 1, 24, or 48 hours (Finan and Taylor, 1940). Medium degrees of hunger were also found to be more favorable to problem solving in chimpanzees than a lesser or a greater degree of hunger (Birch, 1945). Broadhurst (1957) has reported that rats show a curvilinear relationship between motivation and the degree of learning of a discrimination task, with a decrease in learning following motivation which is more intense than the optimum. It was also reported that the optimal motivation decreased with increasing difficulty of the task. Since the degree of activation presumably varies with the degree of motivation, these findings are in harmony with the conception of a U-shaped curve of relationship between activation and performance, though other interpretations cannot be ruled out.

The effects of the injection of adrenalin upon various performances are apparently represented by the inverted U-curve. A very low dose had a beneficial effect on maze learning in the rat (Akimov, 1936). Injection of 0.6 milligram/100 grams of adrenalin in oil (a massive dose) caused a striking decrease in the frequency of conditioned avoidance responses (Kosman and Gerard, 1955). Dibenzyline, which blocked the peripheral effects of the drugs, provided complete protection against this loss.

Berry and Davis (1958) found that a U-shaped curve represented the relationship between the learning of nonsense syllables and muscle potentials from the jaw and forehead, but their curve was quite different from the one suggested here. The best and the poorest learners had higher muscle-potential scores than the mediocre ones. The relationship was significantly nonlinear. No significant relationship between arm potentials and learning scores could be discovered.

Kling, Williams, and Schlosberg (1959) failed to find any clear evidence for an optimal level of skin conductance and a rotary pursuit performance.

Paul Obrist (1959), measuring the level of skin resistance and of heart rate before and during serial learning, believed that his data suggested a curvilinear relationship between these measures and learning in some subjects, though he thought that the two measures reflected differential functioning rather than over-all arousal.

Effects of a Low Degree of Activation

A level of activation which is very low may, it appears, be associated with lack of alertness, or lack of readiness for response, and with generally diminished activity. The type of defect in performance associated with this condition would presumably be slowness in responding, the missing of cues, a relatively small output of work, and, frequently, some degree of disorganization of performance.

Jacobson (1930) found that thirteen subjects whom he studied reported that mental activity was "approximately in abeyance" during advanced muscular relaxation. Mental images diminished or disappeared. With progressive muscular relaxation, Jacobson (1929) claims, not only imagery but also attention, recollection, and thought processes gradually diminish. His subjects reported, during general relaxation "a certain inertness of voluntary activity, and unreadiness to start to move."

Studies by R. C. Travis and Kennedy, referred to previously, have shown a progressive decrease in the quality of performance as muscle-action potentials decreased progressively (from an initially moderate level). When the subject operated a hand control in a tracking task which simulated the job of a pilot, truck driver, or helmsman, and required continuous visuo-motor adjustments to follow the movements of a target, there was in general a poorer tracking score when there were fewer muscle-action potentials (Kennedy and Travis, 1948). The poorer tracking score may well have been due to the subject's inability to remain alert and to co-ordinate his responses successfully at a low level of activation. W. L. Jenkins and Connor (1949), using a very small number of subjects, also found muscular activity during a tracking performance to be closely related to the tracking score.

In a simulated lookout task, failure to respond was associated with low muscle tension (R. C. Travis and Kennedy, 1949). In fact, only one failure to respond occurred at a high tension level. It seems probable that the errors associated with too low a level of muscle tension are likely to be predominantly errors of "omission" rather than errors of "commission."

Adding weight to the findings of R. C. Travis and Kennedy (1949) is the fact that, with a reversal of the degree of tension, there was a reversal in performance. As electrical potentials from the muscles were increased (by appropriate stimulation), there was an increase in the accuracy of performance and a decrease in reaction time.

Improvement in performance through an increase in muscle tension was demonstrated in some of the earliest studies of the relationship between tension and performance. J. J. B. Morgan (1916), in an experiment previously referred to, showed that distraction in the form of noise while the subject was striking keys on a typewriter both increased the pressure with which the keys were struck and improved the quality of the performance. A. G. Bills (1927) later showed that pulling on a dynamometer, when the optimum degree of pressure was determined for each subject, improved the learning of nonsense syllables, the adding of columns of digits, the perception of letters, and the learning of paired associates. Sharp (1941) showed that higher residual tension from a task previously performed increased the output in subsequent work. A number of other investigators have demonstrated improvement in a wide variety of performances by means of increments in muscle tension (Courts, 1939, 1942a; Bills, 1927, 1943). Among these performances, described in a review by Courts (1942b), are pursuit learning, memorizing, finger oscillation, letter naming, tapping, maze learning, and the acquiring of a conditioned salivary response.

Gradients in muscle tension, or a progressive increase in muscle potentials from the beginning to the completion of a task, have been reported to be related to the quality of performance in mirror tracing (Bartoshuk, 1955b). With the subjects equated for practice, the gradient slope (especially for the right-forearm extensor) was found to be directly related to the speed and accuracy of performance. Gradient slope was interpreted to be a function of the strength of motivation.

W. D. Obrist (1950) found that the degree of excitation, as indicated by the magnitude of the GSR and the frequency of the alpha rhythm, was positively related to the rate of learning nonsense syllables. The correlation coefficient between the subjects' alpha frequencies and their rates of learning was .60, but alpha voltage was not significantly related to the rate of learning or to the magnitude of the GSR. He concluded that his GSR findings supported the hypothesis that learning is associated with a high degree of arousal or attention and that, for a given group of syllables, attention was greatest during the time when the greatest amount of learning took place. He suggested an explanation of serial position effects in terms of a factor of excitation.

Perceptual organization as indicated by time scores on the Kohs Block Designs appeared to improve after mild physical exercise and to deteriorate after sleep loss (Lybrand, Andrews, and Ross, 1954). In other studies referred to by these authors, it appeared that a day of physical work decreased the accuracy of perception. Shipyard workers tested at the beginning and at the end of the day, showed, at the end of the day, an increase in each of five illusions. It was suggested that in general "fatigued subjects displayed a lack of ability to form relationships among various stimuli or to relate these stimuli to past experience" (Lybrand, Andrews, and Ross, 1954, p. 704).

Drugs which presumably raise the energy level have been claimed by some investigators to improve the quality of certain performances. Benzedrine Sulfate, for example, has been reported to facilitate reliably the performance on tests of multiplication, of substitution, and of speed in arithmetic (Kleemeir and Kleemeir, 1947). It is said that Benzedrine has some boosting effect which is connected with the mobilization of blood sugar (Crichton-Miller, 1947). While the effects of the drug vary from individual to individual, many, but not all, investigators have reported that it produces an increase in the speed of performance.

Performance on a complicated compensatory pursuit task has been shown to be significantly different under clinical doses of an analeptic drug (Dexedrine) and a depressant drug (Benadryl-Hyosine) from that with no drug at all or with a lactose placebo (Payne and Hauty, 1955). The depressant hastened and maximized work decrement over a number of trials, while the stimulant minimized it. In both this and an earlier study (Payne and Hauty, 1954) it was shown that the performance effects could not be accounted for by concomitant subjective effects. The investigators concluded that the drugs seemed to define "a range of capacity within which proficiency variation due to other influences could occur."

While the effects of drugs upon performance do not appear to be wholly consistent, and N. E. Miller (1957), among others, has pointed out the fact that conclusions must be drawn with an eye to the side effects of the drugs, there does appear to be a general tendency for drugs classified as depressants to have one kind of effect upon performance and drugs classified as stimulants or excitants to have an opposite effect. It might be expected that the findings would vary with variations in the level of activation at which the drug was introduced—certainly if there is indeed a U-shaped relationship between activation and performance. Size of dosage, adequacy of controls, and other factors would also affect the results. We may, however, review briefly some of the findings which have been reported.

Rats given amphetamine, as compared with untreated rats, worked more steadily on a strained fixed-ratio schedule of bar presses (Boren, 1958). In performance on the Porteus maze, Porteus and Barclay (1957) reported that twenty-two patients suffered an average loss of 2.08 years or 15 test quotient points when chlorpromazine was administered. A single dose of 400 milligrams of chlorpromazine also impaired significantly the performance on a continuous task involving the rapid discrimination of either all X's or all X's preceded by A's from a series of letters presented briefly and rapidly (Primac, Mirsky, and Rosvold, 1957). With increasing amounts of chlorpromazine, there was increased impairment on such relatively simple tests as the pursuit rotor and the digit symbol test (Kornetsky, Humphries, and Evarts, 1957). The effect on normal subjects, as compared with schizophrenics, was greater when a single dose of chlorpromazine was administered and the subjects were tested on simple psychomotor tasks (Kornetsky and Humphries, 1958).

Data from two studies using a continuous performance test were analyzed to show that there was a significant negative correlation between the effects of chlorpromazine and those of dextro-amphetamine (Kornetsky, 1960). This finding was interpreted as showing that responsivity to drugs was accounted for by the same variable or variables in the case of both depressants and stimulants. The conditioning of the eye blink has been reported to be facilitated when stimulant drugs were administered and retarded by depressant drugs (Franks and Laverty, 1955; Franks and Trouton, 1958). Continuous work on a pursuit rotor was also facilitated by stimulants and impeded by depressant drugs (Eysenck, Casey, and Trouton, 1957). Congruently, sexual behavior in rats was stimulated by caffeine and depressed by chlorpromazine (Zimbardo and Barry, 1958).

Negative as well as positive findings in regard to the effects of drugs on behavior have been reported. No significant effects were found from either meprobamate or meprobamate plus alcohol on twenty-one measures of such functions as simulated driving, steadiness, and vision (Marquis, Kelly, Miller, Gerard, and Rapoport, 1957). Uhr and Miller (1960), on the other hand, used the same battery of tests, in addition to some others, and found "some impairment in accuracy and braking reaction time under meprobamate." Contradictory findings abound in the field of the effects of drugs upon performance. Perhaps greater agreement would be found if measurement was made of the level of activation at which the drug was administered, if drug dosage and other variables were more strictly controlled, and if the type of subject and the level of previous practice of the performance were more directly comparable. Uhr (1960), in a review of many of these studies, concludes that most of the experimental findings are consistent in their report that "ordinary doses of the stronger tranquilizers (chlorpromazine, reserpine) impair speeded coordinated psychomotor and simple perceptual skills. Indications for the newer phenothiazine derivatives, and for meprobamate, are more equivocal." Apparently, different types of tests tap somewhat different psychological functions, and may be differentially affected by different drugs (Mirsky and Rosvold, 1960). Some drugs apparently have their major effect on subcortical structures, while others have a major effect on the cortex as well. It is interesting to note, however, that Bovet (1959) concludes that various groups of drugs show similarity in their observed antagonisms in the central nervous system and in the viscera controlled by the autonomic nervous system. Incidentally, various investigators have reported that a transient activation of the EEG is produced by both acetylcholine and epinephrin, while an anticholinesterase or amphetamine will produce desynchronization which is both intense and prolonged (Bovet, 1959).

Glutamic acid also has been reported, in a number of clinical studies, to improve the performance on a variety of tests, including some of the items on the Stanford-Binet (Zimmerman, Burgemeister, and Putnam, 1947). Almost all investigators have spoken of the increased alertness and activity produced. The solving of maze problems and the verbatim repeating of sentences were improved, while information and vocabulary scores tended to remain unchanged (Zimmerman et al., 1947). The investigators reported finding it advisable to reduce the dosage of glutamic acid "to the point where the increased activity could be more easily channelized productively" (Zimmerman et al., 1947). They also found it inadvisable to give the dose in the evening since in that case it was likely to cause insomnia.

While clinical studies with human subjects have frequently reported improvement in certain performances with the administration of glutamic acid, investigators who have used rats as subjects have almost as generally reported negative results. It has been suggested that, in the clinical studies, the controls have been inadequate (Marx, 1949). Certainly, as Marx and others have pointed out, there is no evidence that glutamic acid in greater than normal amounts has a special role in psychological functions. On the other hand, there is reason to agree with the further conclusion of Marx that under some experimental conditions "it may be metabolized for energy so as to facilitate performance through increasing general activity and vigor." In at least one study with rats as subjects, it was found that the rats to whom glutamic acid had been administered were significantly superior to the control group in the total time required for the three-table test of "reasoning" and were slightly, but not significantly, superior in number of perfect trials, in total errors, and in the proportion of animals passing the test (Hamilton and Maher, 1947). For our purposes it is of interest to note that, in this test, the animals who had received glutamic acid showed a significantly higher activity level than the control group—that is, they ran faster during the three-table test proper, and they visited more tables during the preliminary exploratory periods.

Apparently, there is fairly general agreement among observers that glutamic acid makes the subject more active. The question is whether this increased activity has any appreciable effect upon the performance of various types of task. A review, by Astin and Ross (1960), of studies in which glutamic acid had been administered to mental defectives, leads them to conclude that, where positive effects have been reported, no control group has usually been employed. They question, as others have, the conclusion that glutamic acid "has a specifically beneficial effect on intellectual functioning."

Reserpine has been shown to block conditioned avoidance responses of cats to both visual and auditory cues when the dosage was sufficiently large (John, Wenzel, and Tschirgi, 1958). When doses were smaller the conditioned avoidance response to a visual cue was much more severely affected than that to an auditory cue, the difference being related to the difficulty of learning the two responses. A difference in the effect of reserpine on two forms of learned behavior which was shown not to be related to the ease of acquisition of the behavior was seen in the more deleterious effect upon conditioned avoidance behavior than upon approach behavior (pattern discrimination with food as a reward). These investigators, after considering other explanations, propose that the selective action of reserpine in small doses is to be attributed to interference with the specific conditioned association between the stimulus and a directed evasion response—i.e., interference with learned associations.

Hormones which presumably raise the level of activation have been found to slow the extinction rate of a conditioned avoidance response (Mirsky, Miller, and Stein, 1953; J. V. Murphy and Miller, 1955). ACTH administered to monkeys produced this result when administered during extinction (Mirsky, Miller, and Stein, 1953). In a study with rats the effect could not be produced when the hormone was administered during extinction but affected the extinction, though not the conditioning, rate when administered during conditioning (J. V. Murphy and Miller, 1955). It is said that preliminary investigations by another experimenter have shown, however, that rats from whom the hypophysis was removed were rendered incapable of forming avoidance responses in a modified Mowrer-Miller shuttle-box (J. V. Murphy and Miller, 1955). After treatment with ACTH, they showed some evidence of learning.

The learning records of male rats that had the hypophysis removed at the ages of 15, 30, and 35 days were significantly inferior to controls during the latter half or two-thirds of their trial series on a 13-choice swimming maze, though the experimental animals were no less active (Stone and Obias, 1955). The investigators pointed out that ablation of the gonads, thyroid, or suprarenal cortex has not heretofore affected learning ability in rats. In the present experiment, there appeared to be "'fixation' of individual response tendencies which perpetuated errors."

Rhinencephalic injury in cats caused the animals to learn a simple conditioned avoidance response more slowly (Brady, Schreiner, Geller, and Kling, 1954). No deficit in the response, was shown, however, if the operation occurred after the training period. Animals that had been operated on were reported to show a "rather marked 'deficit' in autonomic responsivity." Wynne and Solomon (1955) have found that dogs after surgical or pharmacological sympathectomy also showed impairment of avoidance learning.

Effects of a High Degree of Activation

A wide variety of performances has been reported to be handicapped by a very high level of activation as indicated by some physiological measure or implied by the stimulating conditions.

Motor performances which have been reported to suffer under a high degree of muscle tension include accuracy in ball tossing (Russell,

1932), speed of tapping (Duffy, 1932b), manual pursuit (Freeman, 1933), mirror drawing (Freeman, 1938), and the writing of short-hand (Arnold, 1942). When both intelligence and average school standing were held constant, the coefficient of correlation between tension in the unused hand (pressure) and breakdown in the writing of shorthand was .72 ± .07. Breakdown was defined as illegible and omitted words.

"Mental" work also has been found to be adversely affected during conditions producing a high degree of muscle tension. Increased tension resulting from distraction was reported by R. C. Davis (1937) to be accompanied by such an effect, and "super-maximal" effort produced by competition was said by G. L. Freeman (1933) to increase the tension in the quadriceps muscle of the leg and at the same time increase the speed and decrease the accuracy of addition.

Accuracy of discrimination responses was found by the author (Duffy, 1932b) to be lower in nursery-school children with a high degree of muscle tension. The coefficient of correlation between average degree of muscle tension (grip pressure) in both hands and accuracy of performance was —.54 ± .12.[7] The degree of muscle tension was shown to be negligibly related to CA, MA, and IQ, and to be unrelated to muscular strength.

Klein (1961) reported that, with ergographic work, as muscle-action potentials increased, there was a concomitant increase in the amount of breakdown of the work. He concluded that the relationship of muscle-action potentials to performance in motor work is the same regardless of the manner in which the action potentials are induced since the same effect was observed when the changes in potentials were induced by varying the rate of lift and by varying the temperature of a thermal stimulus applied to the working hand. In an earlier study (Klein, 1951), it had been shown that muscle tension produced by a report of failure had the same effect upon an ergographic task as muscle tension produced by an experimentally induced fast rate of work. In both cases high tension scores preceding or accompanying the task were associated with high work output and poor precision. The investigator (Klein, 1951) concluded that "the higher the average tension for any group, regardless of how produced, the higher the output and the greater the variability."

[7] Since muscle-tension patterns in children appear to be more diffuse, or less localized, than those in adults, the sampling of the tension level in any one part of a child's body probably provides a more adequate measure of the general level of bodily tension than is the case with the adult.

With metabolic rate as the physiological measure, a significant relationship was found with the speed and accuracy of performance in a task of mental multiplication (Huxtable, White, and McCartor, 1945). Three subjects engaged in this task for four consecutive 12-hour days. During the latter two days of the fatigue series there was a rise in the metabolic rate, a gradual increase in the percentage of digit error, and an increase in speed. The two subjects who were obviously competing with each other showed the greatest increase in the rate of metabolism.

Fraisse and Bloch (1957), employing mirror drawing as the task, and recording plantar skin resistance to determine electrodermal activity, concluded that, in later trials, electrodermal activity showed a strong negative correlation with accuracy but a strong positive correlation with speed.

Certain performances have been reported to be handicapped by conditions which imply a high level of activation (Courts, 1942b). It has been shown, for example, that when subjects were turning a reel as rapidly as possible, stimulation by competition produced in some subjects a loss of control (Triplett, 1898). The loss of control was accompanied by labored breathing, a flushed face, and a stiffening of the muscles of the arm. With children, overstimulation (and also fatigue) frequently brought a recurrence of the whole arm and shoulder movement of early childhood, or even, if sufficiently intense, the whole body movement.

Excessive motivation has been found to produce disorganization in the behavior of college students in a quadruple-choice apparatus where, in order to escape, they had to discover which one of four doors was unlocked when the order of unlocking on successive trials was fixed by chance (Patrick, 1934). When strongly motivated to escape because they were being exposed to a shower, an electric shock on the feet, or a continuous raucous noise, they frequently tried again and again a door which had just been tried and found locked, even though other doors had not yet been tried. This was contrary to their behavior under ordinary conditions since, in the absence of strong stimulation, they usually tried, in systematic fashion, one door after another.

Similarly, B. D. Cohen, Brown, and Brown (1957) have shown that cats in whom hypothalamic areas were stimulated (and reactions called "rage" were displayed) would learn escape behavior that avoided the central shock. Avoidance learning ceased, however, with stronger intensities of stimulation, which produced disorganized behavior.

Clinical findings are in harmony with the reports from experiments. Spastics, for example, when quiet and at ease, are said to have comparatively good control of their extremities. It is said, however, that any tension, even the mild one of the doctor's visit, may induce strong spasm of the musculature so that neither voluntary nor passive movement at a joint is possible (Kennard, 1947). The ingestion of alcohol frequently produced enough relaxation to restore motor control (Kennard, 1947). Involuntary movements, such as mild tics, may appear only when the individual "is in a tight spot." Moreover, involuntary movements which result from subcortical lesions, chorea, or tremor are said to be absent during sleep and to be either absent or minimal during complete muscular relaxation (Kennard, 1947).

Studies of behavior under "stress," where, however, no physiological measurements were made, have led to such findings as that continued failure produced reckless perceptual responses, characterized by "premature and often nonsensical interpretations of the stimuli" (Postman and Bruner, 1948); that stress increased rigidity in problem solving, as indicated by the number of set solutions of water-jar problems (Luchins, 1942; Cowen, 1952); and that, under "failure stress," there was an increase in the number of errors on a digit-symbol test, which was to some extent compensated for by an increase in speed (Lazarus and Eriksen, 1952).

Children, motivated by being faced with an electric timer and told that speed was the measure of their learning ability, showed a significantly greater number of errors on the light-button pairs which had been changed since their original learning (Castaneda and Palermo, 1955). The unchanged light-button pairs showed a statistically unreliable tendency for stress to decrease the number of errors.

Smock (1955) offers evidence to support the hypothesis that "psychological stress results in (a) premature closure and (b) a tendency to adhere to expectancies (prerecognition hypotheses) in ambiguous task situations."

The conclusion that stress (presumably producing a higher degree of activation) may tend to produce rigidity in behavior is suggested by the fact that a chronic low dosage of chlorpromazine appears to counteract this effect. Chlorpromazine-treated rats, as compared with those to whom a placebo was given, were able to change set more rapidly on the Lashley jumping stand (R. C. Gonzalez and S. Ross, 1959).

H. R. Schaffer (1954) concludes that stress affects the rate and range of activity, exerting either an excitatory or an inhibitory effect, with disorganization of behavior occurring in both cases. He points out that a general constriction of functioning occurs in a stress situation and cites Hamilton and Krechevsky as having shown experimentally that behavior tends to lose its plasticity and assume a marked stereotypy. The characteristics of learning under stress he attributes to a "greatly increased sensitivity of the learning mechanism operative under stress, which fixates whatever response is dominant at the time and prevents its being extinguished even when it is followed by nothing but unfavorable consequences."

A 1959 review of studies of stress examines the various types of definition of stress which have been employed, varying from characteristics of the stimulus situation to variations in internal conditions or in overt response, and cites the findings from a number of studies in this area (Horvath, 1959).

A condition in which it is generally assumed that there is a high level of activation is anxiety. "Anxiety" as used in the studies to be described was defined in terms of high scores on the Taylor Manifest Anxiety Scale (items from the Minnesota Multiphasic Personality Inventory judged to be indicative of manifest anxiety), psychiatric ratings, performance in a laboratory stress situation, or some combination of these measures. In most instances it was defined by extreme scores on the Taylor scale. Physiological measures were seldom used as criteria. Since anxiety is presumably characterized by both a high level of activation and a certain directional trend in behavior, it is difficult to ascribe any given finding to the level of activation alone, though in some cases it would appear that differences in activation are of major significance in determining the results.

There has been considerable discussion of what precisely is measured by the Taylor anxiety scale (Jessor and Hammond, 1957), particularly since the test correlates highly with the MMPI psychasthenia scale (Brackbill and Little, 1954; Eriksen and Davids, 1955) and also with other neurotic inventories (Davids, 1955). While many studies employing the Taylor scale have been based upon the assumption that it measures drive level in the Hullian sense, it has been suggested that stronger defensive or avoidance habits could equally well account for the data (Hilgard, 1953).

It may be pointed out that the Taylor test discriminates with reasonable efficiency between psychiatric and normal subjects (J. A. Taylor, 1953; Matarazzo, Guze, and Matarazzo, 1955), that a number of the items in it are apparently concerned with the "level of energy expenditure" (Jessor and Hammond, 1957), and that the anxiety-scale studies are said to have dealt with the energizing property of drive (Jessor and Hammond, 1957). Since our concern here is not with Hullian drive theory, but with the effect of changes in energy level, it would appear that the Taylor scale, which has been criticized as a test of drive theory (W. F. Hill, 1957), might nevertheless have suggestive significance for our purposes. Farber (1955) in fact comments that "the Taylor questionnaire might better have been termed a test of 'excitability,' or 'level of responsiveness,' or simply, in accordance with the present usage, an 'A scale,'" though, in view of the way in which it was constructed, he concludes that it probably is an index of manifest anxiety as well as drive.

Simple conditioning, with the UCS frequently an electric shock or an air blast, has usually been reported to occur more rapidly in anxious than in nonanxious subjects, while differential conditioning has been reported to be either poorer or better in anxious subjects (Welch and Kubis, 1947a; Welch and Kubis, 1947b; J. A. Taylor, 1951; Hilgard, Jones, and Kaplan, 1951; Bitterman and Holtzman, 1952; Spence and Taylor, 1953; Spence and Farber, 1954; Spence and Beecroft, 1954). Since, as several investigators have pointed out, the response being conditioned has in most instances been an avoidance response to nociceptive stimuli, it would appear that there is no clear evidence as to whether the directional or the arousal aspect of anxiety is primarily responsible for this result. Bindra, Paterson, and Strzelecki (1955), conditioning a nondefensive response, salivation, found no difference in the amount or rate of conditioning between subjects scoring high and those scoring low on the Taylor anxiety scale. The Taylor scale, however, was administered 6 months prior to the conditioning test. Taffel (1955), using recently admitted psychotic and neurotic patients as subjects, found that those with a high score on the Taylor scale showed better verbal conditioning than those with low scores when the reinforcer was the word "good." The group failed to establish a conditioned response to light. The investigator was of the opinion that his findings tended to substantiate the claim that scores on the Taylor scale measured a property of the individual related to the degree of responsiveness, but that this responsiveness was of a discriminating nature.

J. I. Lacey, Smith, and Green (1955) investigated the relationship between the acquisition and spread of new anxiety responses and anxiety level as defined by 35 "nonsomatic" items on the Taylor scale. Measurements of plantar skin resistance, digital blood flow, and heart rate were also made. They concluded that, while their findings were not statistically significant, they showed a consistent pattern. Low-anxiety subjects seemed to condition better to the words in a list which were followed by electric shock, but to generalize less to related words. It is to be noted, however, that this result was obtained *when individual differences in over-all reactivity were controlled,* a factor which there is reason to believe normally differentiates anxious from non-anxious subjects. When differences in reactivity were not ruled out, it appears that high-anxiety subjects conditioned more easily than low-anxiety subjects. In any case, it seems that anxiety is a relatively minor factor in producing individual differences in conditioning (Spence and Taylor, 1953). The correlation coefficient between anxiety and ease of conditioning appears to be rather low in most instances. It is, nevertheless, of interest that anxiety appears to be one of the factors affecting the quality of performance, and with groups representing extremes of anxiety it may be a significant factor.

That anxious subjects are more reactive than nonanxious subjects is suggested by the fact that two groups making extreme scores on the Sarason Test Anxiety Scale differed significantly from each other both during a rest period and during an interview concerned with attitudes toward test-taking (B. Martin and McGowan, 1955). In both instances the high-anxiety group had significantly higher skin conductance. Conductance was not greater during a session immediately preceding the taking of an examination than it was during an earlier session when no examination was in prospect.

In the majority of more complex learning situations, with conflicting responses for a given stimulus, nonanxious subjects, as defined by the Taylor test, have been found to show superior performance (W. F. Hill, 1957). When, however, precautions have been taken to minimize the competition between responses, anxious subjects have frequently been found to be the better performers (W. F. Hill, 1957).

Among the studies in which subjects rated as anxious by the Taylor test did less well than those rated as nonanxious is a study by Taylor and Spence (1952) in which anxious subjects made, on the average, poorer scores in a serial-learning situation. They made a significantly greater number of errors and required a greater number of trials. Similarly, anxious subjects performed less well than nonanxious subjects on a difficult verbal task where many tendencies toward incorrect responses were present, showed improved performance as the task became easier, and surpassed nonanxious subjects on a task of the same type where the tendencies toward incorrect responses were relatively few (Montague, 1953). Since only the highest scores on the anxiety scale marked off a group different from the other subjects, it may be tentatively held that the anxious group was a group functioning at a very high level of activation. In line with these findings is the report that, on a stylus maze test, the performance of anxious subjects was poorer than that of nonanxious subjects (Farber and Spence, 1953). When subjects from the two groups were paired for total scores, it was found that those rating high on anxiety, as compared with those rating low, performed better at the easier choice points and less well at the more difficult choice points. The explanation advanced by the investigators, but later challenged (W. F. Hill, 1957), was that an increase in drive strength improves performance where the task is easy or correct choices are in line with dominant habit tendencies, but impairs performance where the reverse is the case (Farber and Spence, 1953; Montague, 1953). The habit tendencies referred to may include temporary mental sets, as shown in an experiment in which a set for a particular method of solution of a problem was established; it was found that subjects with a high score on the Taylor anxiety scale showed less tendency than subjects with a low score to shift to a more direct method of solution (Maltzman, Fox, and Morrissett, 1953). In the clinician's terminology, they were more "rigid." Rigid maintenance of set was in this instance a handicap to performance. However, when subjects were trained on anagrams having a certain type of solution and were tested on other anagrams having a similar type of solution, anxious subjects made significantly fewer errors than subjects low in anxiety (Maltzman, Fox, and Morrissett, 1953).

Correlating Taylor scores with scores on a 100-word chained association test showed a significant positive relationship between anxiety scores and the productivity of associations (Davids and Eriksen, 1955). Anxiety and association productivity were said to be independent of grade-point averages and performance on college entrance examinations, but to have a correlation of .45 with each other.

Using the Taylor scale as the measure of anxiety, some investigators have reported a negative relationship between anxiety and intelligence test scores (Grice, 1955; Kerrick, 1955). Kerrick (1955) found that scores on mechanical ability, word knowledge, arithmetic reasoning, reading comprehension, and intelligence tests showed a significant negative correlation with anxiety test scores. When "intelligence" was held constant, performance on the other tests was not related to anxiety scores. Though a handicapping effect of anxiety upon many kinds of performance might be expected on the basis of the findings reviewed above, not all investigators have found a negative relationship between anxiety and intelligence (Mayzner, Sersen, and Tresselt, 1955; Calvin, Koons, Bingham, and Fink, 1955). One group (Mayzner et al., 1955) has suggested that the negative relationship between the two variables is limited to test conditions in which anxious subjects feel threatened. Calvin et al. (1955), while failing to obtain a significant relationship between Taylor scores and IQ, did find that several of the subtests of the Wechsler-Bellevue scale showed a significant negative relationship to anxiety as measured by the Taylor test.

The results of investigations in which experimental conditions have been manipulated in such a way as presumably to produce differences in drive have not always been in harmony with the findings in which scores on the Taylor scale have been used as the criterion of anxiety or drive. It has been reported, for example, that with rats as subjects, reversal learning in a maze was more rapid under high drive, as defined by 20½ hours of water deprivation as compared with 1½ hours of deprivation (Buchwald and Yamaguchi, 1955).

Beam (1955), on the other hand, reported findings in harmony with those of many investigators using the Taylor scale, though Taylor scores were significantly related to none of his performance scores, a finding which may be explained by the fact that all of his subjects fell within the middle range of Taylor scores. His subjects learned a list of nonsense syllables prior to exposure to a situation considered to be anxiety-arousing and learned an equivalent list under conditions regarded as "emotionally neutral." Palmar skin resistance and palmar sweat prints were obtained for each subject at the beginning of both the "neutral" and the "stress" test periods. The findings indicated that stress interfered with serial learning, as shown in both time and error scores. It was also reported that the greater the increase in palmar sweating under stress, the greater the increase in the number of trials required for learning. Stress, on the other hand, facilitated conditioning when the galvanic skin response was conditioned to a light, with electric shock as the unconditioned stimulus.

The GSR conditioning of psychiatric patients, when the unconditioned stimulus was a bicycle horn (50 decibels) seems to be significantly affected by the administration of Thorazine (L. E. Mitchell and Zax, 1959). As compared with a control group, the experimental group, who had received the drug for 30 days, required more reinforcements than they had before receiving the drug. In relation to the hypothesis of a U-shaped curve between activation and performance, it is of interest that subjects receiving only a moderate amount of Thorazine seemed more difficult to recondition than those receiving either high or low dosages. The investigators believe the study should be repeated with more rigorous controls.

It has also been reported that, in a trial-and-error learning situation, anxious subjects, defined as those who were highly motivated, made significantly more errors (Palermo, Castaneda, and McCandless, 1956). The effects of anxiety appear to vary with the nature of the task, as indicated by these findings: with college students as subjects, performance on a digit-span test was interfered with by an anxiety-inducing procedure, while performance on a vocabulary test was not (Moldawsky and Moldawsky, 1952).

In the absence of physiological measures, it is hazardous to assume that individuals described as "anxious" necessarily have a high level of activation, yet their behavior is in many respects similar to that which might be expected when the degree of activation is high. They appear to be more responsive to stimulation (though particularly to that of a noxious nature); they show difficulty in shifting set; they show errors in performance which might be ascribed to impulsion to action, which would make difficult the inhibition of response until a correct choice was made. It might be predicted that they would therefore be at a disadvantage in performances requiring a fine co-ordination of responses or a careful survey of alternatives, while they would have an advantage in performances where a given set could be maintained and where alertness was of primary importance.

Lending support to the conclusion that the level of activation may be too high, as well as too low, for effective performance are studies in which presumed lowering of the energy level by means of drugs has been accompanied by improvement in the quality of performance.

Chlorpromazine, which presumably reduces the level of activation, has been reported to enable a pigeon to stand still longer to achieve a food reward (Blough, 1958).

The administration of certain sedatives (bromides or barbiturates) was found to improve the performance on the Pintner General Ability Tests of fifty patients with anxiety neuroses (Damrau, 1946). Sedation with Nembutal or Dial improved the ability to make correct delayed responses in the case of two monkeys who had lost the ability through bilateral lobectomy (Wade, 1947). Small doses of alcohol or of certain barbiturates restored the ability of cats to solve problems which they had become unable to solve as a result of experiencing an airblast (Masserman, 1946).

On the other hand, when chlorpromazine, pentobarbital, meprobamate, or a placebo were administered to comparable groups of normal subjects operating a pointer-pursuit apparatus, there were no significant differences in performance between the groups prior to the introduction of punishment or during punishment (Holliday and Dille, 1958). During trials subsequent to the punishment, only the meprobamate group improved in performance, the other groups showing a rising curve of error. As the investigators point out, a different dose level, another type of task, a different class of subjects, or administration of the drug on more than a single occasion might have produced a different result.

A review of the behavioral effects of "psychoactive" drugs (Uhr, 1960) concludes that it seems "likely that a psychoactive drug brings about more than one change in the subject, and that often these several changes work in opposing directions as far as the behavior being measured . . . is concerned." Uhr believes, however, that, in spite of occasional contradictions in findings, differences are becoming clear between strong tranquilizers, mild tranquilizers, and excitants.

Despite the evidence suggesting that a high degree of activation may present a hazard to co-ordination of response and lead to complete disruption of organized activity, there appear to be instances on record in which performance under a high degree of energy mobilization has been superior to anything of which the individual was capable under ordinary circumstances. Most of the evidence on this point is of the anecdotal variety, and there is sometimes no way of determining whether the degree of activation was very high or merely somewhat above the normal level.

In presenting his emergency theory of emotion, Cannon (1936) cited instances in which, under excitement, feats of strength and endurance were possible which were not possible for the individual under ordinary conditions. For example, a boy when chased by a wild animal jumped over a wall which, when he was not excited, he was unable to clear until he reached maturity. Ceremonial dances which would ordinarily exhaust an individual after a few hours have been known to continue for days on occasions of great excitement. Clinicians have reported that patients with paresis, resulting from known organic lesions, have been found able, under severe emotional stress, to perform acts which were usually beyond their capacity (Kennard, 1947). Individuals confronted with an emergency situation, demanding not only speed and strength of motor responses, but also quick thinking to solve the problem, have been said to arrive at a solution which seemed to them little short of a miracle (Stratton, 1928).

One of the most famous instances of effective behavior under excitement is Stratton's (1928) report of the behavior of his friend, Dr. Ritter, in saving a child from burning. The child's flannel nightgown had caught on fire. Dr. Ritter quickly considered four different modes of action that were possible, decided on one of them, acted promptly and vigorously, and saved the child from suffering more than the singeing of her hair. Such a feat, it will be agreed, was remarkable. It would very likely have been impossible except under the stimulation of excitement. To interpret such action as less efficient than it might have been because the child was handled roughly is to miss the point of the situation, yet a well-known textbook comments that, if Dr. Ritter had been accustomed to saving little girls from burning every morning before breakfast, he might have gone about the task more efficiently and with less damage to the little girl (Valentine and Wickens, 1949). Certainly such practice in the situation would have improved his performance. With such practice he might have solved his problem quickly and calmly and without unnecessary jerking and hauling of the child. In fact, with such experience to draw upon he probably would not have found himself confronted with an emergency situation, for an emergency is defined, not only in terms of the problem, but also in terms of the resources for meeting the problem. The relevant question is whether without such practice he would have met the emergency more successfully if he had not been excited—if, for example, he had been functioning at a low, rather than a high, level of activation. Both Dr. Ritter and his friend, Professor Stratton, were of the opinion that he would not have done so. Though the excitement produced unnecessary roughness in the handling of the child, yet it produced also quick, vigorous, and judicious action, which might have been impossible without the excitement.

Flying personnel of the AAF are reported to have said that fear led to improvement of their performance in combat, mild fear being more advantageous than intense fear (Shaffer, 1947). There was, of course, no objective check on this statement.

One additional type of anecdotal evidence deserves consideration in relation to the present topic. Creative writers have frequently claimed that they wrote under "inspiration" poems or stories which seemed to "just come" to them—products of high quality, which they were incapable of writing under ordinary conditions. It seems possible that the "inspiration" to which these writers have referred is a condition of high excitement (or a high degree of activation) which facilitated the performance. The same effect in lesser degree is no doubt familiar to many of us. Under excitement a student may write a theme or examination paper which, when read later under other conditions, appears so superior to the ordinary performance of the individual that it seems to have been written, not by himself, but by someone else. The flow of ideas, the precision of expression, the penetration of the analysis, all seem superior to that of which he is ordinarily capable. Or, again, the "flash of insight" which puts an old problem in a new light seems frequently to be a function of excitement, though it has also been reported to occur when the individual is relaxed and not seeking a solution to the problem.

Stratton (1925), a number of years ago, expressed the opinion that emotion does not usually reduce the adequacy of the individual's responses. He wrote:

> Emotion, when it is not of extreme violence, . . . involves no general disruption of even complicated muscular acts. Certain movements, it is true, may become difficult or even impossible. . . . But movements suited to the impulse then prevailing . . . are not only possible during emotion, but come forth finished, as part of emotion's usual train (p. 54).
>
> . . . The intellectual processes move at a more rapid tempo than when there is no excitement. Second, there is a lowering of the threshold for the entrance of ideas. Thoughts come more easily; they are aroused in greater variety; there are more of them available. The intelligence is thus more fertile when under emotional stirring. Third, there is an added strength of organization, a more effective integration of certain of the ideas present. And fourth, there is with this heightening also some loosening of organization, a dis-integration amongst certain other constituents, so that these are omitted from the active system and are either suppressed or are left to form relatively independent and non-adaptive systems of their own (p. 59).
>
> . . . Excitement may become excessive, and then the commotion or disarrangement of our usual mental combinations is not succeeded by a rearrangement which is more suitable and which helps us to meet the crisis with prospect of success (p. 60).

The extent to which Stratton's position is justified is open to question, but it does appear probable, on the basis of general observation, that for some people, at some times, a relatively high degree of activation improves the quality of performance. Evidence is abundant, however, that for most people, under most circumstances, a very high degree of activation exerts a handicapping effect.

Fluctuations in Activation

Fluctuations in activation of both the skeletal musculature and the autonomic effectors have been observed. To some extent at least, these fluctuations appear to be either independent of the degree of activation or to bear a curvilinear relationship to activation.

The conditions which produce fluctuations in the activation of the skeletal musculature, as represented by body sway and tremor of the hand, or by irregular grip-pressure curves or ergograph curves, are similar to the conditions which generally produce either a high level of activation or a very low level of activation.

It has been reported that "in general, external stimulation of the human organism [which presumably raises the level of activation] tends to increase body sway and seldom or never to decrease it" (Edwards, 1947). Caffeine, which is a stimulant, increases the individual's unsteadiness (Thornton, Holck, and Smith, 1939). Stress, such as that of anticipating an important examination, produces tremor, especially of the hands and fingers. Luria (1932) demonstrated that motor in-co-ordination in the form of finger tremor (recorded as irregular, rather than smooth, curves of pressure) occurred so unfailingly during "emotional" excitement that it could be used as an indicator of this condition. Murray (1938) and others have reported findings in complete agreement with those of Luria. Jost (1941), for example, found that, when children were frustrated by being asked to learn a list of digits which were too difficult for them, there was an increase in tremor of the hand, accompanied by a decrease in skin resistance. J. W. French (1944) reported that an increase in finger-tremor amplitude occurred when subjects squeezed a dynamometer with the opposite hand, and Skaggs et al. found that body sway was more pronounced when the subject stood with the muscles of the legs or the body generally tensed (E. B. Skaggs, I. S. Skaggs, and M. Jardon, 1932; E. B. Skaggs, 1937).

Muscular in-co-ordination appears to occur also in conditions where the level of activation is very low. General observation indicates that in drowsy states or in states of extreme fatigue, there is often in-co-ordination of speech and of movements. Fumbling, rather than precision, appears to be the rule. However, controlled studies in which the factor of muscular co-ordination is isolated from other factors in the performance are few.

Féré (1900) reported that the dynamometer or the ergograph curve under fatigue (and in cases of hysteria) had a slower and more wavy ascent than under normal conditions. The differences between the normal curves and the curves characteristic of fatigue are remarkably similar to the differences found by Luria between the normal curves and the curves characteristic of "emotional" excitement. Apparently, both fatigue and "emotion" frequently produce motor in-co-ordination.

Ash (1914) studied the effect upon motor control of fatigue developed by muscular exertion. He used a modified ergograph which measured both the voluntary movements of the finger which the subject was instructed to flex and also the involuntary movements of adjacent fingers. He found that, at the beginning of the performance, some subjects were able to hold the adjacent fingers motionless, but sooner or later during the work period all subjects were flexing the adjacent fingers over even greater amplitudes than those of the finger they had been instructed to flex. This "irradiation" of the activity was interpreted as a loss of control.

Golla (1921) reported that when a wand, to be held in a small ring without touching the sides, made most frequent contacts with the ring bag, there was a decrease in the tension of the quadriceps muscle. He observed that these periods of inaccuracy in handling the wand became more frequent as the subject became fatigued, and that in certain cases of neurosis in which the subject complained of nervous asthenia, they were particularly frequent.

Bartlett (1943), finding no simple relationship between the length of time during which work is continued and such measures of performance as errors or reaction time, advanced the hypothesis that the "disorganization" of performance which occurs during prolonged work comes from a disturbance of the timing of the various components of the skilled response. Such an explanation might be considered to lend support to the conception of in-co-ordination as an accompaniment of fatigue.

Studies in which an investigation has been made of the relationship between fluctuations in activation and the level of activation have agreed in finding little or no relationship between the variables (Duffy, 1946; Malmo, Shagass, Belanger, and Smith, 1951; Malmo and Smith, 1955; J. I. Lacey and B. Lacey, 1958b). In the first three studies cited, the irregularities were in skeletal-motor response; in the latter, the fluctuations were in skin resistance and heart rate. In one of these studies (Malmo and Smith, 1955), however, measures of motor irregularity, while correlating poorly with measures of muscular tension in the neck and forearm, showed a significant correlation with frontalis-muscle tension. The problem is one which requires further investigation. To determine whether a curvilinear relationship exists between the variables, measures of activation should be made at a very low level such as is not ordinarily found in an experimental situation, as well as at a very high level of activation. Further investigation is needed in regard to the choice of a suitable measure of fluctuations. In the case of motor irregularities, for example, a few large-sized deviations from a base line, of relatively long duration, might have an entirely different significance from frequent, and not necessarily large, deviations such as those observed in tremor, yet certain scoring systems have given them equal weight.

Variations in performance have been observed to be related to variations in the fluctuations of activation, as indicated by irregularities in grip pressure or by "spontaneous" changes in skin resistance and heart rate.

It is of interest that, when a sedative was administered, there was a decrease in both the galvanic skin response and in spontaneous fluctuations in skin resistance (S. I. Cohen, Silverman, and Burch, 1956). Graded doses of epinephrin produced a continual increase in the spontaneous fluctuations in resistance, but produced, first an increase, and then a decrease, in the galvanic skin response. No measurement of performance was undertaken.

In an experiment which is described more fully in Chapter 10, it was found that nursery-school children with irregular grip-pressure tracings more frequently made errors of "commission" than of "omission" in a discrimination task—i.e., they were more impulsive. (Duffy, 1932b). Very irregular pressure tracings were significantly associated both with poor performance and with responding when no response was called for, as opposed to omitting required responses.

J. I. Lacey and B. C. Lacey (1958b), in a more extensive investigation of the topic, have reported that adult subjects with more "spontaneous" fluctuations in skin resistance and heart rate made a greater number of erroneous motor responses in a discrimination task. The errors were of a type which could be called "impulsive." Their interesting investigation is described in detail in Chapter 10.

Though no physiological measurements were made, D. R. Davis (1948) reports findings which should perhaps be viewed in the present context. He found that the errors made by pilots in a simulated aircraft cockpit were of two kinds: those of overaction and those of inertia.

If speculation may be permitted in this area where there are so few facts, it would appear that fluctuations in activation may represent a deficiency of inhibition in neural centers. Such a deficiency would account for "impulsive" responses or "overaction." It would account also for the disorganization or in-co-ordination of responses which seems to occur frequently, but not always, when activation is either very high or very low. The co-ordination of responses requires the inhibition of certain response tendencies in favor of other response tendencies. Correct responses to relationships, and hence the maintenance of suitable direction in behavior, demands the inhibition of responses until all relevant factors (cues) can be brought to bear upon the choice of response. The forward movement of the solution to a problem must not be so rapid as to exclude consideration of modifying cues. Otherwise, there is likelihood of rigidity of set or of impulsive, erroneous response. In Easterbrook's (1959) terminology there would be reduction in the range of cue-utilization. In other terminology, we might speak of premature closure of perceptual responses or of impulsive motor reaction. In any case, the field would be narrowed, with respect to both perception and action. The more complex the choices required in a performance, or the more finely co-ordinated the movements to be executed, the more would a successful performance depend upon the ability to inhibit, and hence to select and co-ordinate, responses. Deficiency in inhibitory ability, which may conceivably be represented by frequent "bursts of activity" in various systems, to use the Laceys' (1958b) term, may perhaps account for poor performance of the in-co-ordinated or impulsive type.

(While the critical ability of my colleagues makes it unnecessary for me to point out that the formulations presented above are mere speculations, perhaps it is prudent for me to state that I recognize them to be such.)

FACTORS AFFECTING THE RELATIONSHIP BETWEEN THE DEGREE OF ACTIVATION AND THE QUALITY OF PERFORMANCE

With a scheme of explanation such as that presented here, it becomes unhappily apparent that any relationship found between activation and performance can be explained. If the quality of performance increases with an increase in the degree of activation, then the preceding level of activation was too low; if it decreases, then the preceding level of activation was too high. As discouraging as this outcome is to the preservation of rigor in scientific thinking, it is significant nevertheless that few investigators have failed to report some sort of relationship between direct or indirect indicators of the level of activation and the quality of performance. A null hypothesis has found some, but relatively little, support.[8] The task before us then is to discover what the

[8] Among the studies in which no relationship has been found between performance and a physiological indicator of the level of activation or a condition presumed to be associated with either a high or a low degree of activation are

variables are which determine whether a given degree of activation will increase or decrease the quality of performance. It seems likely that the answers will be found in (1) the nature of the task and the conditions under which it is performed, (2) the locus or patterning of the activation, and (3) certain characteristics of the individual performing the task. The nature of the task should be interpreted broadly to include such factors as the stage of learning of a given performance, and the characteristics of the individual should be interpreted broadly to include his developmental status as well as his more or less persistent characteristics. On none of these factors do we have evidence which is conclusive. It may be worthwhile, however, to indicate some of the possible relationships.

The Nature of the Task

Most of the early studies of the effect upon performance of variations in the level of activation were studies of the effect of differences in muscle tension. It was apparent at once that the effect upon performance depended not alone upon the degree of muscle tension but also upon the nature of the task. The author (Duffy, 1932b), for example, offered the following hypotheses, without, however, having data available to support them:

It is not to be assumed that high tension is equally advantageous or disadvantageous for every type of activity. Muscular activities may be handicapped by high tension, since it diminishes ease of movement. Other activities requiring speed and alertness, but not emphasizing choice with its accompanying requirement of inhibition, may in general be favored by relatively high degrees of excitation. Sudden insights and the facile flow of words may, for example, be encouraged, while the careful weighing of evidence may be made more difficult. High degrees of excitation, and consequently of muscular tension, may increase the efficiency of performance of a definite task for which the subject is "set," but may decrease flexibility of reaction and thus make more difficult the adjustment to new and unexpected situations (p. 545).

G. L. Freeman (1933) reported that finger-oscillation scores improved while manual-pursuit scores decreased when there were increases in muscle tension. Mental arithmetic was said to be seriously handicapped by tension increments, while sensory discriminations and reflex responses were facilitated (Freeman, 1938).

Brožek and Taylor (1954) stated that "it has been our general ex-

studies by the following investigators: H. Block (1936); A. C. Williams, Jr., J. W. Macmillan, and J. G. Jenkins (1947); J. A. Adams (1954); and R. Loucks (1944). Courts (1942b) reviews other studies in this category.

perience that motor performance is more susceptible to deterioration under stress than the sensory and intellective functions." The only motor performance studied which showed statistically significant changes under all five types of biological stress employed was complex reaction time, which was said to require the participation of large muscle groups and some hand-foot co-ordination.

There is fairly wide agreement that the nature of the task is a determinant of the effects of varying degrees of activation upon performance. Hypothetical explanations of the way in which this effect is exerted show some variation. R. C. Davis (1956a) prefers a highly specific explanation—i.e., the effect of one response system upon another. He hypothesizes that there are patterns of muscular response which will facilitate or inhibit other responses according to their similarity. While the hypothesis is appealing, both because of its logic and the modesty of its claims, its predictive usefulness is severely limited. Davis (1956a) says: "There is, it would seem, no way of predicting a priori what the response pattern of a particular stimulus is going to be nor how it will affect another response." He hopes, through empirical investigation, to discover the nature of many different response patterns and thus to be able to make statements of a more general nature.

Others have suggested that, in general, tasks of a more complex nature, requiring a high degree of selectivity in the response to cues, may be handicapped by a high degree of activation, while relatively simple tasks, such as a conditioned response, may be facilitated (Farber and Spence, 1953; Montague, 1953; Easterbrook, 1959). The explanation of this phenomenon offered by Farber and Spence, by Montague, and by others who judged "drive" by means of the Taylor Manifest Anxiety Scale, has been presented in an earlier section of this chapter. The author's abstract of Easterbrook's (1959) hypothesis is presented below:

The number of cues utilized in making a response [9] becomes smaller during "emotion," "increased drive" (described as general covert excitement), or increased activity in the brain stem reticular formation (Callaway and Dembo, 1958). Under these conditions the use of "peripheral (occasionally or partially relevant) cues" is reduced, while the use of "central and immediately relevant cues" is maintained.

On some tasks, both perceptual and perceptual-motor, performance is

[9] Easterbrook says that "In general, the range of cue utilization is the total number of environmental cues in any situation that an organism observes, maintains an orientation towards, responds to, or associates with a response" (Easterbrook, 1959).

improved by a reduction in the range of cue utilization. Concentration is then greater, irrelevant cues are excluded, and reaction may be expedited. In the case of other tasks, however, proficiency requires the use of a wide range of cues. Difficult tasks, and those for which the most complex responses are required, are said to be those "which demand long and a priori improbable sequences of responses, and accordingly reflect the transfer of great amounts of information." He believes that a mere increase in general excitement, in the absence of conflict, can disrupt complex action sequences. Among the situations in which a reduced level of performance can presumably be accounted for by a higher level of activation, with consequent reduction in cue utilization, are the reduced memory span for digits which has been found in anxiety (reported when anxiety was determined by questionnaire, induced by threat, or chronic as neurosis), the reported shrinkage of the field of perception under stress, and the handicapping effect of anxiety upon demanding nonrepetitive serial operations such as serial coding, tracing a complex maze, paced problem-solving, tracking with preview, mirror drawing, syntatic speech, and the Luria association-motor task.

Whether a course of action is disrupted or facilitated by "drive" or "emotion" is said to depend on the complexity of the action and on the range of cue utilization left unimpaired by the excitation. Task complexity itself is defined in terms of the number of cues which must be simultaneously utilized to achieve success in the performance. The inverted U-shaped curve representing the relationship between activation and performance would be accounted for by the fact that continued reduction in the range of cue-use would first improve and then impair proficiency. Easterbrook concludes that there "seems to be an optimal range of cue utilization for each task."

At least partial support for Easterbrook's position is seen in a number of studies reviewed by Callaway and Stone (1960) in which it was shown that certain drugs which can produce electroencephalographic arousal make people less responsive to things occurring at the periphery of attention, while other drugs, such as atropine, make them more responsive to peripheral stimulation. Thus the degree of arousal appears to be correlated with the extent of focus of attention. In tasks where response to peripheral, or apparently irrelevant, stimuli can improve performance, a lower degree of arousal is of advantage.

Because the nature of the task changes somewhat in the course of learning a performance, it seems probable that a level of activation which improves performance at one stage of learning may conceivably handicap the performance at another stage of learning.

Kausler and Trapp (1960) have suggested that the net effects of "increasing motivation" on the utilization of cues during incidental learning depend upon such factors as whether the motivation is generalized or there is an "incentive-oriented set," and upon the difficulty of the intentional task, as well as upon the central versus the peripheral position of the irrelevant cues as compared with the relevant cues.

D. R. Meyer (1953) claims, chiefly on the basis of the findings of Courts (1942a) on a rotary pursuit test and of G. L. Freeman (1938) in regard to mirror drawing, that the optimal degree of muscle tension becomes progressively less in the course of practicing a performance, and that the detrimental effects of extreme degrees of tension become more pronounced. Telford and Swenson (1942) report, however, that in mirror drawing, muscle tension in the used hand shows a decline for fifteen or twenty trials and then rises irregularly to the end of the learning. Stroud (1931) reports a decrease in tension during the learning of more difficult mazes and an increase during the learning of easy mazes. He attributes the latter phenomenon to a sort of "end spurt," or a desire to terminate the task and make a good score.

Failure-threat stress (unmeasured physiologically) was reported to be a handicap when introduced during the early stages of learning a rotary pursuit task but, when introduced after considerable practice in the performance, to produce the reverse effect (Deese and Lazarus, 1952). The findings in regard to the effects of failure-stress did not meet statistical tests of significance.

It appears that the requirements of a task may be different at different stages of learning. In learning a maze, for example, it has been suggested that the elimination of errors is the chief problem during the early stages of the learning process, while an increase in speed is the chief problem during the later stages of the same performance (Daniel, 1939). In any case, it is apparent that the stage of learning of a task must be considered when assessing the effect upon performance of any given factor.

The Patterning of Activation

Studies of the patterning of activation in relation to performance have been chiefly studies of the locus of muscle tension. G. L. Freeman (1933, 1937) concluded from his investigations that the most advantageous location of muscle tension was in the muscle groups most closely related neurologically to the responding part of the body. Another investigator found some indication that the best performers in two-board tapping were those who showed increasing pressure in the used hand and decreasing pressure in the unused hand (Arnold, 1942). Supporting the position that the patterning of muscle tension is of basic importance in determining certain characteristics of the response is the finding of R. C. Davis (1948) that the extent of implicit muscular response shows a close relationship to the amount of prestimulus tension, and that the patterning of the tension immediately prior to the response is of dominant importance in determining whether response at a given point will be facilitated or inhibited.

Studies of muscular tension by Oldroyd and Moskowitz (1952), however, have led them to the tentative conclusion that the degree of muscular tension overshadows the locus of the tension in its effect on a task of high qualitative demand.

D. R. Meyer (1953) offers an explanation of the effects of muscular tension upon performance through considering the effect of the interaction of simultaneous responses. He conceives this interaction to be due to "a convergence of impulse patterns upon the motor pathways of the central nervous system." Whether increments in muscle tension will improve performance or interfere with it is presumed to depend upon whether the increased excitation will facilitate the response of more appropriate or of more inappropriate neurones. The fact that a moderate degree of excitation is more likely to lead to superior performance than extreme degrees of excitation is explained by the assumption that small amounts of added excitation are more likely to bring into action neurones which would contribute to the response. Greater degrees of excitation are believed to recruit more remote pools of neurones, with the likelihood that more inappropriate than appropriate neurones would be activated. Interference with performance, therefore, would be due to the facilitation of competing responses. The effect of increases in excitation is held to be specific rather than general—that is, to be the effect of one response system upon another response system. Meyer believes that facilitative effects can be exerted only through changes in the magnitude or latency of responses, not through changes in the selection of responses. The rate of acquisition of a conditioned response may be affected, however, by the promotion of response elicitation.

Supporting Meyer's position is a study in which muscle tension induced during recall only (paired adjectives) was found to be as facilitative of performance as tension induced during both learning and recall (Bourne, 1955). It was concluded that the tension facilitated the ability to respond but did not have any effect upon the learning process. On the other hand, another investigator reported that there is reliably better recall of nonsense syllables when lying on a couch in a state of induced relaxation than when sitting or when lying on the couch without instructions to relax (Pascal, 1949). Relaxation after learning, rather than immediately preceding recall,

showed no difference over a control condition. It has also been reported that rats with a strong hunger drive (22 hours of deprivation)
not only ran significantly faster than rats with a low hunger drive (4
hours of deprivation) but also chose significantly more often the more
frequently reinforced bar in a double-bar Skinner-type box, thus showing improvement in the selection of responses (Ramond, 1954). In
other studies selective learning has sometimes been reported to be a
positive function of drive (D) and sometimes not. Since an increase
in drive probably involves not only an increase in activation but also
a greater urgency with respect to the maintenance of a particular goal-
direction in behavior, it is questionable whether studies of changes in
behavior as a result of changes in the strength of drives could afford
conclusive evidence in regard to the question under consideration.

Evidence is not lacking in support of the position that a higher level
of activation,[10] at least up to a certain point, increases the magnitude
and decreases the latency of responses. There appears to be reason,
however, to question the conclusion that it does not also affect the
selection of responses, and not merely through the recruitment of
more remote pools of neurones, with the likelihood that more inappropriate than appropriate responses would be activated. Alternative suggestions have already been presented—e.g., Easterbrook's (1959) reduction in cue-utilization, attributed here to increased impulsion to
response. The level of activation appears to affect directly the dynamic aspects of behavior rather than the directional aspects. These
dynamic aspects of response may be presumed, however, to exert influence upon the selection of responses, and hence upon the general
quality of performance—not merely upon the speed and vigor of action.

Organismic interaction, rather than the isolated functioning of
parts, appears to be the rule. Nevertheless, within the total pattern of
response we may note focal points at which the activity is greater
than that found at other points at a given moment. These focal points
shift from time to time with variations in the demands of the stimulus
situation and with variations in conditions within the organism. None-
theless, excitation in one part of the organism appears in general to be
accompanied by excitation in other parts, and not, as might conceivably
be the case, by compensatory inactivity in other tissues.

There seems to be fairly general agreement that, in the course of

[10] Meyer speaks only of muscle tension, and not of the level of activation. Since,
however, muscle tension represents activation of one bodily system and may be
roughly indicative of activation in general, the present discussion makes use of
the broader term.

learning, muscle tension becomes more focalized in the performing member of the body, and that this focalization tends to improve performance (Freeman, 1931; Shaw, 1938; D. R. Meyer, 1953). Though no direct comparisons have been made, it appears probable that young children, when performing a task, seldom attain the degree of localization of muscle tension achieved by adults.

Individual Differences

Individual differences probably constitute an additional, and relatively unexplored, factor in determining the effects of a particular degree of activation upon a given performance. If it is a fact that a high degree of activation presents a hazard to organized response, then the maturational status and other characteristics of the individual, affecting (as they appear to do) the ability to inhibit and co-ordinate responses, would be determinants of the quality of performance under a given degree of activation. The studies of Luria (1932), as mentioned above, apparently indicate that children have less ability than adults to make a simple movement as slowly as possible. Luria postulates weakness of the "functional barrier" which restrains excitation from a "direct transfer to the motor sphere." It has been said that Lewin has shown that the behavior of the young child shows a tendency to a direct discharge of the tension created, and that many actions of the child are explained by this characteristic. Certainly, however, some children have developed inhibitory ability to the extent necessary for smooth, co-ordinated performance under high degrees of excitation. One such subject was observed in a study of a small group of nursery-school children (Duffy, 1930). Luria states that psychoneurotic adults are also characterized by a tendency to a direct discharge of tension. Presumably "normal" adults as well would show differences in the characteristic, as indeed Luria implies in his description of certain subjects as "reactive-stable" and of others as "reactive-labile."

It seems probable that individuals who rank high in the ability to restrain action until adequate perceptual and conceptual organization has been attained, and motor co-ordination achieved, are individuals who, with other factors constant, would perform better than other individuals under a high degree of activation. Indeed their optimal degree of activation might be relatively high since, hypothetically, they would be able to profit from increased alertness, vigor, and speed of response without being handicapped by the disorganization of response which is the frequent concomitant of a high level of activation.

Hence, though a high degree of activation appears to present a hazard, it may be a hazard which, if successfully met, can lead to a performance of unusual excellence. Conversely, individuals who for any reason are likely to become easily disorganized would probably function better at a lower level of activation, especially if the task to be performed is a complex one, requiring difficult discriminations or fine co-ordination of motor responses. For all individuals there must, however, be a point at which the degree of activation would become sufficiently high to lead to disruptive behavior.

Factors varying within the individual, as well as differences between individuals, may conceivably serve as determinants of the effect of a given level of activation upon performance. Perhaps certain features of the directional aspect of behavior interact with the arousal aspect in determining the outcome. An attitude of self-confidence in regard to a situation may, for example, reduce conflicting responses and make possible the effective organization of responses at a level of activation at which an attitude of insecurity and lack of confidence would lead to disruption. A clearly defined goal might be conducive to the organization of responses, while conflicting goals would lead to disorganization. Instances in which there are competing goals may be seen in the soldier's breakdown under enemy gunfire, where he desires both to fight the enemy and also to retreat to safety, or in cases of "going to pieces" on an examination because the individual's response systems, which should be directed toward the task at hand, are directed only partly toward the task and partly toward consideration of the dire consequences which would result from failure in the task. Under such circumstances the co-ordination of responses is made more difficult, not merely because the level of activation is high, but also because there are more competing response-tendencies. In certain situations commonly labeled emotional, the competition of goals is frequently a factor in producing disorganized response. In other so-called emotional situations the individual may be exceptionally single-minded—as for example when the boy was chased by the bear or Dr. Ritter wished to save the child whose clothes had caught on fire.

It appears, then, that it is impossible to state what particular level of activation is most conducive to good performance. The answer might be considered to depend upon the requirements of the task at the moment, and certain characteristics of the individual, some of which may be temporary and others more or less permanent. If the assumptions made up to this point are tenable, it seems certain that there is an "optimal" level of activation for a given task to be performed by a given individual at a given time. It would appear also that for most individuals and for most tasks that optimal level is a moderate degree of activation, high enough to assure reasonable speed and alertness, and low enough not to present a hazard to the organization of responses. Therefore, it would be expected that studies in which the degree of activation was the independent variable and the quality of performance was the dependent variable would yield results which, when plotted, would form an inverted U-shaped curve.

SUMMARY

The degree of activation of the individual appears to affect the speed, intensity, and co-ordination of responses, and thus to affect the quality of performance. In general, the optimal degree of activation appears to be a moderate degree, with the curve expressing the relationship between activation and performance taking the form of an inverted U. However, the effect of any given degree of activation upon performance appears to vary with a number of factors, including the nature of the task to be performed and certain characteristics of the individual. Organismic interaction is the basic explanatory principle suggested to account for the particular effects upon performance of various degrees of activation.

part III

INDIVIDUAL
DIFFERENCES
IN ACTIVATION

chapter 9

The extent and consistency
of individual differences in
activation

In both human and animal subjects individual differences in activation have been observed. These differences are of considerable magnitude and of more than a fair degree of consistency. Data have been obtained from observations of the overt behavior of children and of lower animals, as well as from physiological measurements of children and adults.

OBSERVATIONS OF OVERT BEHAVIOR

Studies of Children

Studies in which the behavior of children has been observed over an extended period of time have led to reports of constancy in what have been called "temperamental" characteristics. Mary Shirley (1931), who made an intensive study of the development of twenty-five children during the first two years of life, reported the following:

> Differences in behavior appear very early in life. Indeed, in these subjects they appeared at the first observation and examination which was given sometime within the first twenty-four hours. They were different in irritability, in tone and timbre of the cry, in activity, and in tonicity of the muscles, as well as in the quality of reactions to the test situations (p. 216, Vol. 3).

These differences tended to persist. For example, irritability in the test situation (one form of ease of activation) decreased with age, but the child who had been the most irritable at the first examination remained the most irritable, and the child who had been the least irritable remained the least irritable. Shirley reported that this characteristic seemed to a considerable degree to be a function of the individual child rather than of the situation in which he was placed. She concluded: "Although the personalities of the babies are undoubtedly influenced by training and treatment, strong characteristics are not ironed out by training." Shirley believed that her studies indicated that "personality has its origin and physiological basis in the structure and organization of the nervous system and of the physicochemical constitution of the body as a whole."

Personality sketches of Shirley's subjects written by another investigator fifteen years later were correctly matched with the sketches prepared by Shirley to an extent not likely to occur by chance (Neilson, 1948). Both sets of sketches included, however, many aspects of personality not under consideration here.

Consistent differences in behavior during the first year of life have also been reported by Washburn (1929), who found individual differences in excitability and serenity (as indicated by laughing, smiling, and crying) which did not vary from observation to observation, and which in most instances persisted into the second year of life.

Studies of Rats and Mice

Observations of lower animals have likewise led to reports of consistent differences between individual animals. An aspect of response closely related to our present concern is that of activity level. Activity level, however, as defined in the studies referred to, should not be considered synonymous with the degree of activation as that concept is employed here. It appears rather to be a particular form of overt expression of the degree of activation. This interpretation is supported by the absence of a high degree of correlation between activity level as measured on an activity wheel and activity level as measured in a diffuse activity cage (Reed, 1947); yet it seems reasonable to suppose that both forms of activity would be related in some degree to the underlying degree of activation of the organism.

Studies of rats have demonstrated wide individual differences in the extent of activity on the wheel, even when the animals were litter mates. Some rats had a score of 200 revolutions per day, while others had a score of 20,000 (Reed, 1947). After the tenth day the individual differences remained relatively constant. In fact, there is evidence that the activity of an animal tends to fluctuate around a relatively constant level during the major part of the life cycle (Shirley, 1928; Slonaker, 1912). When such factors as conditions of motivation changed, the activity level changed, but the activity of a given rat tended to maintain a constant relationship to the activity level of other rats in the group (C. S. Hall, 1941). This is shown by the fact that the level of activity when "unmotivated" showed a close correlation with activity level when hungry, when thirsty, and when sexually aroused.

Both genetic and environmental factors affect the level of activity of rats. The influence of genetic variables is seen in the fact that active and inactive strains can be established by selective breeding (Rundquist, 1933). Rats making extremely low activity scores were bred together. At the fifth filial generation, the animals were divided into two groups, active and inactive, and after that time all matings occurred within the group of which the animal was a member. By the twelfth filial generation the two strains of rats were so well differentiated that there was no overlapping in the scores of the males of the two strains, and very little in those of the females. To eliminate the possibility of a chance finding, the parents of the sixth filial generation were remated and the new offspring tested. Their scores were as closely similar to those of the first set of offspring as the scores which might be obtained on a retest of the same animals. Selection of genes had evidently produced two groups of animals which differed sharply in activity level.

Cross-matings between the twenty-first and twenty-second filial generations of these strains of rats led to the conclusion that the two strains differed in a single gene which apparently behaved as a dominant in the males and as a recessive in the females (Brody, 1942). Inactive backcross males were found to be as inactive as the inactive strain, while active backcross females tended to be as active as the active strain. The extremely inactive rats were described as making virtually no movements during the entire period except to obtain food and water, and after the twenty-fifth filial generation this strain could not be continued because no offspring were obtained from the majority of the matings.

Activity level is, however, affected by factors other than the genes. Age, for example, affects the degree of activity. Pregnancy affects the number of animals that are very inactive (Brody, 1942). Both phosphate feeding and starvation (up to a certain point) have been shown to increase the activity level. Many other environmental agents undoubtedly influence the animal's level of activity.

Rats have been found to differ also in characteristics described as "wildness" and "savageness." Differences in these modes of behavior were observed before the age of 20 days, and it was said that they persisted into later life. Yerkes (1913), in an early study in which different strains of rats were observed under controlled conditions, claimed that his "results . . . prove[d] conclusively that savageness, wildness, and timidity are heritable behavior complexes." Stone (1932), in a later investigation, reported similar findings. Different strains of rats, reared under similar conditions, differed in wildness. Half-breeds obtained a score about midway between that of the full wild and the tame rats. It seems likely that "savageness" and "timidity" are different modes of expression of a high degree of activation, while "wildness" incorporates many diverse forms of highly activated behavior.

A positive correlation has been reported between what might be called hyper-responsiveness, or a high degree of arousal, in two different types of situation (Keeler, 1942). Rats who were most disturbed by nose-tickling with a brush were, in general, those who were most disturbed by being held for one minute in the hand. Of the rats who made no reaction to the holding test, 75 per cent made no reaction to the nose-tickling test. It was said that excitable animals can be clearly distinguished from relaxed animals if we take into account, not a single type of response, but a cluster of responses, and especially if we consider the intensity with which the observed behavior occurs (Keeler, 1942).

It is apparent that both genes and environment affect excitability. Different strains of inbred rats and mice (with different genes) show differences in excitability when reared under very similar environmental circumstances. The gray Norway rat, for example, has been reported to differ from the Wistar albino in this characteristic. Yet the "savageness" of the Norway rat can be greatly reduced by an environmental factor—that of handling. In fact, a month of handling has been said to be almost as effective in changing the behavior of the rat as interbreeding the first filial generation (C. S. Hall, 1941). A wild strain of rats bred for 14 years, with no new rats introduced into the strain, changed their behavior greatly in the course of the years (C. S. Hall, 1941). It was found that their nervous tension and fear of man decreased; they gradually became less vicious and wild. Yet, even after domestication for fifty-five generations, these rats continued to show a "distaste for restraint" by making vigorous attempts to escape (Farris and Yeakel, 1945). It was observed also that they were startled by slight noises which produced little or no response from the albino rat.

Whether tamed or not, they were said to react with overt behavior to stimuli which left the albinos apparently unmoved. Greater responsiveness, or excitability, on the part of the Norway rat is suggested by the following comment:

> Even when the savage element (i.e., the tendency to bite) of the gray Norway temperament is suppressed by training, some residuum of wildness, in the sense of ready excitability of the nervous system, remains. Observers familiar with tamed gray rats look upon them as (in anthropomorphic terms) sensitive, nervous, excitable, and emotional (Farris and Yeakel, 1945, p. 109).

Selective mating for eight generations has been shown to increase greatly the difference between two strains of rats in a mode of behavior which C. S. Hall (1941) called "emotionality." Since the criterion for this behavior was defecation or urination in an open field, it may perhaps be suggested that the animals were showing excitability expressed in withdrawal behavior and disturbance of internal functions rather than in attack upon the external environment. In other words, they were showing a high degree of arousal with little overt activity.

Differences in excitability have also been found in mice (W. M. Dawson, 1932). "Wild" mice were observed to be easily excited and to run rapidly about the cage or to hide in the paper when their pen was disturbed. When picked up, they struggled to escape. "Tame" mice moved about more slowly and were less likely to struggle when caught. This behavior suggested that a test for wildness or tameness might be the length of time consumed by a mouse in running from one end to the other of a runway. Using this test, Dawson bred together the fastest mice and also the slowest mice. The difference in time between the first generation wild and the first generation tame was more than twenty-four times its probable error. There was little or no overlapping in the two groups. Both weight and age were shown to be without effect on the time of running.

To test the influence of environmental association upon the response, the fathers were removed from the pen either before the birth of the young or one or two days afterward. This left the offspring of a wild male by a tame female to be reared by the tame female, and the offspring of a tame male by a wild female to be reared by the wild female. No differences were observed in the speed of running of the two groups of young.

Dawson not only found a decided difference between the wild and the tame stocks, but also found that this difference was increased by selecting the parents through four generations. He demonstrated, too, that mating the first filial generation back to the wild stock produced very different results from mating it back to the tame stock.

A most striking feature of these studies of rats and mice is their almost unanimous agreement that the genes play a major role in determining differences in excitability or, more accurately, in determining modes of behavior which appear to have in common the factor of excitability. This has been the conclusion from the early study of Yerkes, in which behavioral characteristics were identified by ratings, to later studies with more objective ways of measuring responses and more refined statistical treatment of the data.

Studies of Dogs

Rats and mice are not, however, the only animals which have been observed to show differences in excitability. It has been pointed out that some breeds of chickens are more excitable than others, that draft horses have quieter dispositions than race horses, and that dairy cows are usually more nervous than beef cattle (W. M. Dawson, 1932). Studies of dogs have emphasized the differences between individual animals.

An extensive investigation of differences in excitability among dogs has been carried out by Stockard (1941) and his co-workers. Dogs of different breeds and physical types were trained by W. T. James (1941) in conditioned reflex experiments under identical conditions. They showed differences in excitability, both in their general behavior and in their behavior during conditioning. Probably this characteristic would show a normal distribution curve if it were finely measured. James divided his dogs into two main groups and two subgroups. The A dogs were lethargic; the B dogs were excitable. A+ dogs were slightly more excitable than A dogs; B— dogs were slightly less excitable than B dogs. James points out, however, that the groups shade into each other.

The dogs designated as excitable were said to be slow to make friends with strangers (note the similarity to the "wildness" of excitable rats); they showed a tendency to become hysterical; and they showed hyperactivity. They struggled violently against the leash when it was first used. At this time they jumped, pulled, bit, trembled, whined as if in intense pain, breathed rapidly, and had an accelerated heart beat and dilated pupils. They were slow to adapt to the laboratory situation. At first, they had to be forced into the room and on the platform, and they refused food until they had been starved for at least 2 or 3 days. They showed many spontaneous undirected movements (no doubt similar to the restless behavior of nervous children). James (1941, p. 556) says: "They (the excitable dogs) appear to have an excess of energy which must be released, either through directed movements to definite signals or undirected movements to non-specific signals."

The lethargic dogs, on the other hand, quickly made friends with the experimenter, did not struggle against the harness, were not greatly disturbed when brought into the laboratory, and appeared to be able to restrain themselves in every way. James says: "It seems that the organism is eliminating useless actions, making short cuts, and retaining only the movements essential for taking food. Spontaneous activity, which is low even in the beginning, is reduced to zero." Such dogs were easy to handle and to train.

In the experimental situation further differences in behavior appeared. The excitable dogs were greatly disturbed by the loud buzzer; the lethargic dogs responded with little noticeable reaction. Whereas the excitable dogs moved the head, tail, and legs, the lethargic dogs moved only the head. Furthermore, the responses of the excitable dogs continued for a longer time.

Adaptation to the experimental situation followed a different course in the two groups of dogs. The excitable dogs never became inert and inactive in an habitual situation. They over-reacted each time the signal was presented—that is, they showed reactions which had no connection at all with food-getting. Most of them showed a tendency toward increased activity and annoyance as the experiments progressed. Lethargic dogs were in their most active phase at the beginning of the experiments, and quickly became inactive and sluggish. The excitable dogs were disturbed by changes in the laboratory; the lethargic dogs appeared almost completely insensitive to change. Excitable dogs showed a deficiency of ability to inhibit their responses. Although they seemed to recognize the difference between the positive and negative signals, even after a long period of training they repeatedly reacted to the negative signal almost as strongly as to the positive. B dogs (excitable) gave a vigorous conditioned salivary response within a short time after the signal was presented. A dogs (lethargic) showed a long delay between the beginning of the signal and the flow of saliva.

James' intermediate type dogs, which he calls A+ and B—, were regarded as better balanced and better able to make suitable adjustments to the situation than either of the extreme types. The B— dogs, though alert and active, did not become too excited to enter into the performance, and they could restrain themselves and differentiate in their responses to different types of signal. The A+ dogs, unlike the A dogs, were not so sluggish that they lost all interest in the experiments. The A dogs finally became so relaxed that they did not bother even to orient to the signals or the food pan but held the head just beside the pan until the food was presented. Sometimes they rested the head on the board beside the pan and went to sleep between signals. The B dogs, on the other hand, continued to orient to the food pan and were impatient of waiting. They always expended energy, even when it seemed unnecessary.

In another experiment by James (1941), twenty-three dogs were trained to raise the foreleg when a certain signal was given, and thereby to avoid an electric shock. A summary of the differences in behavior of A dogs and B dogs is given below.

A Dogs (Lethargic)	B Dogs (Excitable)
Required 1–7 days training before they would stand in harness.	Required 10–15 days training before they would stand in harness.
Generally required slightly stronger shock to produce flexion of leg.	Generally flexed leg in response to weaker shock.
Moved only a segment of the leg in response to liminal electric shock.	Moved all leg segments and postural systems of head and neck in response to liminal shock.
Weak after-discharge of excitation.	Extensive and long-continued activity after shock.
Became progressively less disturbed by shock as experiment proceeded. Strength of shock had to be increased.	Continued to give vigorous general reactions until they learned to avoid the shock.
Never developed a true sustained conditioned avoiding reaction (low excitatory value of stimulus?).	Developed conditioned avoiding reaction very quickly.
Longer time interval between signal and conditioned response.	Shorter time interval between signal and conditioned response.
Did not react to all signals introduced.	Responded to every signal presented, no matter how much it differed from the one used in the initial training.
Became progressively less active as the experiments continued.	Continued at high level of activity.

The vulnerability to stimulation of highly excitable animals was shown by the fact that some of the B dogs were apparently so disturbed by the shock that they held the foot in an avoiding position throughout the experiments and never placed it on the floor. Other B dogs held the leg in a half-flexed position. As would be expected, the animals who held the leg up all the time were those most disturbed by the shock when it was first given.

Again the dogs of the intermediate groups were more successful than either the A or the B dogs in learning to respond to the two signals in the desired way. Especially successful were the B— dogs, who were somewhat excitable, but less so than the B dogs.

James reports that, as a rule, the animals who were excitable under laboratory conditions were excitable in the kennels also, though this was not always the case. A dogs slept or were inactive the greater part of the day, while some of the B dogs moved almost constantly, running or walking back and forth, playing and barking. The B dogs responded to distant noises or other stimuli, were easily roused from sleep, and were the first to give warning when anyone entered the kennel lot.

The difference in behavior of these groups of dogs appears to represent characteristic differences in activation. Some breeds of dog, for example, the basset hound, were said to be characteristically phlegmatic, while other breeds, for example, the shepherd dog, were said to be characteristically excitable. In pure lines the characteristic mode of behavior was associated with a certain body form. In crosses between lines, however, dogs showing a great resemblance in body form might show a wide divergence in behavior (W. T. James, 1941). Hybrid offspring of active and inactive breeds made activity scores (on a pedometer and on a runway mounted on springs) which were intermediate between the two extremes.

James' description of differences in the temperament of dogs has been presented here at considerable length because the kinds of differences reported by him are similar to those we shall discuss later in human beings. It is to be regretted that the number of subjects was relatively small and the statistical treatment of data so incomplete as to leave us uncertain as to the degree of confidence with which we can accept his findings. Nevertheless, the internal consistency of his observations, as well as their consistency with the results of experiments with other animals and with human beings, makes it appear probable that there exist true differences of the types which he reports. Moreover, later studies by James (1953) have been entirely consistent with the findings of the earlier ones. They are also consistent with the reports of Pavlov (1927).

Other studies of dogs have confirmed the findings of differences in activity level and in response to stimulation, and they have produced evidence that certain genetic differences are accentuated by training (Fuller, 1948; Scott and Charles, 1954).

The effect of an environmental agent upon an animal's excitability is seen in the report that two phlegmatic dogs were temporarily changed to excitable dogs by the administration of a drug, prostigmine methylsulfate (W. T. James and B. E. Ginsburg, 1949). Before taking the drug the dogs had shown sluggish muscular responses and poor muscle tone. After administration of the drug, one dog, the more phlegmatic of the two, developed a regularly appearing and vigorous avoidance response to a conditioned stimulus which had been responded to only once in the previous 101 trials. The response to the conditioned stimulus was now more than four times as intense as the response to the unconditioned stimulus (an electric shock) had previously been, and it was sustained for a much longer period. Upon presentation of the conditioned stimulus, cardiac and respiratory rates were increased, whereas previously only a slight slowing of a single inspiration had occurred. The animal now stood alertly upright, responded to slight noises which had previously been ignored, and was said to be unmistakably more responsive to the experiments. The change in behavior lasted for several hours. The other dog, more excitable to begin with, showed a marked increase in excitability, but no increase in the percentage of conditioned avoidance responses after administration of the drug. This animal, said to act now precisely like animals with a naturally high level of excitability, showed alert posture, restless movements, whining, continuous flexions of the foreleg, attempts to pull out of the harness, and apparent inability to restrain her movements until the presentation of the signal.

It appears that the same difference in excitability which may be caused in one instance by a difference in genes may be caused in another instance by an environmental agent, in this case a drug. Other environmental factors, such as nutrition, disease, and various aspects of the social environment, may also presumably influence the degree of excitability of the individual. In fact, the responses of 202 normally reared dogs, of 10 breeds, compared with those of 28 other dogs, belonging to two of the same breeds, but reared in a more restricted environment, showed complex interactions of constitutional and environmental factors (Mahut, 1958). When the 10 breeds of dogs were reared in homes as pets, the breeds showed statistically significant differences in "susceptibility to fear" and in the patterns of response "in both fearful and non-fearful behavior." When boxers and Scottish terriers, two of the 10 breeds studied in a home environment, were reared in kennels, both breeds became more fearful. Cage-restricted animals of these 2 breeds appeared to develop "diffuse excitement" when taken out of the cage and exposed to presumably fear-producing objects.

MEASUREMENT OF PHYSIOLOGICAL PROCESSES

The consistency of the individual with respect to his relative degree of activation, and to fluctuations in activation, is shown most clearly in studies where repeated measurements have been made of one or more physiological processes. Among the processes studied have been the electrical phenomena of the skin, heart rate, electrical potentials of the brain, and tension of the muscles. Measures of these phenomena, when repeated over short intervals of time in the same experimental situation, remain relatively constant. As the time interval between measurements increases, the degree of relationship between successive measurements tends to decrease. This finding might be expected as a result of developmental changes as well as changes in the environment. Nevertheless, some degree of consistency in the responses of individuals has been reported over periods as long as those in which measurements have been made. Such consistency might be expected on the basis of constitutional factors (i.e., type of nervous system and of endocrine system) and also, perhaps, on the basis of established habits of meeting situations in particular ways.

The present chapter reviews data concerning individual differences in physiological measurements and the degree to which certain physiological measurements show consistency on retest. The chapter which follows will discuss the relationship between individual differences in these measurements and differences in various aspects of behavior.

Metabolic Pattern

A biochemist who has made extensive studies of the chemical content of the saliva and of the urinary excretions of normal individuals reports that "each human being has a metabolic pattern which differs in some respects from that of all his fellows" (R. J. Williams, 1946). He points out that dogs, "which have a keen sense of smell, have made use of this fact throughout the ages to identify individuals" (R. J. Williams, 1950). This biochemist argues that observable individual differences in behavior have their basis in fundamental differences in metabolism. He says: "If we could imagine two individuals whose various bodily structures even down to the minutest details were the same, then the metabolism in their various internal organs, in their glands and in the nerve cells throughout their bodies and in their brains would be the same and we would have duplicate individuals without individual differences" (R. J. Williams, 1946, p. 22). Some of the chemical differences between individuals would, we may suppose, be related to characteristic differences in the level of activation and in the lability of response.

Electrical Phenomena of the Skin

Successive measures of palmar skin resistance in the same individual correlate highly when the measurements are not too far separated in time. For example, correlation coefficients ranging from .92 to .998 were obtained during rest and during exercise when the tests were made on the same day or on successive days (Elbel and Ronkin, 1946). When, on the other hand, measurements of initial resistance were made on adolescent subjects at intervals ranging from 1 day to 5 years, the coefficients of correlation ranged from .07 to .73, with the highest coefficients being obtained in general for the shorter intervals of time (W. D. Obrist, 1948). Since adolescence is a period of considerable change in the individual, higher coefficients of correlation between successive measures might be expected at other times of life. Freeman and Giffin (1939) report a coefficient of .40 ± .21 for measurements which were "often widely separated in time," compared with a coefficient of .91 ± .02 when the second measurement followed immediately after the first. Both sets of measurements were made under basal conditions, and both showed greater reliability than measures of basal metabolism which were simultaneously recorded.

When startle stimuli of equivalent intensity are presented, the skin-conductance index of the individual is said to remain fairly constant (Freeman, 1948a). It is also reported that individuals tend to maintain the same position in skin conductance, as compared with other individuals, during a frustration situation and a rest period (Haggard, 1941). J. I. Lacey and B. C. Lacey (1958a), studying palmar conductance, systolic and diastolic blood pressure, heart rate, pulse pressure, and variability in heart rate during rest and during several different types of stimulation, found that the skin-resistance reaction was "possibly the single most reproducible response from one stressor-episode to another," though it was also the response most independent of the others. Apparently measures of the galvanic skin response, as well as measures of the initial resistance of the skin, show fairly consistent differences between individuals except when the measurements are widely separated in time.

Participation of the genes in determining differences in the galvanic skin response is suggested by the fact that identical twins have been found to resemble each other more closely than fraternal twins of the same sex in the extent of this response (Carmena, 1934). Thirty-six pairs of identical twins were found to respond to repeated stimulation (noises, odors, a suddenly appearing bright light, and a slight pin-prick) with a galvanic response that, in 70 per cent of the cases, showed a difference of less than 4 centimeters between members of a pair in the extent of deflection of the galvanometer needle. Fraternal twins of the same sex showed such similarity in only about 4 per cent of the cases.

Individuals differ, not only in basal skin resistance and in the change in resistance which occurs as a result of stimulation, but also in the extent to which skin-resistance responses occur when there are no observed stimuli. Mundy-Castle and McKiever (1953), recording GSR's when auditory stimuli were presented at 30-second intervals, were able to classify their subjects into three groups: (1) stable, who gave skin responses only to observed stimuli and showed a consistent pattern of resistance changes, (2) stable/labile, who gave a few "endogenous" responses or had an unstable resistance level, or both, and (3) labiles, who gave many "endogenous" responses and often showed an unstable resistance level.

The Laceys (J. I. Lacey and B. C. Lacey, 1958b) found that there were individual differences in the number of galvanic skin responses of individuals reclining in an easy chair when no stimulation was administered. The frequency of appearance of GSR's during rest was a reliable individual characteristic which, upon 48-hour retest, tended to be fixed in magnitude. It was a continuous variable, but individuals were classified as "stabiles" or "labiles" according to whether their scores were above or below the median for the group. The frequency of fluctuations in skin resistance during effortful activity was also reliable upon 48-hour retest, though here adaptation effects were observable.

Individuals differ also in the speed of "recovery" of skin resistance from the displacement produced by stimulation. Darrow and Heath (1932) and later Freeman and Pathman (1942) demonstrated this fact. It is possible that the speed of recovery from the activating effects of stimulation may be of more prognostic significance in relation to certain forms of behavior, including susceptibility to breakdown, than the characteristic level of activation of the individual. This question will be discussed further in Chapter 11.

The Electroencephalogram

The electroencephalogram (EEG) has also been found to differentiate individuals and to show consistency of pattern for the same individual (C. E. Henry, 1941a and 1941b). In normal adults there is said to be very little variation from day to day or even from month to month in such characteristics as the frequency of the alpha waves (Lindsley, 1944). Differences between individuals in the EEG are clearly apparent, but variations in the EEG in the same individual tend to be small. Lindsley (1944) remarks:

> The EEG of the individual person during the course of a single recording period shows moment to moment variations in frequency, amplitude, and pattern and no particular section of the record appears precisely like another. Yet as the record streams on and on, one cannot help being impressed with the high degree of similarity all the way through. Averages of frequency, amplitude, and per-cent-time from meter to meter of record show very narrow variability (p. 1047).

Knott (1941) concludes:

> Over fairly long intervals of time the "pattern" of the EEG and, quantitatively (but more narrowly), the per cent time an alpha rhythm is present on the record tend to be repeatable for a given individual. . . . There also appears to be a tendency for different persons to show different types of record, although there is enough similarity between the records of some persons to render positive identification by this means impossible (p. 947).

In line with this opinion is the statement of Lennox, Gibbs, and Gibbs (1945, p. 236) that "Cortical potentials have been compared to fingerprints, but comparison with handwriting or with facial features seems more apt." Perhaps the most substantial demonstration of consistency of the individual in his EEG pattern is to be found in the analysis of Grass and Gibbs (1938) of the frequencies found in repeated samples of the same person.

P. A. Davis (1941a) reported that the alpha index, if recorded under standard conditions, remains approximately constant over a period of years. Others have found a mean standard deviation of 7.1 for the alpha index (Brazier and Finesinger, 1944). In adults over 47 years of age, the dominant alpha frequency is said to be less stable than in younger adults.

The electroencephalograms of children are more variable than those of adults, yet in children also certain characteristics tend to persist.

Henry (1944), who analyzed the records of 95 children over a 5-year period, states: "In general, . . . a child with a fast alpha rhythm (above 11/sec.) will tend to remain on the fast side, and a child with a slow alpha rhythm (below 9/sec.) will tend to remain on the slow side." Some children, however, showed some variation in alpha frequency from day to day. A number of investigators have reported that the EEG pattern of an individual does not change essentially over a long period of time after the age of about 14 years, when cerebral maturity is reached (Werre, 1957).

Note age here.

Genetic influence on the EEG is suggested by the fact that identical twins show electroencephalograms which are more similar than those found in fraternal twins (Lennox, Gibbs, and Gibbs, 1945). In a sample of 55 monozygotic and 19 dizygotic twins, it was reported that, in the monozygotic twins, the EEG's were identical in 85 per cent, nonidentical in 4 per cent, and in doubt in 11 per cent of the cases. In the dizygotic twins the EEG's were alike in 5 per cent of the cases and unlike in 95 per cent.

The differences between the EEG's of different individuals appear to be greater during waking states than during sleep, and during the later hours of the day than upon waking in the morning.[1] Other physiological measures also, as for example tension of the muscles, have been found to show greater differences between individuals during active than during passive states.

Tension of the Muscles

In almost every investigation in which tension of the skeletal musculature has been measured, wide differences between individuals in the degree of tension have been noted. In the same stimulus situation, one individual would respond with a relatively low degree of tension, another with a moderate degree, and a third with a high degree of tension. Moreover, when observed in a different stimulus situation, the subjects, while varying in their absolute level of tension, would tend to preserve their ranks with respect to tension of the muscles. It thus became apparent that individuals differ in the tendency to release more or to release less energy as indicated by this measure of energy release. In other words, the muscle tension of different individuals varies around different central tendencies, so that one individual may be characterized as being generally tense, and another as generally relaxed.

[1] Reviews by Lindsley (1944) and by Knott (1941) cite investigations which provide the basis for these conclusions.

One of the earliest reports of measured differences in response which were indicative of differences in muscle tension between normal individuals was the report of J. J. B. Morgan (1916) that his subjects struck the keys of a typewriter with a force ranging from 100 grams in one individual to 1200 grams in another. He believed, however, that the differences between individuals, as distinct from the differences shown by the same individual, might be due merely to differences in the manner of touching the keys.

From the early nineteen-thirties on, a number of investigators have reported individual differences in measurements of muscle tension made during various performances. To cite only a few of these reports, the author found that one group of eleven, and another group of eighteen, nursery-school children showed marked individual differences in grip pressure while engaged in various tasks (Duffy, 1930, 1932a, 1932b). During tapping, for example, the pressure in the used hand ranged from 20 millimeters for one individual to 73.6 millimeters for another, with a mean variation of 13.1 millimeters. When a discrimination performance was repeated after a week or so there was a correlation coefficient of .74 ± .08 between tension measures on the first and on the second occasion. When average grip pressure in the used and the unused hand during tapping was correlated with a similar measure during a discrimination performance, the coefficient of correlation was .58 ± .12. Evidently, the subjects tended, at least to some degree, to maintain their respective ranks in tension during successive performances of the same task and during the performance of different tasks.

Allport and Vernon (1933) also found a high degree of consistency in level of muscle tension from session to session.

Arnold (1942), measuring pressure in the used and the unused hand during relaxation, tapping, and the taking of shorthand, reached a similar conclusion. When tension during one task was correlated with tension during a different task, 5 out of 12 coefficients of correlation were in the seventies or eighties, 3 were in the sixties, 1 was in the fifties, and 3 were in the forties.

Grip pressure has been found to correlate with point pressure ($r = .76$), and both measures to show a high degree of reliability (Wenger, 1945). The measurements were made during the writing of a sentence by 427 subjects. Test-retest reliability for grip pressure was .94, and for point pressure, .90.

Adult subjects showed pronounced individual consistencies in action potentials recorded from the arm muscles (R. C. Davis, 1937), and infants have been reported to have a preferential level of sucking pressure which was characteristic of the individual (Halverson, 1938).

Airplane pilots in training have also been found to show marked individual differences in muscle tension, some showing excessive pressure on the stick and on the rudder pedal in both take-offs and landings, while others showed little tension on either maneuver (A. C. Williams, Jr., J. W. Macmillan, and J. G. Jenkins, 1947). No individuals were found who in general tended to be tense during take-offs alone or during landings alone. Analysis of myovoltmeter readings from the muscles of the thigh indicated that the major source of variability in the scores was that of variation between individuals. These individual differences were statistically significant.

While tension of the skeletal musculature is not uniform throughout the body, the condition of tension is to a considerable degree general rather than specific. The focal point of the tension depends upon the stimulating conditions, or the nature of the task in which the individual is engaged; yet parts of the body other than those directly involved are also affected. R. C. Davis (1942), for example, found evidence of considerable muscular contraction in all four limbs when only one of them was engaged in a simple voluntary motion. From his own work and that of others he concluded that activity in more remote muscles develops simultaneously with activity in the focal muscles and is a result of the same neural process.

The degree of correspondence in tension of any two parts of the body varies not only with the task and with the areas sampled but also, it appears, with the maturational status of the individual. During infancy and early childhood, tension of the musculature seems to be more generalized or diffuse than it is in adulthood. In infants, for example, it has been reported that the degree of tension of the finger flexors as measured by grip pressure is indicative of the state of tension of the skeletal musculature in general (Halverson, 1938). Thus it was found that tension of the flexor muscles varied directly with the strength of sucking (Halverson, 1938).

In adults also there is in general corresponding, rather than compensatory, variation in the tension of muscles in various parts of the body; yet the correspondence is frequently not close. When action potentials were recorded simultaneously from the neck and from the arm, it was found that there was relatively little correspondence between them during work on problems ($r = .35 \pm .05$) (R. C. Davis, 1938). The arm showed a much greater increase in muscular activity than was shown by the neck.

In other studies with adults, reports have been made of varying degrees of relationship between the tension in one group of muscles and that in another. Stroud (1931) found that subjects learning a stylus maze had scores showing correlation coefficients of .67 ± .02 between grip pressure and downward pressure, .44 ± .03 between jaw tension and downward pressure, and .33 ± .03 between jaw tension and grip pressure. Arnold (1942) found coefficients of correlation between right-hand pressure and left-hand pressure in the same task ranging from .42 ± .12 to .85 ± .04. A. C. Williams and his collaborators found that some pilot trainees consistently showed grip pressure on the stick but no rudder-pedal pressure, while others consistently pressed on the rudder but showed little pressure on the stick (A. C. Williams, Jr., Macmillan, and Jenkins, 1947).

Some years ago, an attempt was made (Duffy, 1946) to determine the degree of generality of skeletal muscle tension in adult subjects by making a factor analysis of measures of tension secured on different occasions, during the performance of different tasks, and by different techniques of measurement, some involving grip pressure and some point pressure. Twelve measures of muscle tension, some from the used and some from the unused hand, were obtained while the subjects were performing the following tasks: color naming, maze tracing, tapping, crossing out digits and letters, and adding numbers. The measures were secured on three separate occasions, the first separated from the second by three months, and the second separated from the third by one week. One of the five factors obtained was widely general and was interpreted to be a factor of general muscle tension. This factor incorporated many different tasks, all three techniques of tension measurement, and all three experimental sessions. The presence of this factor was taken as evidence that individuals tend to function more or less consistently at a relatively high or a relatively low level of tension during the performance of a wide variety of tasks, presented on occasions as much as three months apart.[2] It should be pointed out, however, that all the measures recorded were obtained from the hands.

In Malmo's laboratory, where electromyographic studies have been made of muscles in several parts of the body, the findings are, with one exception, in harmony with those mentioned above. Action potentials from the flexor muscles of the forearm were reported to show considerable individual consistency from one stress situation to another,

[2] The confidence with which this finding can be accepted is limited by the fact that only twenty-five subjects were employed in the investigation.

and to show a small but statistically reliable correlation $(+.36)$ with potentials from the neck during a pain-stress test (Malmo and Shagass, 1951). In another study, muscular activity recorded from five different channels showed in all channels a tendency to decrease as therapeutic progress occurred (Shagass and Malmo, 1954). In a third study, a factor analysis performed on tension measures from six different muscles revealed that five of these measures were grouped together in a single factor of neck and bilateral-forearm tension, while the sixth measure, that of frontalis muscle tension, fell into another factor (Malmo and Smith, 1955).

Frontalis muscle tension itself has, however, been reported by Sainsbury and Gibson (1954) to show significant concordance with the tension in three other muscle groups. Using as subjects "thirty anxious and tense patients," they obtained electronically the summation of action potentials in the frontalis muscle, the forearm extensors, and, in some, the neck muscles, while the subjects relaxed.

It appears that, on the whole, skeletal muscle tension in one part of the body tends to be positively related to that in other parts of the body, though the relationship between the tension in any two areas may not be very close. Parts of the body more remote from each other, or more widely differentiated in function, yield tension measures which are less closely related than those which are closer together or functionally more similar. When tension measures taken from different parts of the body, recorded during different tasks, or made at widely separated intervals of time show, nevertheless, a significant positive correlation with each other, it must be concluded that there is at least some degree of "generality" in skeletal muscle tension. It appears possible, however, that individuals differ in the area in which maximum tension is ordinarily found. If this is the case, consistent differences in tension would still permit us to conceive of one individual as "tense" and another as "relaxed," though adequate measurement of the individual might be difficult.

Individual differences in fluctuations in muscle tension, as indicated by hand-arm steadiness, also appear to be fairly consistent. For example, measurements made a month apart showed substantial correlations (Lovell, 1941).

Other Measures of Activation

Consistent differences between individuals have been reported, not only in the indicators of activation discussed above but also in a number of other measures. Measurements of basal metabolism, systolic blood pressure, pulse rate, and respiratory rate, repeated forty-five times over 90 days, gave evidence that characteristic individual levels for these variables may be fixed when the measurements are taken under standard conditions (Herrington, 1942). The range of scores for basal metabolism and systolic blood pressure was about twenty-five times the typical standard error of the individual means. For pulse rate, the range was about thirty-three times the typical standard error of the means, and for respiratory rate it was over one hundred times the standard error.

It has also been found that the number of bursts of cardiac activity during rest showed a fair degree of consistency when the subjects were retested after 48 hours (J. I. Lacey and B. C. Lacey, 1958b). The co-efficient of correlation was .58, significant at better than the .01 level. Moreover, cardiac activity during rest was correlated with cardiac activity during the performance of various tasks.

Genetic factors have been reported to be of importance in determining blood pressure, pulse rate, and the electrocardiogram (Muller, 1935).

Measurement of changes in skin temperature has shown that some subjects are, in this respect, more reactive than others (Helson and Quantius, 1934). In general, subjects who were more responsive under experimental conditions had also been more reactive during the control period when no stimulation was presented.

The rate of respiration during the flying of an airplane has been found to differ significantly between individuals (A. C. Williams, Jr., et al., 1947). In fact, it was said that a reasonably accurate prediction of a person's respiratory rate at a given time during a flight could be made on the basis of knowledge of his "normal" respiratory rate and the name of the maneuver to be performed.

Apparently there are wide and consistent differences between individuals in respiratory rate, in pulse rate, in blood pressure, in cardiac activity, in basal metabolic rate, and in many other measures.

Individual Differences in the Patterning of Activation

There remains for consideration the question of individual differences in the patterning of the various processes involved in the activation of the organism.

Different profiles of response were found for different individuals by Darrow and Heath (1932), who recorded simultaneously a number of physiological changes when their subjects were given the same stimulation. There were periods in the reaction of each subject when measures of two or more of these responses showed parallelism, and other periods when the same responses showed compensatory action. Darling (1940) also attempted to differentiate between individuals by means of a group of physiological measures. Both of these investigations will be discussed more fully in the following chapter.

In the early studies of individual differences in groups of physiological responses, no attempt was made to determine the consistency with which the individual showed a given patterning of responses. In later studies, undertaken by Wenger and others, this question has been investigated. Wenger (1942) obtained from 62 school-age children measures of 20 physiological variables related to the functioning of the autonomic nervous system. Repetition of the tests after 6 months, and again after 12 months, yielded test-retest coefficients of correlation ranging from very low values to values in the sixties and seventies. Factor analysis of the measures produced, among other factors, one designated as an autonomic factor and defined chiefly by sparcity of saliva, high percentage of solids in the saliva, rapid heart rate, little sinus arrhythmia, much palmar and nonpalmar sweating, high basal metabolic rate, and low pulse pressure (Wenger, 1941). A regression equation was worked out in order to obtain for each individual a score on this autonomic factor. The tests finally included in the factor were salivary output, heart rate, palmar and nonpalmar skin conductance, pulse pressure, respiration rate, and dermographia persistence (length of time the skin remains red after application of a constant pressure). Test-retest coefficients of correlation of scores on this factor, when measured 6 months later and again a year later, were .57 and .69 respectively. Seasonal variations were presumed to account for the less close correspondence in scores after 6 months than after 12 months. Forty-eight subjects were available for the comparison.

Wenger (1943b) reported that, in a later study, employing somewhat differently weighted measures for obtaining the autonomic factor, he had found that, while individuals differed greatly in scores on this factor, the correlation coefficient between early and later factor scores did not drop below .64 over a 2-year period. Evidently, then, the physiological processes included in the factor differentiate one individual from another with some degree of consistency over a period of at least a couple of years.

The early studies of Wenger were based upon the hypothesis that the functioning of the autonomic nervous system involves antagonistic action of the adrenergic (sympathetic) and cholinergic (parasympathetic) branches of this system, and that individuals differ in tendencies with respect to autonomic imbalance, some individuals tending toward predominance of the adrenergic, and others toward predominance of the cholinergic branch. Autonomic imbalance, when measured in an unselected population, was presumed to be continuously distributed about a central tendency defined as autonomic balance (Wenger, 1947). Inspection of the raw data upon which his measurements of the autonomic factor were based led Wenger to conclude, however, that this factor had appeared because of patterns of interrelated physiological processes which characterized fewer than half of his subjects. The other subjects showed no consistent pattern for these functions and therefore could not be considered as adequately measured for the autonomic factor.

A later study by Wenger (1957) led to the conclusion that the autonomic factor previously reported was to be found in several different populations, but that it afforded a description of somewhat less than one-third of each population. Most subjects showed mixed patterns of autonomic functions judged by the criteria he employed for sympathetic and parasympathetic activity.

Wenger's concept of autonomic balance is accepted by Richmond and Lustman (1955) but challenged by Terry (1953). The former investigators, measuring reflex vasodilation to immersion of the right limb of thirty-one newborn infants, found marked individual differences. At least two of the infants could, by statistical criteria, be called hyperreactors. Twenty-nine infants were observed for reflex pupillary dilation when a bell was struck. Gross observation on three occasions led to a classification of the subjects as showing a positive reflex, a negative reflex, or being variable. Only four were variable. On the basis of a factor analysis of a number of measures of autonomic functioning, Terry (1953) has reported, not "generalized autonomic balance," but factors which represent chiefly the functioning of single organs and systems, i.e., skin conductance, heart period, and blood pressure. Terry's findings are consistently negative, not only with respect to autonomic balance, but also with respect to other conclusions which have apparently been more clearly established in the work of others (e.g., the relationship between the Féré effect and the Tarchanoff effect).

Genetic factors are believed by Jost and Sontag (1944) to be primarily responsible for differences in "autonomic constitution." Measurements of the physiological processes comprising Wenger's autonomic factor were made on a small number of identical-twin pairs (5 to 6), a somewhat larger number of siblings (10 to 23), and a large number of unrelated individuals, on three occasions, one year apart. In general, identical twins resembled each other most closely, siblings came next in similarity, and unrelated individuals showed least resemblance. This general trend was found in almost every instance, but not all measures showed statistically reliable differences between the groups. Among the measures which showed significant differences between various groups in the greatest number of instances were vasomotor persistence (measured by the time required for the disappearance of a red mark left by pressure on the arm), standing palmar conductance, reclining pulse pressure, and total salivary output.

It appears that what the investigators call "autonomic constitution" tends to be most alike in individuals who are most closely related, but the greater similarity cannot be attributed to the genes alone, since the environment, as well as the genes, of identical twins is more similar than that of other siblings, and the environment, as well as the genes, of siblings is more similar than that of unrelated individuals. Nevertheless, it is a fact of some significance that the type of functioning of these physiological processes "runs in families," and must therefore be determined to a considerable extent by the factors, genetic and environmental, which differentiate one family from another.

While all autonomically innervated structures have been reported to be activated during stress, usually in the direction of sympathetic predominance, the various structures have been found not to show equal increments or decrements of function (J. I. Lacey, D. E. Bateman and R. Van Lehn, 1953). Instead, as was pointed out in Chapter 5, there was individual patterning of response. When different individuals were subjected to the same stress, a given individual might be above the mean of the group in one physiological measure, at the mean for another measure, and considerably below the mean for a third measure. The individual pattern of response showed some degree of consistency, but was not highly consistent even upon immediate retest. When test-retest reliability coefficients were computed for paired physiological measures, the correlation coefficients for girls were all significant and ranged from .57 to .76. The coefficients for boys ranged from .32 to .74, and all except five were significant. Individuals were said to differ in the extent to which they showed a consistent pattern of autonomic response, some showing the pattern very consistently, while others showed random variation (J. I. Lacey et al., 1953).

In a later study, J. I. Lacey (1956) concluded that the individual differences in autonomic reactivity which he found were not a mere sampling variation, but were due to individual differences in "homeo-static efficiency." In one experimental situation, he correlated the heart-rate change of each individual with the prestimulus heart rate in each of two parts of fifty-two serial reactions. When these pairs of correlations were then correlated by the method of rank-differences, he found a correlation coefficient of .60, significant beyond the .01 level. He concluded tentatively that there are reliable and systematic individual differences in homeostatic efficiency.

Further testing of the "principle of relative response-specificity," under noxious stimulation and "effortful 'mental' activity," with meas-urements of systolic and diastolic blood pressure, pulse pressure, skin resistance, heart rate, and variability of heart rate, led to the following hypothesis:

> For any given set of autonomic functions (greater than two), all Ss ex-hibit, in response to effective stimulus-conditions, idiosyncratic patterns of autonomic activity, in which the different physiological functions are dif-ferentially responsive. These patterns of response tend to be reproduced from one stressor-episode to another. This is true even though the phys-iological and psychological demands of the stressor-episodes are uncorre-lated, or very poorly correlated. Finally, there are quantitative individual differences in this tendency to reproduce a response-hierarchy from one stressor to other stressors (J. I. Lacey and B. C. Lacey, 1958a, pp. 72–73).

Age Differences in Measures of Activation

Most of the measures used in assessing activation show differences in different age groups. A few examples of age differences in physio-logical measures will be presented below.

Skin Resistance. Evidence of changes in the electrical resistance of the skin with changes in age comes from a number of sources. Harold E. Jones (1950), for example, has reported that infants from 3 to 11 months of age have galvanic skin responses which are usually smaller and less easily aroused than those of older children.

Data from the California Growth Study, in which 100 subjects were tested and retested over a period of 6 years, have shown that the level of skin resistance follows a downward trend with age, from 12 years of age to late adolescence (H. E. Jones, 1949). At this time it reaches a level about half that found at the age of 12. The relative change in resistance in response to stimulation (the galvanic skin response) was found to increase with age. This increase was due to the fact that, while the absolute resistance change remained approximately con-stant, the initial level of resistance had declined, thus producing a larger ratio of change to initial resistance.

An analysis of the findings of this Growth Study, made by W. D. Obrist (1948), shows not only age trends in resistance level, but also a relationship between resistance level and physiological maturation as represented by the menarche. There was a significant drop in the level of resistance before the menarche, a stabilization of the level for about two years following the menarche, and a significant fall in level again after this period of stability. The investigator suggests that the final leveling off of the curve may represent the attainment of adult levels of resistance. An attempt to discover a similar phenomenon in boys by relating the resistance level to physiological age as represented by skeletal maturity failed to demonstrate a clear-cut correspondence.

An adult group, consisting of 73 university students and 30 staff members, with a mean age in the early twenties, showed no relationship between resistance level and age, but a significant relationship between galvanic skin response and age (Mundy-Castle and Mc-Kiever, 1953). Young persons were more responsive.

Age differences have been shown also in the number of active palmar digital sweat glands (Mackinnon, 1954). One hundred and twenty-three healthy males, ranging in age from 7 to 96 years, were classified according to their decade of life and compared for the number of active sweat glands in 4 square millimeters of the right middle finger. Consecutive pairs of decades were shown to differ significantly from each other in this respect, the later decades having a lower count. For example, there were more active sweat glands in the first and second decades than in the third and fourth decades, and more in the third and fourth decades than in the fifth and sixth. The maximum rate of decrease was found when subjects in the first two decades were compared with those in the next two decades. This finding is of interest since measures of skin resistance have been said to show a fairly high degree of correspondence with activity of the sweat glands (McCleary, 1950). Wilcott (1959), however, reported that the Silverman-Powell index of sweating, with measurements taken from the volar surface of the finger, showed little correlation with skin conductance from the same area, but a high correlation with a humidity index of skin moisture.

The Electroencephalogram (EEG). Major changes occur in the EEG during the developmental period from infancy to adulthood. During the years of maturity there is relatively little change until, with senescence, the changes again become more marked.

In general, the younger the child, the larger and slower are the electrical rhythms of the brain (Lindsley, 1936; Henry, 1944; W. G. Walter, 1950b). Lindsley (1939) recorded EEG's from 132 children over a period of several years and found an increase in the average frequency of the occipital rhythms as the child grew older. F. A. Gibbs and Knott (1949), studying records from the occipital area of 930 subjects ranging in age from 71 days premature to 29 years, reported an increase in voltage in successively higher frequencies throughout the period studied. Newborn infants had a concentration of voltage at 1 to 3 cycles per second; children up to 2 years of age showed an increase with age in electrical activity in the 4-to-6-cycles-per-second range. In the group as a whole, increases in age were in general accompanied by a steady increase in voltage in the 10-to-12-cycle band and a slight increase in the 18-to-22-cycle band.

A rhythm known as the theta rhythm has received particular attention from W. G. Walter (1950b). This band of activity, of 4 to 7 cycles per second, and recorded from the parieto-temporal region, is said to occur as the dominant rhythm in records of children between 2 and 5 years of age. Some investigators have been of the opinion that the theta rhythm is merely an acceleration of the delta activity found primarily in younger children. Later studies in which the alpha rhythm has, in many records, been found throughout early life, apparently negate the hypothesis that the theta rhythm is a transitional pattern between the delta rhythm of infancy and the alpha rhythm of the older child (Melin, 1953). The theta rhythm is quantitatively similar to electrical activity found in organic lesions and in behavior disorders in adults. W. G. Walter (1950b) regards the rhythm as a sign of "relative immaturity of the mechanisms linking the cortex, the thalamus and the hypothalamus." Between the ages of 10 and 12 years, the rhythm begins to disappear in most children. According to Walter, many records in which a slowing of the alpha rhythm or a deceleration of the dominant rhythm is described are actually records in which the theta rhythm was present and was masking, or being masked by, the alpha rhythm.

C. E. Henry (1944), studying a cross-section of 540 children, reported that, during the normal process of growth, there was a progressive decline in the percentage of time during which slow activity occurred in the EEG and a progressive increase in the rate of such activity. It was not until the age of 13 years that the distribution of frequencies in the EEG corresponded to that of the normal population. He found no correlation between alpha frequency and skeletal age or IQ. There appears, however, to be considerable uncertainty as to when the adult EEG pattern becomes stabilized (D. Hill, 1955). Presumably, this occurs some time between 18 and 20 years of age.

Electroencephalograms of children from 1 to 10 years of age (71 Ss), studied by means of automatic frequency analyses as well as by visual inspection, have been reported not to show a simple progression from low to higher frequencies as the child grows older (Corbin and Bickford, 1955). Such a shift, it was pointed out, would be expected if uniform neurones had shown a gradual change in frequencies. Instead, the evidence was thought to point to complex maturational changes taking place in "individual neuron populations (delta, theta, and alpha)." There was agreement with Walter (1950b) that the delta rhythm (1 to 3 cycles per second) may be the dominant rhythm up to 4 years of age, and that the theta rhythm (4 to 7 cycles per second) and the alpha rhythm (8 to 12 cycles per second) are about equally prominent in records of subjects around 5 or 6 years of age. Within any given age group, these investigators, as well as Walter, noted extreme variability in the rhythms found. In fact, one reviewer of the literature points out that children and young adults regularly show EEG's which are "more reactive and less set" than those of older persons, so that a record which is considered normal at the age of 12 might have too much variability to be regarded as normal at the age of 30 (Kennard, 1953).

Studies of the EEG in normal old age show a slowing down of the alpha rhythm (W. D. Obrist, 1954; Mundy-Castle, Hurst, Beerstecher, and Prinsloo, 1954), a slight increase in the incidence of delta waves (W. D. Obrist, 1954), and, in many of the records, the presence of fast waves (W. D. Obrist, 1954; Mundy-Castle et al., 1954). Obrist (1954), who studied 150 normal males ranging in age from 65 to 94 years, says his findings suggest that the EEG shows a progressive change toward slower frequencies in old age. The records of aged persons resembled those of children in slow-wave activity. They differed from those of children, however, in showing a general lowering of voltage and the presence of fast waves in many of the records. Both Obrist and Mundy-Castle noted that normal seniles have more beta activity than young adults.

Though relatively small changes in the EEG occur during the middle years of life, several investigators have found that, when large numbers of cases are studied statistically, slight but significant differences appear (W. D. Obrist, 1954). Obrist, in reviewing studies of this age period, notes that Gibbs and Gibbs found a decrease in the occurrence of "slow" electroencephalograms up to age 60, at which time there appeared to be a reversal of the trend. These investigators are also said to have found an increase in "fast" electroencephalograms during middle age. Greenblatt, who observed similar trends, is reported to have shown that changes of this sort account in large part for differences in the EEG in certain neuropsychiatric conditions, the incidence of which varies with age.

Metabolic Rate, Heart Rate, and Body Temperature. The basal metabolic rate has been found to decrease regularly from early childhood to adolescence, at which time it reaches the adult level (Lucas, Pryor, Bost, and Pope, 1933). Measurements were made on 680 children between the ages of 3 and 18. In this study, the findings of other investigators were quoted to establish the fact that parallel changes occur in heart rate and in body temperature, heart rate showing a progressive decrease until the adult level is reached, and the body temperature being lower for adults than for young children. In harmony with these findings is the report that energy expenditure (average calories per kilogram per hour) decreases with age in a group of subjects between 7 and 14 years of age (C. M. Taylor, Lamb, Robertson, and MacLeod, 1948). This was found to be true during both quiet play and cycling.

In adolescence, it is said that on the average basal metabolism decreases, pulse rate diminishes, systolic blood pressure increases, and the total respiratory volume increases (Shock, 1944a). Individual children frequently show sudden and rapid changes in physiological characteristics, and different children vary greatly in the rate of physiological maturation.

After adulthood is reached, heart rate shows no significant change with age (Malmo and Shagass, 1949c). Heart-rate variability under stress, on the other hand, was found to decrease in linear fashion with age in both a group of psychiatric patients (13 to 63 years) and a group of normal subjects (18 to 39 years) (Malmo and Shagass, 1949c). The investigators suggest that the decrease in lability of the heart rate with age is the result of diminished autonomic nervous system influence, both vagal and sympathetic, which is believed to occur as the individual grows older.

Sex Differences in Measures of Activation

Sex differences appear to exist in some of the indicators of activation. Evidence of such differences has been found in the course of reviewing the literature on other subjects. No systematic survey of the topic has, however, been undertaken.

Most measures of arousal have been reported either to show no difference between the sexes or to show a difference in the direction of a higher degree of activation on the part of females.

In rats, females have been reported to be consistently more active than males (Rundquist, 1933; Brody, 1942). One investigator is said to have found that, in an unselected group of rats, the activity of the males was only 56 per cent of that of the females (Rundquist, 1933). Differences in activity level appear to be correlated with differences in metabolic rate. In one study a correlation coefficient of .72 ± .09 was reported between the two (V. E. Hall and M. Lindsay, 1938); in another study the mean metabolic rate of an active strain of rats was found to be significantly higher than that of an inactive strain (Rundquist and Bellis, 1933).

In dogs, the heart rates of females were significantly higher than those of males when stimulation was minimal (Fuller, 1948). Under intense stimulation, however, this difference was greatly reduced.

In human subjects, greater tension of the muscles of the upper extremities, shoulders, back, and thorax was found in a group of 64 women than in a group of 46 men (Lundervold, 1952). Electromyograms showed "resting activity," or activity at the time of insertion of the electrode, in 81 per cent of the women and in only 37 per cent of the men. Other investigators have reported shorter periods of relaxation in the electromyograms of women than of men (Ruesch and Finesinger, 1943).

Electroencephalograms have been variously reported to show no characteristic correlated with sex (Brazier and Finesinger, 1944); to show higher alpha frequencies for females than for males, both in childhood and in adulthood (Henry, 1944; Kennard, Rabinovitch, and Fister, 1955; Lindsley, 1938); and to show a higher percentage of fast activity, including beta rhythms, in females and a higher percentage of alpha rhythms in males (Kennard et al., 1955; Henry, 1944; Mundy-Castle, 1951). Though at least one investigator has reported more theta activity in females (Mundy-Castle, 1951), this report seems questionable in view of the fact that other investigators appear to have found either no sex differences in slow activity or a greater incidence of theta rhythm in males (Henry, 1944; Kennard et al., 1955).

The body temperature of women, taken at the time of a basal metabolism test, was found to be slightly higher than that of men (Jenkins, 1932). Heart-rate variability was also said to be somewhat greater in women (Malmo and Shagass, 1949c).

Girls in each of four age groups (7, 8, 9, and 10 years) showed greater volar skin conductance and a shorter mean heart period than boys of the corresponding age (Wenger and Ellington, 1943). The critical ratios of the differences for volar skin conductance closely approached significance, while those for heart period indicated a less dependable relationship. Measures of dermographia persistence, palmar conductance, respiration period, systolic blood pressure, and diastolic blood pressure for the same subjects failed to show consistent sex differences.

Between the ages of 12 and 18 years, girls have been reported to show a tendency toward a higher level of skin resistance than boys of similar ages, though differences significant at the .01 level were not found until after the age of 16 (H. E. Jones, 1949; W. D. Obrist, 1948). In this instance, the degree of activation was greater for males.

No sex differences in the type of galvanic skin responses were found when the responses were grouped into three categories on the basis of the number of reactions in the absence of observed stimulation and the tendency toward a stable or an unstable resistance level (Mundy-Castle and McKiever, 1953).

Sex differences in metabolic rate appear to vary with variations in the age of the subjects. The average basal metabolic rate of 169 girls between the ages of 3 and 9 years was found to be plus 10 per cent, and that of 140 boys of this age group, plus 14 per cent (Lucas, Pryor, Bost, and Pope, 1933). A group of 134 girls between the ages of 10 and 18 years had, however, an average metabolic rate of plus 2½ per cent, while 130 boys of similar age had an average rate of plus ½ of one per cent. Apparently, in this measure, the relationship between the sexes reverses itself at adolescence.

In a study of autonomic and skeletal-muscle responses to certain pictures, R. C. Davis and Buchwald (1957) found sex differences which may well be related to the nature of the stimuli and might not hold for other types of stimulation. In three variables, pulse-cycle duration and breathing time and amplitude, females showed a greater response than males, but the muscular tension change, and the change in all the measures combined, was greater for males than for females. The investigators suggest that the males respond more in distal, and the females in axial, regions, with the choice of measures in this study favoring the finding of greater total responses for males. They point out also that the smaller responses of the females in more distal areas would not necessarily mean lower female responsiveness in this sector, but could imply the opposite, i.e., "that the distal mechanisms are already so excited that our stimuli are working near an asymptote." They found certain hints that the latter interpretation might be the correct one, but the evidence was insufficient for drawing a conclusion.

From these and other studies, it appears that both sex and age are factors which must be considered in making comparisons between groups.

SUMMARY AND CONCLUSIONS

Evidence has been cited which tends to support the conclusion that individuals differ to a marked degree in the extent of activation in the same situation; that these differences in activation tend to persist and to characterize the individual; and that, in general, the individual who responds with a high degree of activation in one situation is likely, as compared with other individuals, to respond with a high degree of activation in other situations also. Justification is thus given for conceiving of some individuals as being excitable or responsive, and for conceiving of other individuals as being phlegmatic or unresponsive.

There are few data available which permit us to determine the extent to which such a characterization remains valid throughout the life span of the individual. Most of the investigations of consistency in this aspect of behavior have covered a period of a few months or, at most, a few years. Since they have shown that the degree of consistency varies with the span of time, it is reasonable to assume that such characterizations are not immutable. Variations in the tendency toward a high or toward a low degree of activation might be expected to occur with variations in the developmental cycle, with infections and physical trauma, and, most significantly perhaps, with variations in environmental demands or problems of adjustment. A considerable degree of consistency in the extent of activation appears, however, to be provided by such constitutional factors as type of nervous system and endocrine system, and by established habits of meeting a situation in one way or in another. Genetic and environmental factors are thus seen to interact in producing differences in the degree of activation.

Age differences have been reported in most of the measures of activation. Sex differences have been reported in some of them. It seems probable that there are true differences in the ease of arousal at different periods of the life span, and it is at least possible that the female sex is, on the average, more easily activated than the male. In rats there is evidence that both age and sex affect the level of activity (Brody, 1942). Overt activity, however, is not synonymous with the level of arousal.

chapter 10

Behavioral correlates of individual differences in activation

Though consistent individual differences in almost every known indicator of activation are clearly established, the behavioral correlates
of these differences are less certainly known. In fact, the majority of
investigations of the relationship between physiological variables and
various aspects of the normal personality have produced results of a
rather disappointing nature. The relationships discovered have usually
been slight and not very definitely proved. It is not necessary, however,
to assume an absence of relationship in order to account for this state
of affairs. Before discussing some of the factors which may be responsible for it, I shall review a few of the studies in which covariation in behavior and in one or more of the indicators of activation has
been either suggested or established.

Well-designed studies of differences in activation of normal individuals are relatively few. In such a situation we face the choice of
omitting altogether this topic of discussion or presenting such presumptive evidence as is available, even where statistical treatment,
sampling, or controls appear to be inadequate. The latter course has
been chosen since it has the advantage of indicating the significance
of the area of investigation, of suggesting possible relationships, and
of focusing attention upon certain opinions about which there appears
to be striking agreement among investigators. In the present chapter
only those studies will be reviewed which have sought to establish
relationships between variables in a presumably normal population.

Comparisons between normal subjects and behavioral deviates will be discussed in Chapter 11.

Activation may vary in degree or level, and it may vary in constancy, or the extent to which there are fluctuations in the measures of activation. It may vary also in the speed of "recovery" from the effects of stimulation. Each of these aspects of activation will be discussed separately.

THE DEGREE OF ACTIVATION

A number of lines of evidence converge to suggest that individuals who, as compared with other individuals, tend to respond to situations with a high degree of arousal, tend to differ from these other individuals in other characteristics also. This conclusion would follow if it is indeed true, as suggested in Part II, that the level of activation has some influence, however small, upon sensory sensitivity, reaction time, the co-ordination of responses, and other behavioral phenomena. The aspect of behavior which appears to be most closely related to differences in the characteristic degree of activation is that of excitability or responsiveness. If such a statement is regarded as tautological, it may be pointed out that indicators of the degree of activation are seldom employed in clinical assessments of personality, where the degree of responsiveness of an individual is a factor of major importance. Physiological responsiveness and general behavioral responsiveness should, it is contended, be regarded as two sides of the same coin. Moreover, differences in responsiveness appear to be the basis of many further differences in behavior, including perhaps some aspects of the differences called abnormal.

Individuals who are exceptionally responsive to the environment may show their responsiveness in behavior which, from a directional point of view, may be described in diverse ways. A tendency toward a high degree of activation does not determine which aspects of the environment an individual will approach or will have a tendency to approach (i.e., have a favorable attitude toward); nor does it determine which aspects of the environment he will withdraw from or have a tendency to withdraw from (i.e., have an unfavorable attitude toward.) On the contrary, the orientation of the individual in his environment is determined largely by other factors. These are, of course, the factors, both genetic and environmental, which have given to various aspects of his environment the nature of their significance, or their "cue-function." There are, nevertheless, differences in the dynamic aspects of approach or withdrawal responses which appear to be direct or indirect expressions of differences in the level of activation. Among these may be mentioned differences in such characteristics of behavior as alertness, impulsiveness, irritability, distractibility, and the degree of organization of responses. Moreover, greater responsiveness may, it appears, facilitate the development of aggression or withdrawal, enthusiasm or anxiety. The more responsive individual in a certain kind of environment is no doubt more susceptible to the effects of that environment. It would seem that he may become, depending upon circumstances, more anxiety-prone, more conscientious, more sympathetic, more devoted, or more irascible than a less responsive person would become under similar circumstances. We should therefore expect to find an association between a high degree of activation and easily aroused or intense responses of various kinds (e.g., anxieties, resentments, enthusiasms, or attachments). From knowing the individual's tendencies with respect to activation we should not, however, be able to predict the direction which his behavior would take. A more dependable association might be expected between individual differences in activation and differences in the "dynamic" characteristics of behavior such as those mentioned above.

Unfortunately there are relatively few studies to which we may turn for support or denial of these hypotheses. Physiological psychologists have, with a few notable exceptions, been little interested in individual differences, and students of personality have seldom been interested in physiological psychology. There are, however, some studies of individual differences which have a bearing on the problem.

Biochemical Differences

Early attempts to discover physiological differences associated with differences in the personality of normal individuals were focused primarily upon biochemical factors. From the well-known studies of Ludlum (1918), of Starr (1922), and of Rich (1928) there emerged the suggestion that individuals who tend to excrete an alkaline saliva and urine are more excitable or emotionally unstable than those whose excretions are more acid. In a review of studies of the acid-base balance, Shock (1944b) points out that, while animal studies show that muscles and nerves are more easily excited under conditions of increased alkalinity, studies on human beings have failed to yield clear-cut results in regard to complex behavior. Nevertheless, Hamilton and Shock found greater alkalinity of the blood in more excitable individuals (Shock, 1944b). They attributed this finding to the fact that excitable persons, when confronted with what would now be called a "stress" situation, rendered their blood more alkaline by changes in respiration. Shock also states that slight displacements of the acid-base balance toward the alkaline side are associated with subjective reports of well-being, while other investigators are said to have found that slight displacements toward the acid side are associated with depression.

At approximately the same time that the studies of Ludlum and Starr were taking place, Hammett (1921) was investigating the hypothesis that differences in "temperament" are associated with differences in the manner in which individuals handle their intermediary metabolism. He reported that excitable individuals, as compared with phlegmatic ones, showed greater total variability of the soluble nitrogenous constituents of the blood stream as determined by analyses made from week to week. He conceived of bodily constitution as influencing behavior, and of behavior as influencing bodily constitution.

Since chemical as well as neural factors are known to affect the level of activation, it may be presumed that the constituents of the blood stream will show covariation with variations in activation. It remains uncertain, however, whether there are consistent differences in behavior which correspond with these variations. It is known that changes in the composition of the blood stream must occur within fairly narrow limits if life is to be preserved (Cannon, 1939). Are there, in spite of homeostatic correction, consistent differences in blood components which bear a constant relationship to differences in behavior? Some investigations suggest that this may be the case. No attempt will be made, however, to survey the studies in this area since the present undertaking already has more than sufficient scope. Attention may nevertheless be directed to the possibility that, if individual differences in the particular contents of the blood stream are not of significance in relation to personality, differences in the degree of variability in blood constituents may be related to such differences. One investigator reported, for example, that basal biochemical determinations (inorganic phosphorus, cholesterol, sugar, chlorides, calcium, creatinine) made at intervals of three weeks showed no significant correlation with each other, and hence were of no value as guides to personality (Goldstein, 1935). The degree of variability of the blood contents conceivably, however, bore some relationship to "emotional stability," as was suggested by a not-quite-significant correlation coefficient of $+.41 \pm .13$ between the degree of metabolic variability and neurotic tendencies as measured by the Bernreuter Personality Inventory. Other studies have suggested that abnormality of behavior (at least in its acute stages) may be associated with a high degree of variability in the contents of the blood stream. More recently there has been interest in a possible relationship between a particular chemical excretion, hippuric acid, and the degree of anxiety experienced by normal subjects in a controlled situation which was different from the one in which the hippuric acid determinations had been made (Basowitz, Persky, Korchin, and Grinker, 1955). An attempt was also made to relate this chemical variable to certain responses of psychiatric patients (Persky, Grinker, Mirsky, and Gamm, 1950).

Electrical Resistance of the Skin

Studies of the electrical resistance of the skin have a long history; nevertheless, dependable data on the correlates of individual differences in skin resistance are relatively few. In many studies, skin resistance has been investigated either in conjunction with other physiological measures or as a means of deriving a "Recovery Quotient" representing the speed of recovery from the effects of stimulation. These studies will be discussed in a later section of this chapter.

Among the studies which might be mentioned in the present section is one by Haggard (1943) in which, using a relatively small number of subjects (eighteen), and presenting no extensive statistical treatment of his data, he reported that subjects who showed the "greatest degree of autonomic activity" (i.e., skin conductance) at the end of an experimental session in which they had taken an association test and had been given electric shocks, showed a tendency to respond with larger GSR's ($r = .55$), to manifest less adaptation to the shock ($r = .62$), to show a more variable level of "autonomic activity" ($r = .51$), and to recall fewer stimulus words at the end of the session ($r = .53$).

Mentioned in Landis' (1932) extensive review of investigations of the electrical phenomena of the skin, is a study by Weiss and Lauer in which accident-prone automobile drivers were said to show consistently greater intensity of galvanic responses to sensory stimuli than those who were safe drivers, and a study by Lauer and Evans in which a correlation coefficient of $-.42$ was reported between skin resistance and intelligence. Neither of these findings is inconsistent with the hypothesis that lower and more unstable skin resistance is indicative of greater responsiveness.

More direct evidence was obtained from twenty-two subjects whose skin-resistance tracings were recorded while they were alert with minimal external stimulation (E. Z. Levy, Thaler, and Ruff, 1958). Subjects who could relax easily gave in general hyper-responsive tracings, while those who could not relax easily gave hyporesponsive tracings. The explanation of this finding may conceivably be due to the fact that hyper-responsive subjects had approached their ceiling of response before the administration of the mild stimulation.

In a differential conditioning experiment, it was found that the adequately conditioned subjects (US was an electric shock) had higher conductance levels and showed less decrease in conductance levels in the course of the experiment (P. A. Obrist, 1958). It appeared that the change in conductance was independent of the basal level of conductance. Adequately conditioned subjects could not be distinguished from poorly conditioned subjects by means of MMPI scales.

W. T. James (1953) points out that there appears to be a constitutional factor in the difference in "emotionality" in the response of dogs to a liminal shock. His statement that "we have been so much concerned with learning, as such, that we have neglected" the study of the relationship between "emotionality" and "excitability or inhibitive tendencies" appears to be valid. James points out that we do not know whether a dog that reacts vigorously to mild pain ever can be trained to inhibit this response.

There are a number of studies in which measures of skin resistance, considered singly or in conjunction with other physiological measures, have been compared with responses on the Rorschach test which have sometimes been said to be indicative of "emotion." A group of normal subjects who showed "color shock" on the test were reported to be significantly different in total palmar skin resistance changes during the test from a group who showed no color shock (Rockwell, Welch, Kubis, and Fisichelli, 1947). Other investigators have failed, however, to find a significant difference between the skin-resistance responses of normal subjects to colored and uncolored plates (Levy, 1948), or to find that color and noncolor Rorschach responses can be distinguished by differences in galvanic skin responses, heart rate, blood pressure, or respiration (Hughes, Epstein, and Jost, 1951).

J. I. Lacey and his associates (J. I. Lacey, Bateman, and Van Lehn, 1952) reported a correlation coefficient of +.47, significant at the .02 level, between the Form-Color Index of the Rorschach test and the maximum physiological response in four different stress situations.[1] The measures employed were palmar conductance, heart rate, and heart-rate variability. When, however, individual physiological measures in each of the stress situations were correlated with the Form-Color Index, the only variable with which the index showed a significant relationship was palmar conductance during the cold-pressor

[1] All measures were represented by T-scores.

test ($r = +.43$). These findings with respect to the Rorschach test were not verified in the same laboratory with a different Rorschach examiner, a different group of subjects, and a different context with respect to the interaction between the subject and the Rorschach examiner (J. I. Lacey, 1959). Other investigators have, however, reported that the use of the maximum physiological response as the criterion of physiological reactivity produced correlations with a number of psychological variables, whereas certain other ways of evaluating autonomic reactivity failed to do so (Vogel, Baker, and Lazarus, 1958).

The Electroencephalogram (EEG)

The clinical use of electroencephalography has developed rapidly. Studies of the behavior disorders have been followed by studies of individual differences in the electroencephalograms of presumably normal subjects. Again, as with other indicators of activation, there is both direct and indirect evidence that differences in this measure are associated with differences in responsiveness or excitability. In fact, such differences in ease of arousal may well be the basis of a number of the more specific differences in behavior which have been reported.

A series of studies by Mundy-Castle and his collaborators support the suggestion that certain characteristics of the EEG are indicative of differences in excitability (Mundy-Castle, 1953a; Mundy-Castle, 1953b; Mundy-Castle and McKiever, 1953). A significant relationship was found in normal adults between the frequency of the alpha rhythm and ratings on the behavioral continuum called by Heymans (1929) and Wiersma (1932) "primary-secondary function" ($r = .46$, $P = .01$). Individuals in whom the alpha rhythm was more rapid tended to show more "primary functioning," or to be "quick, impulsive, variable, and highly stimulable." Those with relatively low frequencies of the alpha rhythm tended to show more "secondary functioning," or to be "slow, cautious, steady, with an even mood and psychic tempo. . . ." Mundy-Castle hypothetically ascribed these behavioral differences to differences in excitability within the central nervous system, the primary functioning individuals showing the greater excitability. On this basis he accounted for the fact that both Wiersma (1932) and Biesheuvel (1935) found a higher critical fusion frequency associated with less secondary function.[2] He also employed this hypothesis to account for his own finding of a significant difference in the EEG activity evoked

[2] Mundy-Castle (1953b) points out, however, that the correspondence between alpha frequency and flicker-response characteristics is far from perfect, and that a

by rhythmic photic stimulation in subjects with a mean alpha frequency above 10.3 cycles per second and those with a mean alpha
frequency below that rate.[3] The significantly greater incidence of second and third harmonics in the evoked responses of those with the
more rapid alpha rhythm (and more primary functioning) was attributed to more rapid trains of neural impulses being generated by
the visual stimuli, which in turn would favor discharge rates in the
optic nerve trunk at double or treble the stimulus frequency, and would
be reflected as second and third harmonics respectively. A significant
association was found between the occurrence of these harmonics and
the existence of spontaneous beta rhythm. Greater neural excitability
was also the basis of explanation of the greater incidence of "following"[4] in the beta range by those subjects showing little alpha rhythm,
even when the eyes were closed, as compared with those subjects
showing persistent alpha rhythms. It was suggested that, in the former, the receptors might be able to maintain a higher discharge-rate
and the cortical neurones show individual responses at higher frequencies.

In a later report, Mundy-Castle (1957) cites a significant correlation coefficient of .464 between the frequency of the alpha rhythm
and the evaluation of temperament, and a coefficient of .61 between
the alpha-rhythm frequency and a battery of psychological, speed,
and tempo tests. Among the motor tests correlating significantly with
the frequency of the alpha rhythm were speed of tapping ($r = .403$),
tapping at the subject's preferred rate ($r = .381$), and rapidity of
walking ($r = .332$).

Gastaut and his collaborators have also reported individual differences in cortical excitability (H. Gastaut, Y. Gastaut, Roger, Corriol,
and Naquet, 1951). They studied, by means of photic conditioning
stimuli and test stimuli, the "cycle of excitability," or the modifications
which occurred in the excitability of a population of neurones follow-

_____

better understanding of factors contributing to variations in the frequency of the
alpha rhythm is required before the relationship between these measures can be
regarded as more than an indirect and somewhat obscure reflection of individual
differences in "temperament."

[3] The process by which electrical rhythms in the brain can be evoked is believed
to be similar to that of resonance (Mundy-Castle, 1953b). If rhythmic stimulation
corresponding to the latent or actual frequency of the electrical activity of a given
area of the brain is applied, it is thought that oscillation may occur in that area
of the brain for as long as stimulation is maintained. Activation may also be produced, it is thought, by harmonically related stimulation.

[4] "Following" refers to electrical responses in the cortex occurring at the stimulus frequency.

ing preliminary excitation. While their major purpose was not the investigation of individual differences, they made the incidental observation that calm individuals had a slow, high-voltage alpha rhythm (8 to 10 cycles per second), with little "driving" of occipital rhythms by photic stimulation. Neurones showed a long recuperation time, synchrony of response was said to be noticeable, and recruitment poor. "Nervous" individuals, on the other hand, were said to have a high-frequency, low-voltage alpha rhythm (10 to 13 cycles per second), which at times was not perceptible. They were described as having a short neuronal recuperation time, little synchrony of response, good recruitment, and considerable driving by photic stimulation. In other words, "calm" as compared with "nervous" individuals showed less cortical excitability.

According to Gastaut's (H. Gastaut, 1954) concept of the "excitability cycle," neurone systems are able to reorganize nervous messages either by variations in the excitability of each neurone, producing a corresponding amplification or damping of signals, or by dividing the neurones into functional groups in which the waves are out of phase, the frequency of each group being that of the EEG rhythm. A balance between the two ways in which nervous messages may be reorganized produces the optimal condition for the "coding" of impulses and is perhaps the reason the alpha frequency is rather strictly regulated at about 10 cycles per second. The individual with more rapid rhythms would have more functional groups at his disposal and would therefore have more information transmitted and be more quickly disturbed by an excess of information. The individual with slower alpha rhythms would have a lower rate of transmission of neural impulses and would be insufficiently informed. A lack of stability in the regulation of cortical excitability would produce constant variation between the two extremes of hyperexcitability and hypoexcitability. Werre (1957, p. 77) has reported that Gastaut (H. Gastaut, 1954), making use of these concepts and citing the findings of various investigators, suggests three types of personality which are found in association with three types of EEG. They are as follows:

The hyperexcitability syndrome

The EEG has "rare and rapid alpha rhythms (11 to 13 cycles per second) of small amplitude, grouped in short bursts on desynchronized activity. Beta waves (15 to 20 cycles per second) in the middle regions." Intermittent photic driving has been reported.

The associated personality characteristics are variously described.

Some of the terms used are strongly reacting, hypersensitive, hyper-active, nervous, unstable, dynamic, impulsive, hyperemotional, enthusiastic, and showing a tendency toward anxiety and toward leadership.

The hypoexcitability syndrome

The EEG has "frequent alpha rhythms (8 to 9 cycles per second), continuous large amplitude, no desynchronized intervals. No appreciable beta activity. No intermittent photic driving."

The associated personality characteristics are variously described as, among others, calmness, slowness, even temper, passivity, submissiveness, dependence, cautiousness, and firmness.

The lability syndrome

The description of the EEG is: "alpha rhythm (9 to 11 cycles per second) rare, associated with slower (theta) or more rapid (beta) waves or with both, very variable amplitude. Intermittent photic driving."

Among the personality characteristics said to be associated with this type of EEG are impatience, aggressiveness, violence. These individuals are said to be "calm and not anxious but susceptible to rapid and violent reactions."

Studies of 113 young soldiers (Gallais, Collomb, Miletto, Cardaire, and Blanc-Garin, 1957), of 309 cadet pilots (Picard, Navarranne, Laboureur, Grousset, and Jest, 1957), and of 100 neurotic subjects (M. Dongier, S. Dongier, G. Angel-Villegas, and A. Angel-Villegas, 1957) later led H. Gastaut (1957) to question some of his earlier conclusions in regard to the relationship between the EEG and personality.[5] He nevertheless concluded tentatively, according to Werre (1957, p. 73), that "rapid alpha rhythms (11 to 13 cycles per second), appearing as short spindleformed bursts in desynchronized EEG's (cortical hyperexcitability), are seen mainly in hypersensitive, hyperemotional, and hyperactive 'nervous' individuals," and that "slow alpha rhythms (8 to 9 cycles per second), appearing as long spindleformed bursts with periods of desynchronization (cortical hypoexcitability), are encountered mainly in slow, steady and calm subjects."

Differences in psychological characteristics associated with differ-

[5] Cadet pilots showed rather slow alpha rhythms; yet, on the basis of psychiatric interviews and tests, they were judged to show "dynamism, dominance, and aggressiveness strongly directed to the outside world." It is questionable that these characteristics necessarily indicate a high degree of responsiveness. Gastaut may therefore have been correct in his original conclusions.

ences in the electroencephalogram have also been reported by Rémond and Lesèvre (1957).[6] Studying two groups of normal adults (Air Force recruits and truckdrivers) by means of psychomotor tests, the Rorschach or Zulliger test, a personality questionnaire, a clinical examination, and other means, they reported that, when the subjects were grouped according to the total picture of the EEG (organization, distribution, and reactivity of the basic rhythm), they showed statistically significant psychological differences. Their first "electropsychological" group, characterized as hyperexcitable, was said to be composed in large part of "hyperemotional people of the impulsive type, or else people of the inhibited type." They were vulnerable to stimulation, the least stimulus being said to perturb them greatly. These subjects were slow on the psychomotor tests, presumably as a result of emotional instability rather than "real bradypsychia." Their basic EEG rhythm was "essentially complex, polyrhythmic, with a tendency to desynchronization and marked reactivity to all sensory-affective stimuli and to metabolic variations." The second group of subjects, with a basic rhythm which was "a mainly slow, monorhythmic, widely distributed, alpha rhythm which does not react much to sensory-affective stimuli," was characterized as hypoexcitable and apparently stable emotionally. On the psychomotor tests, their performance was usually slow and regular. Because of the relatively small number of subjects in this group the investigators point out the need of confirmation of their findings. The third group had a "more or less fast alpha rhythm (9 to 11 cycles per second) which appears in well-organized parieto-occipital bursts and which reacts normally to sensory-affective stimuli." These subjects showed more speed and better control on psychomotor tests, a finding attributed to their good emotional adaptation.

Again, it may be noted, there is association between hyperexcitability and desynchronization of the EEG, and between hypoexcitability and an alpha rhythm of low frequency. The subjects characterized as psychologically hyperexcitable had an EEG which was highly responsive to stimulation, while the subjects characterized as psychologically hypoexcitable had an EEG which was not very responsive to stimulation. Responsiveness is, as might be expected, a psychophysiological phenomenon.

The relationship between the EEG and the individual's responsiveness to stimulation is indicated also in a comparison of the electroencephalograms of normal subjects with deep reflexes which are difficult to elicit and those with deep reflexes which are hyperactive. Ken-

[6] All quotations from this article are translations.

nard and Willner (1945) found that the former showed a high percentage of alpha activity and little or no fast activity, while the latter
had little alpha activity and a high percentage of fast activity. Groups
at the two extremes of reflex responsiveness differed significantly in
the percentage of alpha activity, but there was wide variation in the
extent of such activity within any one of the groups formed on the
basis of reflex status. The rate of alpha activity showed some correlation with the reflex status of the individual, a finding which, as the
investigators point out, might be expected on the basis of the fact that
slow rates are more often found in records with a high percentage of
alpha activity. Amplitude of rhythm was observed to be greatest in
EEG records showing pronounced alpha activity. In summary, the
investigators (Kennard and Willner, 1945) conclude:

> Subjects with deep reflexes of high threshold, which are hence difficult
> to elicit, have EEG's which are of relatively high amplitude, high percent
> alpha activity and slow alpha rate. Those with easily elicited and active
> deep reflexes have EEG's with relatively little alpha activity, fast alpha
> rate and low amplitude. Fast activity is present to greater degree in the
> EEG's of normal individuals with high reflex activity and low percent of
> alpha activity (p. 342).

Both the type of electroencephalogram and the type of reflex activity are known to be characteristic of the individual to a considerable
degree, yet both vary in the same individual with variation in factors
affecting the general level of excitation. Kennard and Willner (1945)
point out that the extent of reflex activity may be affected by exercise,
fatigue, drugs, or excitement, and that the EEG is affected also by
such factors as produce general organic changes. The knee-jerk, for
example, is increased by large doses of Benzedrine, or ephedrine, and
these drugs also produce increased fast activity in the EEG. Alpha
activity is reduced or eliminated by failure to relax, and the extent of
the knee-jerk is in similar fashion increased during excitement and
decreased during muscular relaxation. Differences in the EEG's of different individuals under similar stimulating conditions appear to be
correlated with differences in the threshold of deep reflexes—i.e., with
differences in another form of responsiveness.

It has been noted also that individuals vary greatly in the ease of
arousal and the extent of the startle response (S. Dongier, Y. Gastaut,
and M. Dongier, 1957). Certain persons are said not to show signs of it
even when a revolver is unexpectedly discharged, while others respond
at the least sound or sudden contact. Both extremes were found to be
rare, most subjects falling somewhere between the extremes. Some

subjects gave a complete reaction, while others showed only certain elements of the response. Finally, there were individual differences in the occurrence of the response and in the speed of adaptation to the stimulation. The components of the startle response recorded were: (1) a brief muscular tremor, (2) a blocking of the alpha rhythm, (3) an evoked potential at the vertex, and (4) a galvanic skin response. The investigators conclude that the startle response is a total reaction which affects the cerebral cortex and the somatic and vegetative nervous system.

Evoked vertex potentials were suggested by Y. Gastaut (1953) to be the result of afferent impulses received by a hypersensitive cortex. One-third of the subjects who showed vertex spikes were characterized as being, not only hypersensitive to sensory stimuli, but also "hyper-emotional," "emotionally" labile, and deficient in ability to inhibit responses. Conversely, Rémond and Lesèvre (1957) found little vertex spike activity in hypoexcitable, calm subjects.

Differences in responsiveness may find expression in, or may perhaps be the result of, characteristics varying widely in directional aspects. Any correlation between these characteristics and the EEG is presumably to be attributed to the arousal, rather than to the directional, aspect of the characteristic. Among the modes of response studied in relation to the electroencephalogram are anxiety-proneness, aggression, passivity, and introversion-extroversion.

Proneness to develop anxiety under stress, as measured by psychological tests and rated in psychiatric interviews, was found by Ulett and his associates to be related to certain characteristics of the EEG as determined by automatic frequency analysis (Ulett, Gleser, Winokur, and Lawler, 1953). Subjects of the study were 151 normal persons and 40 psychiatric patients of comparable age and sex judged to have a disorder in which anxiety was a major feature. Both patients and anxiety-prone normal subjects showed a significantly smaller percentage of their resting brain-wave activity in the alpha region than did the nonanxiety-prone subjects. The anxiety-prone groups showed more fast activity (16 to 24 cycles per second) or more slow activity (3 to 7 cycles per second) below the alpha range. The EEG response to intermittent photic stimulation was found, in the anxiety-prone subjects, to be least for stimulus frequencies at or near the alpha range and to be greater for higher or lower frequencies. If the response to photic stimulation is, as has been claimed by certain investigators (Ostow, 1949; Toman, 1941), greatest at or near the dominant frequency of the resting EEG, this finding would be consistent with the report that anxiety-prone subjects show less resting alpha activity. Many subjects, however, who did not show a fast or slow resting record showed, under photic stimulation, a predominance of response ("driving") in the extreme ranges, or showed marked harmonic responses in the higher frequencies, thus showing a readiness to respond at these frequencies. For the normal subjects, there was a correlation coefficient of .42 between ratings on characteristics of the EEG and the criterion rating on anxiety. With the psychiatric patients included, the coefficient was .51.

Fast activity may be presumed to be indicative of a high level of activation. It has been observed, for example, at the beginning of EEG recording in normal subjects who are unusually apprehensive about the procedure, and it has been found to disappear with reassurance and the attainment of relaxation (Lindsley, 1944). Slow activity (theta and sometimes delta) has been found in adults during the showing of "shocking and horrifying" motion pictures (Melin, 1953). Both Faure (1950) and W. G. Walter (1954b) have reported an increase in the amount of theta activity when a person is disturbed, anxious, or annoyed during the recording of the EEG. Darrow (1947) comments that "a normal alpha rhythm . . . apparently requires that there be neither great excess nor great deficiency in the conditions favoring cortical activity" and points to a well-developed alpha rhythm as indicating an absence of excessive tension. In fact, he finds evidence to support the view that in "emotionally less stable" individuals there is a tendency for the slow alpha-like or theta activity in precentral portions of the brain to be increased by stimulation (Darrow, 1953).

Fast activity in the EEG was also reported by Kennard, Rabinovitch, and Fister (1955) to be associated particularly with anxiety. Thirty-three prison farm inmates, forty-four schizophrenics, and fifty controls were given a group of psychological tests (Rorschach, Bender-Gestalt, Shipley-Hartford, and Wechsler-Bellevue). EEG's recorded from frontal, motor, parietal, and occipital regions were subjected to frequency analysis. Though no statistical tests of significance are reported, it is said that activity at 16 to 20 cycles per second was found in all records, but that activity above this rate appeared in significant amounts only in the records of those who, as rated by the psychological tests, showed anxiety to a marked degree. Slow activity (theta) was not very prevalent, but when it did occur was found most often among the patients. Single scoring categories of the Rorschach test showed no reliable relationship to EEG patterns. Subjects whose Rorschach responses indicated anxiety showed, however, significantly different EEG patterns from those of subjects whose responses did not.

These and other studies suggest that anxiety-proneness may be conceived of as a particular form of over-responsiveness. The EEG's of the anxiety-prone seem very similar in most instances to the EEG's of other normal subjects whose exceptional responsiveness to the environment is indicated by active reflexes or by ratings on "primary function." If this is the case, the EEG pattern of anxiety is indicative, not of anxiety, but of degree of responsiveness. Only by showing that the pattern is evoked more easily or in more marked degree by certain kinds of stimuli than by others, can it be demonstrated that the EEG characteristics found in the anxiety-prone have any closer relationship to anxiety than to any other kind of responsiveness. It appears that anxiety may be conceived of as over-responsiveness which takes a particular direction. Difficult to reconcile with this interpretation, however, is the fact that rhythms of low frequency (theta) have sometimes been reported in anxious patients. This question will be discussed in the chapter which follows.

"Passivity," as judged during psychoanalytic treatment, has been said to be associated with a high alpha index, i.e., the percentage of time that a readable alpha rhythm is found in the EEG of a subject who is awake and relaxed (Saul, H. Davis, and P. A. Davis, 1949). Passive individuals were reported to show considerable alpha activity, usually of low frequency (8.5 to 10.5 cycles per second). Women with strong "masculine trends" (independent, dominant, drive to activity and leadership) were found to have EEG's with little alpha activity. Sisson and Ellingson (1955) considered the evidence for these conclusions unconvincing, as they did that of subsequent studies by other investigators reporting similar conclusions. H. Gastaut and his collaborators are also said not to have been able to confirm the correlation (Werre, 1957).

Findings in regard to the relationship between the EEG and Rorschach scores have been various. L. E. Travis and Bennett (1953) reported that normal subjects with an alpha index over 50 gave significantly more whole responses (W per cent) than those with an alpha index below 50, while those with the lower alpha index gave significantly more total responses (R), color responses (sum C), unusual details plus space responses (Dd, 5 per cent), more absolute whole responses (W), and took significantly more time on the test. They tentatively suggested that individuals with a high alpha index had a "passive-receptive manner of organizing stimuli." Sisson and Ellingson (1955) point out that their brief report does not make it clear how these conclusions were deduced from the Rorschach data.

Other findings with the Rorschach test include those of Brudo and

Darrow (1953), who found a significant rank-order correlation of .532 between the alpha index and the incidence of human movement responses (*M*) in 11 normal children, and a correlation coefficient of .636 for 10 behavior problem children with possible brain damage; and those of Sisson and Ellingson (1955), who found no significant differences in Rorschach scores between a group of 15 male neuropsychiatric patients with alpha indices over 90 and a similar group of 15 with alpha indices under 10.

Electroencephalographic studies by Werre (1957), in which the psychological characteristics of 30 subjects were judged on the basis of an interview and of the Rorschach, Wiggly Blocks and Four Picture Tests, led him to report a lack of agreement with Saul et al. (1949) and certain other investigators in regard to passivity, but some concurrence with Mundy-Castle (1956) in regard to primary-secondary functioning. Subjects with "psychic tensions, often leading to anxiety" were found, as reported by others, to have EEG waves of relatively higher frequency (in this instance, more beta waves). An attempt was made to relate the EEG to various other characteristics, such as self-confidence and reaction to frustration, but without success.

Extroversion has been reported to be associated with greater alpha activity (Gottlober, 1938), but this finding has been challenged by other investigators (Henry and Knott, 1941).

Correlation between the EEG and the directional aspect of behavior is, as we have pointed out, scarcely to be expected, except as differences in responsiveness may affect or reflect the direction of behavior. The extent of the relationship of the EEG to a given behavioral characteristic (or trait) will be determined in large part, it appears, by the extent to which the characteristic incorporates differences in activation. Since anxious or highly motivated individuals may be presumed to have a higher level of activation than care-free or easy-going individuals, their EEG's might be expected to be different from those of such individuals. The EEG could not be expected, however, to differentiate, for example, between "anxiety" and other modes of behavior showing a high degree of arousal.

Differences in Muscle Tension

One of the earliest attempts to relate measured individual differences in "spontaneous" muscle tension to the behavioral characteristics of normal subjects was made by Buford Johnson (1928), who reported grip-pressure differences which appeared to be related to differences in a motor performance. After this study, the author investigated the relationship between consistent differences in grip pressure and differences in personality (Duffy, 1930). Despite the fact that the number of subjects was small and the statistical treatment of data was simple—defects which were characteristic of the period—the findings of this study have in essential respects been confirmed by later investigations. The strength of the study lay no doubt in the fact that muscle tension was measured on eleven nonconsecutive days in the same controlled situation, rather than on a single occasion. The "tension" score assigned to an individual was the mean of these eleven measurements. Subjects of the study were nursery-school children assigned the task of making discrimination responses. Grip pressure was recorded from the unused hand, and ratings on excitability were secured from the nursery-school staff. The two measures showed a rank-difference coefficient of correlation of $+.56 \pm .15$.

A later study, with a different group of subjects in a different nursery school, lent support to the earlier findings (Duffy, 1932a). It was shown that during successive performances of the same task (discrimination responses) and during the performance of a different task (tapping), the subjects ($N = 18$) tended to maintain their respective ranks in muscle tension. Grip-pressure scores were shown to be independent of the strength of grip as indicated by dynamometer scores, but to be related to ratings on excitability and on adjustment to the nursery school. The rank-order coefficient of correlation between the ratings on excitability and the mean tension scores in the used and unused hands during five experimental sessions was $.60 \pm .11$.[7] The coefficient of mean square contingency between average muscle-tension scores and ratings on school adjustment was $.58$.[8]

Nursery-school records for the subjects of the first study, as mentioned, supported the hypothesis that individuals with greater muscle tension, as measured by grip pressure, are more excitable than subjects

[7] Rating instructions were as follows: "Rank the children from highest to lowest in excitability, i.e., tendency to become excited. This trait should not necessarily be identified with 'emotionality' or 'instability.' Excitable individuals are often described as 'keyed-up,' 'high-strung,' 'tense,' or 'stirred-up.'" Traits mentioned by the nursery school teachers as having influenced their ratings were high, shrill voice, screaming, exuberance, nervous tension, intense and frequent manifestations of emotion, and type of reaction when asked for any reason to leave the room.

[8] The physician and the nurse at the Child Development Institute were asked to classify the subjects into three categories on the basis of their adjustment to the nursery school. It is apparent that these ratings on adjustment are related to measures of grip pressure to approximately the same degree as are the ratings on excitability made by the nursery-school teachers.

with less muscle tension. Since, however, two out of three of the subjects with high tension scores had irregular pressure tracings, and all five of the subjects with relatively low tension scores had rather smooth tracings, it is possible that the degree of regularity of the pressure, rather than the extent of the pressure, is the variable associated with certain modes of behavior. Conceivably, the degree of pressure may be indicative of the degree of responsiveness, while the presence of marked irregularity of pressure may be indicative of poor control of responses.

Other possible relationships between tension measures and behavior are suggested by data from the second of the two nursery schools in which these investigations were conducted (Duffy, 1932c). Several investigators had collected other data which were then studied by the author in relation to muscular tension. A negative relationship appeared to exist between tension scores and number of physical contacts on the playground ($r = -.46 \pm .15$), and especially between tension scores and contacts judged to be intentional ($r = -.73 \pm .09$). There was also some slight indication, of no scientific validity, that high scores for muscle tension might be associated with speaking fewer words, using small muscle groups more often than large muscle groups, performing less well in tracing a figure, being below the average in weight, and being restless, impulsive, or inattentive. Certainly none of these relationships was established. If, however, the observations should be confirmed, the tense child would appear to be very responsive but, in many instances, not active physically. It might be surmised that greater excitability would lead to overt activity which was either noticeably greater or noticeably less than the mean of the group. Social reactions to others, whether in speech or in playground behavior, might well be affected by the greater responsiveness to stimulation which presumably characterizes the child with a high level of activation. At the present time, however, such suggestions lack the empirical evidence which would be required to remove them from the category of speculations.

A study of the relationship between muscle tension and one type of responsiveness in adults was carried out by Freeman and Katzoff (1932). Grip-pressure scores were correlated with scores on the Cason Common Annoyance Test, and a rank-order coefficient of correlation of $+.49 \pm .07$ was reported. Subjects with higher pressure scores tended to be more frequently or intensely annoyed by everyday occurrences. They were described as being more "irritable."

I. Martin (1958) failed to find any significant differences in muscle tension of either the frontalis muscle or the right-forearm extensor muscles between male university students in any of the four following groups selected on the basis of scales for the measurement of neuroticism and of introversion-extroversion: (1) introverted neurotics, (2) extroverted neurotics, (3) introverted normals, and (4) extroverted normals.

Other Measures

Measures of basal metabolism, pulse rate, blood pressure, finger volume, and other physiological conditions have been studied in relation to behavioral characteristics.

In an early study of the relationship of basal metabolism to test scores on introversion-extroversion, Herrington (1930) found a higher metabolic rate for the introvert group. He believed this finding was due to the greater susceptibility of the test-introvert to excitement, an effect which required considerable time to adapt (Herrington, 1942). If his assumption is correct, the introverts would, by the criteria employed here, be considered more responsive, or more highly activated. As Herrington points out, this physiological difference is not peculiar to the introvert-extrovert axis.

In a later study Herrington (1942) investigated the relationship between rated "general activity and drive" and measures of mean basal metabolic rate, pulse rate, respiratory rate, and systolic blood pressure, as well as indices of variability in these functions. The raters were asked, in judging activity and drive, to consider "(1) physical vigor as suggested by athletic pursuits, speed of movement, and typical postures at work or when idle, (2) excitable speech and pressure for expression in group situations, (3) energy and enthusiasm in meeting class work requirements." It seems likely that some of these characteristics would show no correlation with each other, unless indeed the correlation were a negative one. "Physical vigor as suggested by athletic pursuits" does not, for example, seem likely to be positively associated with "excitable speech" or with other indicators of excitability. Though the excitable individual readily expends energy, his vitality may be low, and he may perhaps be less likely, rather than more likely, to engage in athletic pursuits. Judging from the physiological correlates of the ratings obtained by Herrington, it may be surmised that his raters placed somewhat more emphasis upon the indications of excitability than upon those of vigor. There is, however, no certainty in regard to this conclusion.

The subjects of the investigation were eleven medical students, studied intensively under exceptionally favorable conditions for obtaining knowledge of their behavior and securing accurate measurements of their physiological functioning. Each physiological measurement of a subject was repeated on 45 days, under controlled conditions of living as well as of measurement. It was found that the mean pulse rate showed a correlation of .81 ± .10 with the ratings on activity and drive. Mean basal metabolic rate, respiratory rate, and systolic blood pressure, when correlated with the ratings, gave coefficients of .45 ± .26, .44 ± .26, and .24 ± .29, respectively. Of the variability measures, the one most closely related to the ratings was blood-pressure variability, which had a coefficient of correlation of .56 ± .22. By combining blood-pressure variability with mean pulse rate, the activity rating was predicted with a multiple coefficient of the order of .90. No cross-validation was, however, attempted. While regarding the obtained coefficient conservatively because of the small number of subjects, the investigator suggests that the rated characteristic is correlated with physiological signs which are indicative of much more general properties of the autonomic nervous system. Perhaps the relatively close relationship between certain physiological and behavioral measures reported in this study is due to the extreme care with which the investigation was carried out, the repetition of the measurements, and the fact that the behavioral correlates studied were more closely related to the arousal than to the directional aspect of behavior.

Another study in which the basal metabolic rate was considered in relation to the arousal aspect of behavior was made by Omwake, Dexter, and Lewis (1934). A slight difference was found between the median metabolic rate of twenty college students rated by their classmates as "peppy" and that of twenty rated as "calm" (+2.0 vs. −3.4). The range of metabolic rates of the middle 50 per cent of those rated as "peppy" was from 6 to −2, while the range for the middle 50 per cent of those rated as "calm" was from 0 to −11. Since a high level of activation is often accompanied by inhibition of response in social situations, no very close relationship should be expected between ratings on peppiness and indicators of the degree of activation. Moreover, it is possible that basal metabolism would be less effective than intermediary metabolism as an indicator of individual differences in the degree of arousal since the physiological condition of the responsive individual may conceivably be more different from that of the unresponsive individual during activity than during rest. A further difficulty in employing this measure is the possible role of fatigue (from previous over-reaction) in lowering the basal metabolic rate. A fatigue effect, if any, might however be obscured unless the excitable subject had become sufficiently adapted to the test situation to function at an approximately "basal" level.

A greater proportional increase in pulse rate upon stimulation was found in subjects who had a high normal pulse rate than in those who had a low one (Lauer and E. A. Smith, 1932). Greater responsiveness was thus again observed to accompany a higher degree of activation.

Armstrong (1938) reported coefficients of correlation between .88 and .98 as indicative of the relationship between cardiovascular reactivity and emotional stability in 700 Air Corps candidates.

Little or no relationship has been found between certain physiological measures and scores on various personality inventories. To the extent that these personality tests measure the directional aspect of behavior rather than the arousal aspect, no relationship should be expected. Scores on the Bernreuter Personality Inventory gave low coefficients of correlation with measures of basal metabolism, systolic blood pressure, diastolic blood pressure, and pulse rate (Omwake, Dexter, and Lewis, 1934). Basal metabolic rate bore little relationship to scores on the Minnesota Multiphasic Personality Inventory or the Humm-Wadsworth Temperament Scale (Greenberg and Gilliland, 1952). On the MMPI the only statistically significant coefficients of correlation were with Psychasthenia ($-.32$) and with the Interest Scale ($-.38$), a high score on the latter indicating more feminine interests in males. On the Humm-Wadsworth test the only significant correlation was with the autistic schizoid scale ($-.27$).

Groups of Measures

For reasons pointed out earlier, the level of activation is probably best indicated, not by a single physiological measure, but by a group of measures. Moreover, since there is day-to-day and even hour-to-hour variation in this aspect of response, measurements should be repeated on a number of occasions if an adequate representation of the individual is to be obtained. There are a number of studies in which individual differences have been determined on the basis of the pooled results of several physiological measures. Unfortunately, there are few studies in which such pooled measures of the same individual have been taken on more than one occasion and the findings related to some measure of overt behavior. When this has been done, the number of subjects studied has usually been rather small.

A pioneer investigation of autonomic functioning was made by Darrow and Heath (1932), who studied the interrelationships between several physiological measures (chiefly skin-resistance phenomena and blood-pressure changes) and "personality constellations" as determined by answers to questions on the Thurstone Neurotic Inventory and the Northwestern University Introversion-Extroversion Test. The physiological measurements were made during a session in which the subject was at various times given electric shocks. Continuity was observed in the groups of physiological measures arranged according to their relationship to the personality constellations. One end of the continuum was tentatively labeled "hypo-reactivity" and the other end, "hyper-reactivity," though the investigators thought that these terms did not adequately represent the two extremes of their data. In no instance was a close relationship found between physiological measures and composite personality scores, though there were a number of coefficients of correlation between .20 and .30 with small probability that the correlation was obtained by chance.

A line of investigation seeking to establish relationships between ratings on behavior and measures of autonomic functioning classified as predominantly sympathetic or predominantly parasympathetic was perhaps initiated by Darling (1940). Darling performed a factor analysis of ratings of six behavioral characteristics and five indicators of autonomic activity, chiefly measures of blood pressure and skin conductance. Among the four factors reported were a cholinergic (parasympathetic) factor and an adrenergic (sympathetic) factor. The cholinergic factor had a high positive loading on skin-conductance reactivity and conductance reactivity minus systolic blood pressure. It had a high negative loading on systolic blood pressure. The adrenergic factor had high positive loadings on conductance reactivity, on conductance reactivity minus systolic blood pressure, and on systolic blood pressure. None of the rated characteristics (which included excitement and hyperactivity) showed more than a negligible loading on either of these factors. This finding need occasion no surprise since the interrater reliabilities were in the neighborhood of .35.

Wenger has conducted a number of studies in which he has sought to establish differences between individuals in "autonomic balance" and to relate these differences to differences in behavior. By means of regression scores derived from a factor analysis of physiological variables, he obtained an "autonomic factor," which was described in the preceding chapter (Wenger, 1941). Children at the "parasympathetic" extreme of the distribution of autonomic-factor scores were reported to differ significantly from those at the "sympathetic" extreme in showing less emotional excitability, more emotional inhibition, a lower basal metabolic rate, a more adequate diet, a lower frequency of activity, less fatigue, and more patience and neatness (Wenger, 1947).[9] Many of the differences between the two groups may be conceived to be differences in excitability or in characteristics which might well be derived from differences in excitability. As compared with the Fels Institute sample of children, the group with presumed parasympathetic dominance had a significantly lower basal metabolic rate and were significantly less fatigable, less suggestible, and more dominant. The group with presumed sympathetic dominance were said to have a significantly lower palmar skin temperature than the Fels subjects, to have less dominant mothers (Bernreuter Scale), and to have come from homes that were less child-centered and less well co-ordinated.[10] Ratings on behavior at school and at camp were the basis for the determination of the behavioral characteristics.

It is surprising that subjects at the two extremes of autonomic scores were not compared with those in the middle of the distribution who would, according to Wenger's hypothesis, show better autonomic balance. In fact, Wenger and Ellington (1943) state, without presentation of data:

> Other data indicate that adult psychoneurotics and others manifesting difficulties in adjustment to their social environment appear to have low (sympathetic dominance), or occasionally extremely high (parasympathetic dominance), scores on this weighted battery of tests, while those individuals who manifest adequate adjustment to life show average or slightly higher than average scores (p. 241).

[9] Out of 87 subjects, 14 at each extreme of the distribution were compared. Originally 10 at each extreme were compared. When, however, it was discovered that 35 out of 42 variables showed differences between the two groups in the expected direction, but few of the differences were statistically significant, 4 more subjects were added to each group. It is not clear whether the 8 subjects added were in every instance those with the next lowest or the next highest autonomic factor scores since they were described as subjects "whose deviation was either not so extreme or not so certain" as that of the original groups. The fact that adding the 8 more subjects weighted the group with sympathetic dominance toward a younger age level and toward the female sex cannot be wholly disregarded in assessing the significance of the findings. If we consider only the original groups, we find that the group with "parasympathetic dominance" differed (at the .05 level or better) from the group with "sympathetic dominance" in having greater emotional inhibition, a lower basal metabolic rate, a more adequate diet and more dominant mothers (Bernreuter Scale).

[10] The home environment is probably a factor of considerable importance in determining differences in the functioning of the autonomic nervous system. Genetic factors, however, appear to be of equal or greater importance. For a discussion of this question, see Chapter 9.

An attempt by Wenger (1948) to find significant correlates of the autonomic factor in adults proved to be less successful than the search for such correlates in children. Students in a preflight school showed little relationship between the autonomic factor [11] and scores on the personality inventories of Guilford, or of Guilford and Martin (GAMIN, STDCR, and Personnel Inventory I). Among the few significant relationships were low positive correlations of the autonomic factor (parasympathetic dominance) with depression ($+.31$) and with cycloid disposition or emotional instability ($+.27$), and low negative correlations with co-operation and tolerance ($-.26$), and with objectivity ($-.23$). One of the personality test factors, defined as "lack of nervous tension and irritability," showed a relationship to the physiological measures in a direction opposite to that predicted by Wenger's theory. It was found associated with scores indicating a predominance of sympathetic nervous system function, whereas, according to Wenger, it should have been associated with dominance of the parasympathetic system. Scores on individual physiological tests were even less closely related to personality factors than were scores on the autonomic factor.

Results such as these, obtained from a large number of physiological measurements made on a large sample of subjects, suggest deficiencies in the physiological measurements, the personality tests, or the conceptualization of the study (i.e., the choice of physiological variables or the choice of personality variables to be related to each other). Since measurements of autonomic functioning are notoriously difficult to obtain with accuracy, it is probable that the "autonomic" tests, administered rapidly in a military establishment by three different examiners, were made under conditions which interfered with precision of measurement. It is obvious that many of the personality variables were constituted chiefly of the directional, rather than the arousal, aspect of behavior.

Wenger has several times reported a factor of muscular tension in his measurements of children. In the first study, a factor analysis of the scores of only six subjects was made, and the only direct measure of muscle tension failed to distinguish between the subjects and was dropped from the table of intercorrelations (Wenger, 1938). In a later study, one direct measure of muscle tension (resistance to mechanical abduction of the forearm) was employed, but this measure had a low loading (.18) for the factor labeled "muscle tension" (Wen-

[11] This factor was tentatively defined and differed somewhat in composition from the autonomic factor obtained for children.

ger, 1942). In a third study, no direct measure of muscular tension was employed, but ratings on muscular tension were used as a means of identifying the factor (Wenger, 1943a). When the ratings and sixteen physiological variables were intercorrelated and submitted to factor analysis, a factor defined as muscular tension gave a distribution of scores similar to that of the ratings alone and showed similar relationships to rated personality characteristics.[12] For 74 subjects, factor scores said to represent a high degree of muscular tension correlated positively with "energeticness" (+.46), restlessness (+.48), frequency of emotion (+.46), impulsiveness (+.35), distractibility (+.19), and carelessness (+.22). They correlated negatively with emotional control (—.33) and fatigability (—.35).[13] A high level of "muscular tension," then, was associated to some degree with greater responsiveness and a higher level of activity. To a lesser degree, it was associated also with a deficiency of control or inhibition. The picture is in most respects consistent with the author's report in two earlier studies of nursery-school children referred to previously (Duffy, 1930, 1932a). It is of interest that a factor derived from physiological measures, no one of which was a measure of muscular response, gave a distribution of scores similar to that of ratings on muscular tension and related in similar fashion to personality characteristics. These findings lend support to the concept of a general level of activation which may be indicated roughly by any one of a number of physiological measures.

Groups of autonomic measures of various sorts have been reported by other investigators to be related to behavior. Autonomic responses to mild exercise (the Schneider test) have been said to be related to "frustration tolerance" (Strother and Cook, 1953), to psychiatric status (McFarland and Huddleson, 1936), and to the relative frequency of recall of completed and uncompleted tasks (Abel, 1938).

When continuous recordings were made of skin resistance, heart rate, and respiration of forty male medical students, and the autonomic responses were scaled by a modification of the regression method proposed by J. I. Lacey, it was found that subjects who had high self-rated anxiety for various phases of the experiment (listening to tones and thinking about "emotional" and "nonemotional" questions) tended, as

[12] Tests represented in the factor, in addition to the ratings, were dermographia latency, change in palmar log conductance, respiration period, sigma of the respiration period, and diastolic blood pressure.

[13] This is rated fatigability. The excitable child may, because of his excitability, give little evidence of fatigue until he is all but exhausted.

compared with those who were less apprehensive, to function at significantly higher autonomic levels (Dykman, Reese, Galbrecht, Thomasson, 1959). This was indicated by the extent of the response to the first tone and the first question, and by the maximal response time in skin resistance. Higher "autonomic levels" tended to be found also for subjects who were more proficient intellectually and who had greater motivation toward achievement as indicated by scores on the Medical College Admission Test.

Various investigations employing the technique of factor analysis of physiological measurements, or of behavioral ratings, or both, have led to the report of factors which apparently represent excitability or ease of arousal, either alone or in conjunction with some phase of the directional aspect of behavior. Our purposes do not require a review of these studies, but it might be pointed out that, using physiological measurements made on human subjects, Jost (1940) found a factor called "general emotionality," G. L. Freeman and Katzoff (1942b) a factor called "physiological arousal to stimulation," and R. B. Cattell, A. K. S. Cattell, and Rhymer (1947) a factor called "emotional responsiveness." With rats as subjects, Billingslea (1942) found a factor of "emotionality," and with dogs as subjects Royce (1950) found several factors which appeared to involve the degree of reactivity. Howie (1945), using ratings of school boys, found a factor which he interpreted as showing a contrast between the qualities of the "unrepressed, excitable, irritable, or distractible character" and those suggesting "stability, placidity or perhaps inertia." Eysenck (1947, 1952) in a series of investigations, has reported a factor called "neuroticism" which appears to have much in common with excitability, and he has reviewed studies by others in which factors involving a high degree of arousal have been reported (Eysenck, 1953).

A distinction between the level of arousal and the direction of response is suggested in some of the factor analyses. R. B. Cattell (1946) finds among four second-order factors, which are more general than the first-order factors, a factor called "easy reactivity," which he suggests may be a hyperthyroid or autonomic factor "gaining alternative expressions in cheerful or anxious overactivity" (i.e., different directions of response). Adcock (1952), in findings said to be closely related to those of Burt, reports a factor of "emotional ability" or "excitability" which, it is suggested, may find expression in either "worry and anxiety" or "social activity and adventure." This factor, he believes, is the equivalent of a factor found by at least fifteen other research workers. It is of interest that the factor is said to find expression in more than one direction of behavior.

It appears that factor analyses of measures of personality have regularly led to the isolation of one or more factors incorporating responsiveness. In the measures employed, and in the rotation of factors, this aspect of behavior is seldom separated from the directional aspect. It may, in different factor analyses, be combined with different phases of the direction of response. Thus it may fail to appear as a separate factor but may constitute a part of many different factors.

FLUCTUATIONS IN ACTIVATION

Fluctuations in activation appear to be of at least as great significance as the degree of activation. Such fluctuations have been observed in almost every recorded indicator of activation. Their behavioral correlates will be suggested in the discussion which follows.

Muscle Tension

Among the earliest investigations of the behavioral significance of fluctuations in muscle tension where studies by the author (Duffy, 1930, 1932b) of individual differences in the irregularity of the grip-pressure tracings of nursery-school children. In an experiment in which the instructions were to press, or not to press, a key according to the nature of the picture which appeared, those subjects who had shown a greater number of fluctuations in muscle tension during a different performance (tapping) showed more errors of the impulsive type—i.e., pressing the key when no response was called for. There was a correlation coefficient of .59 (P.E. = .12) between the fluctuations in grip pressure during tapping and the percentage of "false," as opposed to "omitted," responses during the discrimination task. No subject with a very irregular tension tracing had, among his errors, predominantly omitted responses, and no subject with a very smooth tension tracing had, among his errors, predominantly false responses. False responses were attributed to excessive reactivity, or a deficiency of inhibition. Lability in skeletal-muscle activity was therefore shown to be correlated with impulsiveness in a task entirely different from the one during which the muscular tension was measured. Such a finding suggests that both lability of physiological reactions and impulsiveness in behavior are characteristics of the individual.

No statistically significant relationship was found between level of muscle tension (grip pressure) and type of error ("impulsive" or "omitted") in the study in which a significant correlation was reported between fluctuations in tension and type of error (Duffy, 1932b). In an earlier study (Duffy, 1930), it was noted, however, that subjects with low grip-pressure scores tended to have rather smooth pressure tracings, while those with high tension scores showed, in two out of three instances, very irregular tracings. The nursery school records revealed many instances of uninhibited motor response on the part of subjects with irregular tracings and relatively few such instances on the part of subjects with smooth tracings. Descriptions of the three subjects out of eleven who had the highest tension scores and the five subjects who had the lowest tension scores are presented below.

HIGHEST TENSION SCORES:

Subject 1H (Irregular tracing)

"Is the only one in the group who has not succeeded in staying absolutely quiet and relaxed for at least five minutes during the rest period."

"At times seems overflowing with good spirits and madly races around the room. Has not learned self-control upon these occasions. His danger lies in exhaustion coming through overstimulation and nervous tension."

"Needs to be encouraged to hold over his impulses and not so often plunge into situations without forethought."

Further comments found in the records were that this subject often stammered; that during a verbal intelligence test his attention wandered; and that during a motor performance test he showed impetuosity and impatience (Duffy, 1930, p. 44).

Subject 2H (Irregular tracing)

"Talks a great deal. She has a high shrill laugh which seems to result from excitement, but her laugh has a similar quality when she is not excited."

"Worries over things a great deal at times and has a real need of assurance. Asks who is coming for her, does she need a raincoat, etc."

It was reported that during the verbal intelligence test, she became nervous and began talking to herself. During the motor performance test she "talked a steady stream all the time she was working." It was said that "her impulses were little controlled either in speech or in the use of her hands." Her attention was reported to be rather poor (Duffy, 1930, p. 44).

Subject 3H (Smooth tracing)

This subject was said to be stubborn, persistent, and patient, and to have good motor co-ordination. It appeared that he was an intense, easily aroused person whose responses were under control (Duffy, 1930, p. 47).

LOWEST TENSION SCORES (RELATIVELY SMOOTH TRACINGS):

Subject 1L

During the verbal intelligence test showed "a carefree attitude coupled with continued effort." During the motor performance test was said to show excellent motor control and little impatience.

Subject 2L

The comments were: Relaxes well. Eats well. Motor co-ordination excellent. Bites nails. During the motor performance test this subject was said to have "impulses well under control while doing work."

Subject 3L

Comments were: Relaxes well. Deliberate in movements. Persistent. Motor co-ordination fine.

Subject 4L

Comments were: Has learned to relax very well. Shows forethought, persistence, and patience. Has good motor control. Is cautious and deliberate.

Subject 5L

The comments were: Gets wrought up easily. Chews or sucks the forefinger of her glove. Impetuous. Emotions readily expressed. Was quite restless throughout the verbal intelligence test. Showed no special interest or efficiency in any part of the test.

Comments on her motor performance test were more in harmony with the comments on the other four subjects in this group. It was said that she was eager and interested, that her motor impulses were well-controlled, and that her attention, patience, and persistence were excellent (Duffy, 1930, pp. 51–52).

A comparison of the descriptions of children with highly irregular tension tracings and those with relatively smooth tension tracings (and usually low pressure scores) suggests the possibility that the two groups differ, not only in behavior which may be an obvious consequence of a high degree of activation (muscle tension), such as restlessness, difficulty in relaxing, high activity level, a high-pitched voice, and shrill laughter, but also in various forms of behavior which may be less obviously and regularly derived from a high level of activation. Such behavior would include impatience, impulsiveness, distractibility, lack of self-control, and poor motor co-ordination. These characteristics of response might be conceived to stem from deficiency in the control of the directional aspect of behavior. If a high degree of activation imposes a burden upon the inhibition and organization of responses, as was suggested in Chapter 8, it might be expected that inadequately controlled behavior would be associated with a high level of activation, especially in children, in whom the ability to inhibit responses has been said to be less highly developed than it is in adults (Luria, 1932). Much of the problem behavior of children may conceivably have its origin in a level of activation which is too high for the child to manage successfully. Individual differences in the ability to inhibit and co-ordinate responses occurring at a high level of activation are to be expected, and it is possible that these differences may be roughly indicated by differences in the smoothness of grip-pressure tracings, at least in the child.

A pioneer study of differences in the degree of disorganization of motor responses was carried out by Luria (1932), who reports that individuals who show irregular pressure responses manifest: (1) "unconditioned sensibility of the nervous system," and (2) "special defects in the cortical regulators of excitation, in consequence of which every arising excitation manifests the tendency to pass immediately to the motor sphere." [14] Such individuals are called "reactively labile," while those showing smooth pressure response are called "reactively stable."

Luria's stimulating discussion is accompanied by little quantitative data. Subsequent investigations by others have, however, confirmed many of his conclusions. M. I. Morgan and Ojemann (1942) have reported that "the Luria method" differentiates at a high level of confidence between subjects classified into three groups (high, intermediate, and low) on the basis of ratings of the severity of their conflicts. Albino (1948) found that the mean scores on motor disorganization in pressure tracings from the left hand were significantly different for normal subjects in the upper quartile and those in the lower quartile on a neurotic inventory. This inventory had been shown to discriminate between persons who had had and those who had not had a nervous breakdown at some time in their lives.

In-co-ordination, or irregularity, of movement measured in various ways appears to be associated with neurosis or neurotic tendency. Standing steadiness, for example, has been reported to be related to neurosis (Lee, 1931). Studies to be presented in the following chapter will show that measures of irregularity in pressure are among the measures which discriminate best between a normal and a psychiatric population, a fact which is not surprising if, as suggested by the author (Duffy, 1930, 1932b) and by Luria (1932), irregular pressure tracings are indicative of poor co-ordination or lack of control of responses.

"Spontaneous" muscular activity, in the absence of specific stimulation, was found by Lundervold (1952) to occur in some individuals and not in others. Action potentials from the muscles of the upper extremities, shoulders, thorax, and back of 64 women and 46 men were recorded while they were engaged in typewriting. The measurements were repeated one to thirty-six times over a period of 3 years. Subjects were classified as "tense" or as "relaxed" according to whether or not electrical activity occurred after the insertion of the needle electrode and while the subject was sitting in a relaxed position, before stimula-

---

[14] Here Luria (1932) refers to "that fatigue or weakness of the nervous system seen in many of our mental workers." He reports also that children show weakness of the functional barrier between excitation and motor response, as indicated by poor performance on a test requiring that a key be pressed down as slowly as possible.

tion was introduced. Tense subjects were found to show more activity in the muscles when external conditions were changed, as by an increase in noise, the lowering of the room temperature, or the introduction of certain stimuli which caused irritation or anger. In these persons, there was not only more activity in the single muscle, but also electrical activity in more muscles, including muscles which did not participate directly in the movement. At the moment of introduction of noise, 85 per cent of the tense subjects, but only 25 per cent of the relaxed subjects, responded with an increase in action potentials. At the cessation of 30 minutes of noise, 50 per cent of the tense subjects, as compared with none of the relaxed subjects, showed more action potentials than they had shown before the noise began. Again we have evidence that individuals who are more highly activated in one stimulus situation are more responsive to a wide variety of stimuli than are individuals who are less highly activated in a given situation. In addition, the more reactive individuals gave muscular responses when they were sitting in a relaxed position and were not being subjected to any special stimulation. Thus there is evidence in this study also that the degree of responsiveness is a characteristic of the individual.

Skin Resistance

Skin resistance, too, shows "spontaneous" changes or fluctuations. Mundy-Castle and McKiever (1953) divided 109 normal subjects into three groups on the basis of the frequency with which a change in skin resistance (GSR) occurred when there were no observed stimuli. Subjects were classified as "stable" if they showed GSR's only to observed stimuli. They were called "labile" if GSR's occurred without observable stimulation, a condition which was frequently accompanied by an unstable resistance level. They were classified as "stable/labile" if they showed a few, but not many, GSR's when no stimuli were observed, or had an unstable resistance level, or both. Adaptation of the GSR to a noise stimulus (i.e., decrease in the extent of the response to successive stimuli) was significantly greater in the stable group than in the other groups, and the average resistance level of this group was significantly higher. Out of 47 stable records, all except 2 showed adaptation, whereas only 6 out of 35 labile records gave evidence of adaptation. Greater responsiveness was thus shown to be accompanied by less adaptation to stimulation—or, it might be said, less adaptation to repeated stimulation is one of the ways in which greater responsiveness manifests itself.

Some of the skin-resistance measures showed little relationship to

electroencephalograms of the subjects; (EEG's, however, were not recorded at the same time as skin resistance and were not subjected to
automatic frequency analysis). In the stable group, alpha frequency
and GSR adaptation rate were significantly correlated. When, however,
the labile group was included, there was no correlation between the
two measures. Perhaps this finding may be explained by the fact that
the labile group showed only about 17.6 per cent adaptation as compared with 95.7 per cent adaptation for the stable group.

No significant differences appeared in the mean alpha frequencies of
the three GSR groups, a report which is in contrast to that of Darrow,
Pathman, and Kronenberg (1946), who found relationships between
skin conductance and both alpha frequency and alpha amplitude.
Mundy-Castle and McKiever (1953) are not inclined to challenge the
earlier findings.

In summary, stable individuals, who gave GSR responses only to observed stimuli, had a higher average skin-resistance level, ceased more
quickly to respond to noise stimuli with a galvanic skin response, and
showed a significant correlation between GSR adaptation rate and
alpha frequency.

The Electroencephalogram

Differences in the degree of variability or irregularity of pattern of
the EEG also appear to have behavioral significance.

A review by Kennard (1953) suggests that regularity of EEG pattern
is associated with good motor co-ordination and a well-integrated personality, while irregularity of pattern, or absence of alpha rhythm is associated with "psychological or emotional variability."

Werre (1957) noted that the EEG's of some subjects may be described as being "relatively stable, regular, constant," while those of
others are "labile, irregular, inconstant."

Variability of EEG rhythm and concordance of the rhythms in different parts of the cortex have been studied primarily in relation to
abnormalities of behavior. Discussion of these phenomena will therefore be deferred.

Other Measures

Continuous spontaneous variations in the volume of the fingers, toes,
and ears of twelve normal white adults were found by Burch, Cohn,
and Neuman (1942). Measurements were made while the subjects
were in a reclining position and not subject to any special stimulation.
The investigators believed that their observations "tend[ed] to show

that fundamental differences exist in the reactivity of blood vessels in types of people even when no external strain is being imposed." Their general observation of the subjects, some of whom were associates in the laboratory, led them to conclude that the subjects who showed small changes in the volume of these parts of the body were "placid and emotionally stable people" who adjusted easily to the experimental situation. Those, on the other hand, who showed frequent and rather large changes in volume were said to show wide fluctuations in mood and at times to show anxiety about the experimental procedure. They frequently had to be asked to remain quiet long after they should have become accustomed to the experimental procedure.

Lability of physiological responses appears to be correlated with lability of "emotional" responses. A correlation coefficient of .409, reliable beyond the .05 level, was found between "emotional lability," as measured by the Bell Adjustment Inventory, and the rate of change in finger volume during simple tasks (van der Merwe and Theron, 1947). This coefficient was raised to .653 (50 Ss) when measures of the rate of change in finger volume under various conditions were combined with measures of pulse volume in the period before the stimulation, labile subjects showing the greater rate of change (Theron, 1948). A comparison of the ten most stable and the ten most labile subjects on the Bell Inventory revealed a greater rate of change, significant at the .01 level, on the part of the labile subjects. These subjects were said to have more constriction of the peripheral blood vessels and a smaller pulse volume.

Lability of skin resistance and of pulse rate were reported to be greater in subjects judged to be more disturbed by a frustration situation (Thiesen and Meister, 1949).[15] The ratio of change in skin resistance and the ratio of change in pulse rate during frustration, as compared with a control period, were found to correlate significantly with "overt disturbance scores" based on ratings of behavior during frustration. The coefficients of correlation were .83 and .69 respectively. Again, if these findings are accepted, physiological lability appears to accompany behavior which is less stable.

Fluctuations in autonomic activity have more recently been studied in very thorough fashion by John and Beatrice Lacey (1958b). In con-

[15] From the description of the experiment it seems possible that one of the persons who rated the subjects' behavior also recorded the physiological changes. Correlations of the magnitude reported here are seldom obtained between physiological measures and measures of behavior, especially when the physiological measures are taken on only a single occasion.

tinuous records of heart rate and skin resistance, they have shown that there are bursts of activity, or more continuous aperiodic changes, that do not appear to be connected with any stimulus imposed at the moment or any detectable "affective" response. These "spontaneous" fluctuations in skin resistance and heart rate are no doubt similar to the spontaneous GSR's reported by Mundy-Castle and McKiever (1953) in "labile" subjects, the lability of skin resistance and pulse rate reported by Thiesen and Meister (1949) in subjects judged to be more disturbed by a frustration situation, the spontaneous variations of resting peripheral blood flow found by Burch, Cohn, and Neuman (1942), the individual differences in fluctuations of grip pressure found by Duffy (1930, 1932a, 1932b) in nursery-school children, and perhaps with lability of the EEG as reported by H. Gastaut (1954). The Laceys have, however, studied this significant phenomenon more extensively than other investigators. They have, through retesting after a 48-hour period, shown that it is a reliable individual characteristic. They have shown also that it is related to measurable individual differences in behavior, specifically to "hyperkinetic" or impulsive behavior.

During a 15-minute rest period, a computation was made of the number of half-minutes during which "bursts of skin-resistance activity" could be observed and the number of half-minutes in which "bursts" of cardiac acceleration occurred in a group of twenty-eight mothers participating in the Fels Research Institute's study of human development. On 48-hour retest the reliability coefficient for skin resistance was .76, and that for heart rate was .58. The correlation between these two measures was .36 for the first day and .32 for the second, the former coefficient being barely significant at the .05 level, though both measures showed an increase during a paced task of visual discrimination. Such a finding is in harmony with data discussed in Chapter 9. Those subjects who showed bursts of skin-resistance activity and cardiac activity during rest tended to show them also during activity. All coefficients of correlation were statistically significant. Adaptation effects were observed during the activity period, but not during the rest period.

High variability in skin resistance was significantly correlated with low initial (but not final) skin resistance on both days. Heart-rate variability showed no such relationship with initial or final heart rate. The Laceys concluded that there were two reliable but relatively uncorrelated autonomic variables in the resting organism, one the "level of sympathetic tonus," and the other "the frequency of apparently spontaneous variation . . . about this level." Some doubt may be cast upon the independence of these variables in view of the Laceys' report of a significant correlation between initial skin resistance and degree of variability on both days.

The question of the extent of correlation between the degree of activation and fluctuations in activation has been raised by other investigators. It seems probable that some degree of relationship, though not a high one, is to be expected. The problem is a difficult one to resolve. On the one hand, autonomic regulation is such that, if the degree of activation is high, there is a reduced likelihood of its becoming higher upon the presentation of stimulation, or as a result of "spontaneous" variation. On the other hand, higher activation is indicative of a high degree of response and hence, presumably, of greater responsiveness, which might be expected to lead to greater variability in physiological measures. These two tendencies might be presumed to work against each other and thus reduce the correlation between the level of activation and fluctuations in activation, though each of the measures may in itself be indicative of responsiveness. Conversely, a low degree of activation would, from the point of view of autonomic regulation, favor greater variability of response, but low activation is no doubt indicative of low responsiveness; hence the tendency toward variability in responsiveness would be low, and again two physiological tendencies would be working against each other. In the light of our present information, it seems reasonable to regard both the level of activation and fluctuations in activation as indicative of the responsiveness of the individual.

Autonomic measures, because of intricate homeostatic regulation, may conceivably show less relationship between the level of activation and fluctuations in activation than is shown by measures of muscle tension or electrical potentials from the brain, though the latter measures also are not unaffected by regulatory processes, and they also have been reported to show some degree of independence between the level of activation and fluctuations in activation. The extent of independence of these two aspects of activation reported by the Laceys may, however, be due in part to the relatively "crude measurement techniques" which they suggest as one explanation of certain differences in findings in their experiment with Fels mothers and those in a later experiment with male college students. With the former subjects, spontaneous changes in heart rate and skin resistance during the rest period were closely related to those during prolonged stressful activity. In the latter group of subjects there was no consistent relationship between resting and nonresting fluctuations in these measures, and the correlation between cardiac and skin-resistance measures was low. There was also little relationship between initial or final heart rate and skin-resistance level, and the incidence of fluctuations in these measures. The college males showed more autonomic activity than did the selected group of adult women. Their greater activation at rest, which was said to be near maximal in some individuals by the yardstick employed, was offered as another possible explanation of the lack of correlation in this sample between resting and nonresting fluctuations.

When the subjects were divided into those above and those below the median in number of half-minutes of skin-resistance activity during rest, it was found that those with more activity, the labiles, showed a statistically dependable difference from the stables in the number of erroneous responses in the discrimination-reaction task. They made more responses to the lights to which no response was supposed to be made, thus indicating greater impulsiveness. The rank-order coefficient of correlation between the number of erroneous responses and the number of half-minutes of skin-resistance activity was +.41, significant at less than the .05 level. The findings for cardiac labiles and stables were similar. The rank-order coefficient of correlation between false responses and half-minutes of cardiac activity was +.53, significant at less than the .02 level. The greater number of false responses on the part of the labiles could not be attributed to poorer sensory discrimination of light positions since there was evidence indicating that, if there was any difference between the groups in this respect, the labiles had the advantage. It was concluded that both cardiac and skin-resistance lability were positively related to impulsiveness, though they were themselves uncorrelated. Individuals who showed both great cardiac and great skin-resistance lability gave a strikingly greater number of false responses than those who were consistent stables in these measures. Analysis of the data led to the conclusion that, though resting autonomic lability tended to be correlated with a short reaction time, the relationship between the number of false responses and autonomic lability was not due in a significant degree to a tendency of the labile individual to respond quickly. Another form of analysis of the data suggested the conclusion that a stable subject makes a better adjustment to experimental variation than a labile subject. The Laceys interpreted a significant increase in reaction time when experimental conditions were changed, which occurred on the part of the stable subjects, as indicating that these subjects were able to restrain motor responses until discrimination of stimuli had occurred. It will be recalled that, in the preceding chapter, a similar difference in behavior was described in recounting the differences which W. T. James (1941) found between excitable and less excitable dogs in an experimental situation. The excitable dogs continued to respond to all stimuli and showed restlessness, straining in the harness and other forms of excessive motor reaction.

It is interesting to note in the Laceys' study that, though cardiac lability and skin-resistance lability do not correlate with each other, each measure defines a stable and a labile group who differ from one another in reaction time, and in the same direction. Moreover, a similar difference in reaction time was found when the subjects were separated into two groups on the basis of high or low initial and final level of activation during rest. While the pattern of findings was the same in all instances, only the measures of final resting heart rate attained statistical significance. These findings lend confirmation to the position taken here that both measures of fluctuation in activation and measures of the level of activation, even when they do not correlate with each other, may be indicators of responsiveness and of the many characteristics of behavior derivable from differences in responsiveness. The Laceys suggest that "autonomic labiles,"—and it should be noted that the term "autonomic" is a generalization from cardiac and skin-resistance measures which are not correlated—"driven by recurrent facilitatory volleys to the motor cortex and to brain stem formations, cannot voluntarily inhibit the speed of emission of an impulse along final motor pathways." They suggest that the relationship between the number of erroneous responses and autonomic lability is primarily a relationship between autonomic lability and motility, or motor reactivity.

The level of activation, as indicated by initial and final resting measures of skin resistance and heart rate, was related in the same direction as fluctuations in these measures to reaction time, the frequency of erroneous impulsive responses, and to foreperiod phenomena in the reaction-time experiments. The relationship was not statistically significant, however, except in the case of final resting heart-rate level and reaction time.

It seems probable, as suggested by the author in regard to muscle tension (Duffy, 1932b), that excessive fluctuations in activation are indicative of poor control, or a deficiency of inhibition, while a high level of activation, without frequent fluctuations, may indicate intensity of response coupled with adequate control. On this assumption, impulsive errors would be related to fluctuations in activation but not of necessity to the level of activation, except as the level of activation may be correlated with such fluctuations. Interpreted in this way, the early findings of the author are in harmony with the recent, more extensive findings of the Laceys.

RECOVERY FROM THE EFFECTS OF STIMULATION

Individuals differ, not only in their characteristic degree of activation and in the degree of fluctuation in activation, but also in the speed with which the systems affected return to their prior level of functioning. Differences in recovery time cannot be accounted for solely by differences in the degree of activation, for they are apparently found when recovery is measured *in relation to the degree of activation*.

One of the earliest studies of this aspect of behavior was made by Darrow and Heath (1932). Using records of skin resistance, they computed two different measures of recovery: (1) the percentage of increase in resistance 3 seconds after the peak of the galvanic response, and (2) the "recovery-reaction quotient," or the recovery of resistance divided by the decrease in resistance which had occurred as a result of stimulation. The former measure was reported to be positively related to "the general galvanic and motor reactivity of the subject, and negatively related to his resistance level." It was also said to be positively related to general health and to inclination toward social participation. The latter measure was reported to be related to many different measures of " 'neurotic' and emotionally unstable tendencies." The investigators concluded that it was one of their best indicators of the absence of neurotic trend, but that the coefficients of correlation were not high enough to justify the use of the measure for prediction in individual cases.

Measurements of physiological recovery have usually covered relatively short periods of time, but it has been said that there is a positive correlation between the extent of recovery a short time after the peak of effect from stimulation and the extent of recovery at a later time. G. L. Freeman and Katzoff (1942a) state, without presentation of data, that human subjects reach their peak of reaction within a minute after the cessation of stimulation and "tend to maintain the same rank in recovery regardless of whether the scores are based upon readings taken five minutes or ten minutes after this 'peak.'" They report a high correlation in rats between the percentage of decrease in the rate of breathing 5 minutes after a startle reaction has occurred and the length of time required for complete recovery of this function.

Recovery time, according to Freeman, should be considered within the framework of homeostatic regulation. A stimulus "displaces" the physiological functioning of the organism. The speed of recovery of equilibrium is regarded as a significant individual variable which is related to other aspects of response (Freeman, 1939). It is suggested, for example, that "physiological recovery from experimental loads may be useful in estimating individual ability to withstand conflict and related types of nervous strain in ordinary life situations" (Freeman, 1939).

In one investigation "tension" was produced through the voluntary inhibition of micturition (Freeman, 1939). Measurements of galvanic skin resistance, blood pressure, and muscle-action potentials made under this condition were compared with measurements obtained under a "preload" condition and with those made after the "tension-load" had been removed. The recovery quotient (RQ) [16] for each of these measures, or the percentage of "postload return to preload level," was reported to be positively related to the length of time the subject had been able to inhibit micturition, and to the ability to carry on an eye-hand co-ordination performance while under the stress of inhibited micturition. The latter measures, regarded as indicators of "control," were reported to be more closely related to the RQ for skin resistance than to the RQ for blood pressure or for muscle tension. Both long inhibition time and rapid physiological recovery were said to be positively associated with low basal reactivity and low mean reactivity, as shown by high skin resistance, low blood pressure, and relatively few muscle-action potentials. No indication of the statistical significance of the findings is reported. Moreover, since in this study each subject presented himself for testing when he felt the urge for micturition could no longer be delayed, a personality variable was introduced which may have affected the results. Tending to support Freeman's argument, however, is his finding of a coefficient of correlation of .69 between skin-resistance RQ and the length of time an electric shock would be tolerated by fifteen subjects who were tested a year later.

A slow rate of recovery of skin resistance after exposure to a frustrating situation was reported by Freeman and Haggard (1941) to be associated with instability of basal skin conductance and greater reac-

[16] A formula for computing the recovery quotient (RQ) for skin conductance, designed to yield a value independent of the base level at which the "displacement" and "recovery" occur, is presented by Freeman and Katzoff (1942a). Palmar skin conductance is regarded by Freeman (1939) as especially suited to the determination of the RQ.

tivity and variability during frustration. While this conclusion is probably correct, since it links a slower rate of recovery with greater responsiveness, it is based upon evidence which is not beyond question.

In a later study by Freeman and Katzoff (1942b), twenty-four subjects had skin-conductance measurements taken several times in each of four "displacing" situations or, in current terminology, "stress" situations. Other data on the subjects included a time-sample of nervous movements, clinical ratings on emotionality, recorded movements on a pneumatic mattress, and answers to questions selected from personality tests. From thirty variables, three factors were obtained. Two of these were tentatively identified as "physiological arousal to stimulation" and "control of the expression of energy." The third factor was said to show little relationship to behavior in the displacing situations but to be heavily loaded with self-rated emotionality. The "arousal" factor contained primarily the percentage of increase in skin conductance in each of the four situations, but also the recovery quotient in one of the four situations. The "control" factor contained the recovery quotients for skin conductance in three of the four situations, several measures of movement, and the psychiatric rating. It was said that a person ranking high on this factor might be expected to recover rapidly from the effects of stimulation, show little variability in "basal" movement during the various experimental sessions, and be rated as "well-adjusted." While the number of subjects was small, and no final conclusions were believed to be justified, these findings are of considerable interest.

BODY BUILD AND THE LEVEL OF ACTIVATION

Measurements of body build have in a few instances been studied in relation to one or more indicators of the level of activation. In the normal population, such relationships as have been reported have usually been consistent but not very close, and some investigators have failed to find any relationship at all.

A slender body build was found to be associated to a slight degree with a high basal metabolic rate, and a broad build with a low basal metabolic rate (Lucas, Pryor, Bost, and Pope, 1933). For 415 subjects between the ages of 3 and 17 years, the coefficient of correlation between deviations in metabolic rate and deviations in width-length index was $-.26 \pm .04$ for the girls and $-.20 \pm .05$ for the boys. It seems possible that the relationship, if any, between body build and metabolic rate is complicated by the fact that, while thinness is frequently associated with a high metabolic rate, it may also on occasion be associated with a low metabolic rate. Thyroid deficiency, as well as an excess of secretion from the thyroid gland, has been said to produce sometimes a thin, irritable type of individual who is over-responsive to the environment (Hoskins, 1941).

No significant relationship was found between grip pressure and and hip-width/height index in a group of eighteen nursery-school children (Duffy, 1932c). The rank-order coefficient of correlation was —.39 ± .13. It was noted, however, that a line dividing the group into those above, and those below, the median for this index of body build served also to divide the subjects into those above and those below the median in grip pressure, with but two exceptions.

Extremely linear individuals were said to be found almost twice as frequently as usual in a group with "unstable autonomic functions," as indicated by anxiety, tremulousness, blushing, increased perspiration, palpitation, and functional disturbances of the urinary and gastrointestinal systems (Seltzer, 1946).

Other investigators have reported a positive, though only moderately high, coefficient of correlation between body build and a group of measures related to the functioning of the parasympathetic nervous system (Sanford, Adkins, Miller, and Cobb, 1943). These measures were flushing, sweating, skin-stroking intensity, sinus arrhythmia, and palpable thyroid.[17] Using forty-five subjects between the ages of 5 and 14 years of age at the beginning of the study, and correcting for age, they found that parasympathetic dominance was positively associated with a tall, thin body build and also with a wide, heavy, tall build, but was negatively associated with a short, wide build. These findings offer some difficulty in interpretation. Eysenck (1947), speaking of Sanford's study, concludes that both autonomic imbalance and a tall-narrow body build correlate positively with tests of intelligence and with school abilities, while wide-heavy body build correlates negatively. Reviewing a number of studies in the field, he concludes that the relationship between body type and personality traits is not very close, most coefficients of correlation being in the neighborhood of +.30.

A factor analysis of various aspects of the EEG and certain other measures led to the report that "pyknomorphic" constitution [18] had a

[17] Palpable thyroid, though not an autonomic variable, was included in the syndrome because it showed some relationship to certain of the other variables in the group of measures indicative of parasympathetic response. "Skin-stroking intensity" refers to the duration of the change in color produced by stroking the skin.

[18] Constitutional type was determined by Strömgren's index. Pyknomorphic persons have a broader body build; leptomorphic persons, a more linear build.

loading of +.869 on a factor in which the alpha rhythm had a loading of +.402 (Elmgren, 1951). On this same factor, "leptomorphic" constitution had a loading of −.408 and beta rhythm a loading of −.813. It was thus suggested that pyknomorphic constitution is associated with alpha rhythm, while leptomorphic constitution is associated with beta rhythm. The variability of the alpha rhythm was said to be greater in leptomorphics. No correlation between physique and EEG type was found, however, by certain other investigators (Golla, Hutton, and Walter, 1943).

Measures of the galvanic skin response were reported to be different for leptosomatics, athletics, and pyknics (Kretschmer and Enke, 1936).[19] The leptosomatics were said to give the most intense response to stimulation and to require the longest time for the skin resistance to return to the "resting" level. Athletics were said to be intermediate between leptosomatics and pyknics in both the extent of response and the length of recovery time. The subjects of the study were ninety normal individuals, divided equally among the three types of body build.

Using the height/weight ratio as an index of body build, another group of investigators failed to find, in ninety-two male subjects, any relationship between body build and either basal skin conductance or the galvanic skin response to an electric shock (O. L. Lacey, P. S. Siegel, and H. S. Siegel, 1949).

The extensive studies of Sheldon and his collaborators (Sheldon, Stevens, and Tucker, 1940; Sheldon and Stevens, 1942) did not include measures of activation and will not, therefore, be discussed here.

The evidence is not substantial enough to indicate whether there is or is not a relationship between body build and activation. Single measures of a single physiological variable, in this most difficult area of measurement, would not appear to be sufficient to provide reason for assuming that a relationship is not to be found. If a relationship does exist, its direction is clear: a linear body build is associated with greater responsiveness, and a broad body build is associated with less responsiveness. Our best guess is that at some time in the future such a relationship will be established, although the degree of relationship may prove to be slight.

[19] The pyknic has a thick-set, round build; the leptosomatic a thin, lean build; and the athletic has a build which is intermediate between the two.

CONCLUSIONS

Differences between individuals have been found in the degree of activation, in fluctuations in activation, and in the speed of recovery from the effects of stimulation. These physiological differences are apparently associated with certain differences in behavior.

The basic behavioral correlate of differences in activation, from which other behavioral correlates may be derived, appears to be that of a difference in responsiveness. A high degree of activation or frequent fluctuations in activation, appears to indicate greater responsiveness of the organism, or a marked degree of excitability of the nervous system in both its higher and lower centers.

Individual differences in responsiveness have been observed in many forms—in the frequency and amplitude of rhythms in the EEG; in the ease with which reflexes are elicited; in the occurrence of "spontaneous" changes in skin resistance, peripheral blood flow, heart rate, muscle tension, and other functions; and in the extent, frequency, and duration of reactions to stimulation, both of the skeletal musculature and of various functions controlled by the autonomic nervous system. These various forms of reactivity show, in general, intercorrelations, though the intercorrelations are apparently not high enough to make a measure of any one of these modes of response an adequate measure of the general responsiveness of the individual.[20] They appear, however, to give justification to the conception of a responsive or an unresponsive individual, not merely responsive or unresponsive skeletal musculature, skin resistance, or cortical potentials.

Differences in reactivity are shown also in responses of greater inclusiveness, of higher integration. In short, they find expression in modes of behavior commonly classified as personality traits. Combining with one or another directional aspect of behavior, a high degree of responsiveness may be observed in modes of behavior designated, for example, as "anxiety," "aggression," "delight," "enthusiasm," and "drive," or the vigorous pursuit of goals. The effect of the degree of activation upon overt behavior varies apparently with variations in the

[20] The most adequate single measure of the responsiveness of an individual may conceivably prove to be electroencephalographic measures, because they come from the neural centers controlling response, or measures of skeletal muscle tension, because they record activity of the effectors by means of which the organism produces changes in the external environment. Skin conductance, however, has shown many significant correlations with other data.

degree of inhibitory ability (Duffy, 1934), or, as Luria (1932) has described it, with variations in the strength of the "functional barrier" between excitation and response. Depending upon this factor, a high degree of activation may apparently lead to impulsive, disorganized behavior or to sensitive, alert, vigorous, and co-ordinated responses to the environment. Evidence in support of these statements is at present so meager, however, as to leave them in the category of speculations. It is to be hoped that further investigation will provide the basis for a more confident statement of the relationship between "personality" characteristics and individual differences in the level of activation.

Among the behavioral correlates of the degree of activation, and especially of fluctuations in activation, the one which has been most frequently studied, and perhaps most clearly established, is that of emotional instability or a tendency toward neuroticism. A uniformly positive, and sometimes close, relationship has been reported between ease of activation and behavior described as unstable or neurotic. The logic of the association is not difficult to see. The readiness to respond, and to respond in excessive degree, which apparently characterizes the easily activated individual may well lead to what is called emotional instability, social maladjustment, or neuroticism. Conversely, problems of adjustment probably tend to increase both the degree of activation and fluctuations in activation.

The individual who is hyper-reactive no doubt faces problems of adjustment not met by the individual who is habitually less responsive or more relaxed. If the more highly activated individual is more sensitive to the impact of the environment and responds more intensely to it, this readiness to respond might well lead to impulsive action rather than to a well-considered choice of responses. From the basic characteristic of hyper-reactivity many other characteristics may be derived, though the derivation at the present time must rest more upon logical deduction than upon empirical evidence. It seems reasonable to suppose that a relatively intense response to even minor aspects of the environment, or to frustrations easily tolerated by less responsive individuals, might make the excitable individual "hard to get along with" or "difficult to manage." Unless coupled with unusual powers of control, or inhibition of response, it might frequently lead to manifestations of anger or irritation, to impatience with the imposition of restraints, and to problem behavior of various kinds.

It seems clear that constitutional factors predisposing to excitability may predispose also to instability and maladjustment. It seems equally clear that environmental stresses may produce in one individual a tendency toward an habitually high degree of activation, or considerable lability in activation, while another individual with the same constitution may, because of a different environment, be otherwise disposed. A high degree of activation may lead to maladjustment, or maladjustment may lead to a high degree of activation. It should be pointed out, however, that a high degree of activation does not of necessity lead to emotional instability. This point, or one closely related to it, is made by Maberly (1946), a contributor to a British symposium on personality, who suggests that there are two distinct factors included in the factor of "neuroticism, instability, or lack of integration" as described by Eysenck. One of these is said to be "an essential lack of cohesiveness with a tendency to break down under stresses which are within normal limits" and the other to be a factor "associated with sensitivity (such as high intelligence, imaginativeness or autonomic sensitivity) which makes an individual unduly responsive and, therefore, unduly susceptible to life stresses." Maberly (1946) makes this comment about sensitivity:

It involves a delicacy of response, and of the underlying nervous and physiological mechanisms, that carries with it a vulnerability to any strong stimulus. It brings the advantages and handicaps of a chemical balance compared with kitchen scales. The nature of upbringing and education determines whether the condition becomes exaggerated or modified sufficiently to enable the individual to take a normal place in society. . . . Sensitivity is not the same as the factor described as introversion or inhibition, although it may correlate fairly highly with it. . . . The insensitive and the strongly integrated personality will both withstand stress well, but for different reasons. Put in another way, a personality with high sensitivity requires high power of integration to show objective stability (pp. 8–9).

Though in many instances sensitivity has proved to be synonymous with instability, and the sensitive individual has become the maladjusted individual, nevertheless, a distinction between the two seems desirable on both theoretical and practical grounds.

Any survey of physiological studies of personality must recognize the surprising fact that relatively few investigators have reported relationships of any magnitude between physiological measures and measures of behavior within the normal population. Since it is inconceivable that few relationships of consequence exist between differences in behavior and differences in so basic an aspect of response as that of activation, we are led to seek an explanation of the essentially negative findings of perhaps the majority of investigators. The explanation appears to lie in conceptual and procedural defects in most of the studies which have been made.

On the conceptual side we find the absence of satisfactory categories for the description of personality.[21] Lack of attention to the problem of describing the basic ways in which behavior may vary has led to the uncritical use of descriptive categories (trait names) which are "impure" in the sense that they incorporate under one heading more than one dimension of behavior, and often dimensions which vary independently. While differences in activation may be the basis of variations in one of these dimensions of behavior, they may be only slightly related, or related not at all, to the other dimension included under the single descriptive term. Under such circumstances it would be impossible to secure a very high coefficient of correlation between the characteristic degree of, or fluctuations in, activation and the aspects of personality incorporated in the particular descriptive category.

A second reason for the frequent failure to discover relationships between physiological variables and personality appears to be that, aside from the confusion produced by trait names which incorporate more than one variable, investigators have frequently looked in the wrong place for the relationship they sought to establish. They have, for example, calculated coefficients of correlation between physiological measures and measures of the directional aspect of behavior; yet, as has been pointed out elsewhere (Duffy, 1941a, 1949), the direction taken by behavior and the intensity or energy mobilization with which the behavior occurs appear to be relatively independent aspects of response. Low coefficients of correlation might then be expected when some indicator of the degree of activation is correlated with some measure of the directional aspect of behavior, as for instance attitudes or values, or even when it is correlated with such characteristics as aggressiveness or timidity, which are also largely directional in their significance.

One of the difficulties here appears to be the fact that, for many psychologists, the directional aspects of behavior are regarded as constituting the personality. Some years ago, for example, a now well-known article appeared (Ingle, 1935) in which it was asserted that endocrine secretions, when their variations were within normal limits, bore little relationship to personality; yet in the same article it was pointed out that they affected the activity level, the emotionality, and to some extent, the intelligence of the individual! If personality is to be

[21] For a fuller discussion of this topic see Duffy, 1949.

defined largely in terms of its directional aspect, as important as that is, then it may be true that the degree of activation, when it is within normal limits, bears no very close relationship to personality. If, however, personality is conceived to include also the intensity aspect of response and all its probable derivatives and correlates in behavior, such as impulsiveness, sensitivity to the impact of the environment, and other dynamic characteristics, then individual differences in activation must constitute a very significant part of personality. In short it seems that relationships have not been discovered because the wrong relationships have so frequently been sought.

A third reason for the failure to establish clear-cut relationships appears to lie in the inadequacy of the physiological measures employed and the inadequacy of some of the questionnaires, rating-scales, and other criteria with which these have been correlated. The inadequacy of many of the paper-and-pencil tests of personality is well known. The inadequacy of the psysiological measures has come from a number of sources. There have been problems in regard to the technique of measurement, such as the question of what should be measured and how the data could best be obtained. Methodological problems have plagued the field. Also, in most of the early studies, a single physiological measure was studied in relation to the behavioral characteristics of the individual. Yet it now seems probable that such a procedure must inevitably reduce coefficients of correlation since in some individuals one physiological function, and in other individuals another function, may be most affected as the organism increases its degree of activation. Groups of measures, rather than a single physiological measure, appear to afford a more adequate indication of the general state of arousal.

Another defect of procedure has been the tendency to take only a single sampling of the physiological condition of an individual rather than to obtain repeated samplings over an extended period of time. If characteristic tendencies with respect to activation are to be studied in relation to characteristic tendencies with respect to behavior, measurements under a given set of controlled conditions must be repeated often enough to minimize variations produced by changes in the regime of living or by the events of the day. The activation of the individual is more variable and more difficult to measure under controlled conditions than most of the other aspects of response investigated by the psychologist. A single measurement is therefore less likely to be representative of the individual than is a single measurement of many other functions.

Because of the difficulty of making measurements of activation, most of the studies in this area have employed a relatively small number of subjects, and the statistical analysis of the findings has frequently been inadequate. In a few instances, as in certain studies made in the armed services, the number of subjects has been large, but the conditions under which the measurements were made were poorly controlled.

There are a number of recent studies in which a group of physiological measures have been employed under well-controlled conditions and the data have been subjected to adequate statistical analysis. Many, but not all, of these studies have been concerned with differences in the reaction to stress of neurotics, psychotics, and normal control groups, rather than differences within the normal population. In few instances have the measurements been repeated on a number of occasions in order to determine the consistency of the findings. There is still need for studies of normal individuals in which repeated measurements of a number of physiological variables are made under both stressful and nonstressful conditions and the findings are correlated with various measurable aspects of the individuals' personalities. It is a mistaken assumption to suppose that individual differences in activation occur only under conditions of special stress and not under the ordinary conditions of life, or to suppose that differences in activation under more routine conditions are without behavioral significance. Moreover, the psychologist has every reason to be interested in differences in activation within the normal group as well as in differences between normal and abnormal subjects.

Finally, it should be said that, in spite of all the defects of conception and procedure discussed above, investigations of the behavioral correlates of individual differences in activation have nevertheless produced some positive results. The studies reviewed in the present chapter give support to the conclusion that differences between individuals in activation are basically differences in responsiveness or excitability. These differences appear to be associated with differences in certain other characteristics which might be regarded as derived from a basic difference in responsiveness.

Excitability a phenom. of amt. of energy or of threshold or perhaps both ??

chapter 11
Activation and functional disorders

INTRODUCTION

Abnormalities of behavior which are described as functional appear to be accompanied rather regularly by abnormalities in activation. Both neuroses and psychoses have frequently been reported to differ from "normal" conditions in the degree of arousal of the subject. Reports of excessive arousal are perhaps more frequent than those of subnormal arousal, but both conditions have been found among psychiatric patients. In comparatively few instances has a degree of arousal similar to that found in control subjects been reported. Physiological indices of arousal employed in the study of behavior pathology include most, if not all, of the measures discussed in previous chapters.

The deviation from normality in the level, the fluctuations, and the patterning of activation is rather consistently accompanied by a deviation in the directional aspect of behavior. The abnormal individual does not relate himself in a "normal" way to his environment. His attitudes, his overt responses, are oriented in such a way as to be "maladjustive." Adolf Meyer is said to have described the characteristic feature of the "discordant personality" as that of incompatibility of attitudes and the direction of behavior with reality or with other attitudes and other directions of behavior.

Perhaps faulty orientation of behavior leads to deviations in the degree of arousal, for faulty "cue-responses" may well release energy appropriate to those responses but inappropriate to the situation as viewed by others. It is conceivable, on the other hand, that excessive

But also need distinction between intensity of energy and modes of binding— "inhibition," redirection neutral.

arousal may contribute toward poor integration of behavior, or that aberrations in both the direction of behavior and the degree of arousal may stem from some other basic factor. In any case, one of the characteristic features of the neuroses and the psychoses appears to be a deviant pattern of activation.

In considering evidence bearing on the relationship between activation and the functional disorders, many difficulties are encountered. Studies of activation in psychiatric patients are subject to all the problems and defects of method described in the discussion of studies of individual differences in activation in the normal population [1]—and some besides. Psychiatric classifications differ from one institution to another, and from one psychiatrist to another. They do not provide a firm basis upon which studies of physiological correlates can be conducted. Lowell Kelly (1954), for example, has cited data which he says "justify general dissatisfaction as to the meaningfulness of current psychiatric diagnosis." Under such conditions, it is not surprising to find that physiological measures often fail to show a close and consistent relationship with psychiatric categories. The difficulty is compounded when mixed groups of psychiatric patients are compared with "normal" control subjects. Unless it is assumed that all psychiatric conditions, whatever the diagnosis, and whether acute or chronic, show a deviation in arousal in the same direction, it might be expected that in many instances scores representing underactivity would tend to cancel out scores representing overactivity, and the mean score for the group might differ little from that of normal subjects. However, in spite of all these difficulties, physiological studies of psychiatric patients have produced certain findings which are of interest.

Before turning to these studies, we may note that psychiatric conditions are not alone in their apparent deviation from the normal in the level of activation. Both hyperthyroidism and acute infections change the level of activation. They have been said to show in many instances some of the characteristics of manic-depressive syndromes (Rosanoff, Handy, and Plesset, 1935). The metabolic changes of semistarvation have also been found to produce a condition which apparently represents a change in the level of activation. The starved man described himself as being moody, depressed, and apathetic, not alert mentally, and lacking in ambition (Keys, 1952). He was found to have "a low basal metabolic rate, bradycardia, arterial and venous hypotension, polyuria, hypothermia, great muscular weakness, and anemia." Semistarved subjects gave answers on the hysteria, depression, and hypo-

[1] See Chapter 10.

chondriasis scales of the Minnesota Multiphasic Personality Inventory which were not fundamentally different from those given by psychoneurotics. The investigator concluded that simple semistarvation, without unusual psychic stress, could produce behavior describable as mild to moderate psychoneurosis.

Stimulation of the hypothalamic region has been reported to produce excitement, manic reactions, and anxiety, or on occasion depression and irascibility (Alpers, 1940). The type of response was said not to depend upon "the pre-morbid emotional make-up of the patient."

DRUGS AND HORMONES

Certain hormones and drugs, administered to psychiatric patients or "neurotic" animals, may either improve behavior or the reverse, apparently in large part through their effect on activation. For example, the administration of ACTH may, in some psychiatric patients, produce anxiety or manic excitement (Gildea, Ronzoni, and Trufant, 1952). In studies with cats, both alcohol (Masserman, 1946) and sedation with Sodium Amytal (Bailey and Miller, 1952) were found to cause the animals to resume food-getting activities which had ceased as a result of punishment by electric shock. Sedation in human beings reduces pathological tension. It was reported that the "sedation threshold," or the amount of the sedative drug (in relation to weight) which was required to produce a certain effect on the EEG, was an excellent indicator of the degree of tension (Shagass, 1954). Since, in pathological tension, a number of the characteristics of excessive arousal are seen, the investigator suggested that the condition might involve increased activation of the reticular system, which is reduced when barbiturates are administered.

It has been pointed out, however, that it seems likely that more than one change is brought about by a "psychoactive" drug, and that, since these changes often have opposing effects on behavior, it may happen that in one experiment the effects may cancel out, in another experiment one effect might predominate, and in a third experiment a different effect might be found (Uhr, 1960). A dual action of tranquilizers has been reported by Barsa (1957): one, a calming effect; and two, an anti-psychotic effect, eliminating delusions and hallucinations. He says that either of these may occur without the other. Variability of reactions of individuals to particular drugs have also been rather consistently reported (Katz, 1960). As might be expected, those with an autonomic imbalance in the sympathetic direction responded differently from those with an autonomic imbalance in the parasympathetic direction (Kaplan, 1960). In spite of these considerations, the effect of psychoactive drugs on behavior seems to be related in an important way to their effect on activation, as the succeeding discussion will suggest.

The neural site of action of different drugs appears to be different. Among the "tranquilizers," for example, it has been suggested that in order to be effective, reserpine and chlorpromazine must depress the hypothalamus (Himwich, 1955). A second site of action may be found in the activating system, and the possibility of a third site of action is suggested by the therapeutic effects of Frenquel (azacyclonol) (Himwich, 1955). Since these drugs apparently tend to suppress activity, it is believed that they may be effective in psychiatric conditions involving overactivity but perhaps not in cases of depression without anxiety and tension, and not in patients with "burnt out schizophrenic processes who are regressed and without hallucinations." The barbiturates, on the other hand, appear to act most strongly on the cerebral cortex rather than, like the tranquilizers, on the midbrain reticular formation, the hypothalamus, and components of the rhinencephalon (Himwich, 1960).

Administration of glutamic acid to psychiatric patients has been reported to increase emotional responsiveness, productivity, and motor control in the patients with a low level of activity, but to increase hostility, excitability, and tension in those who started with a higher level of activity (Kitzinger, Arnold, Cartwright, and Shapiro, 1949).

LSD is a drug which can apparently cause a "model psychosis," with hallucinations and delusions and other serious disorganizations of normal behavior (R. W. Russell, 1960). The abnormal symptoms of schizophrenic patients are aggravated and, in normal subjects, mild schizophrenic-like symptoms are produced. One observer (Bennett, 1960) reported that a conservative dose of LSD was experienced as a disruption of autonomic functions. It has been found to produce low-amplitude, high-frequency waves in the EEG (Himwich, 1955). Without medication, such waves are said to occur in few normal subjects but to be found in about one-third of the psychiatric patients diagnosed as schizophrenics, manic-depressives, or psychoneurotics and in more than one-half of those with involutional psychosis. Himwich suggested that these EEG's may possibly be due either to a disorder of the cortex or to an overactive alerting system which stimulates the cortex and is in turn stimulated by it.

It has been said that the calming action of certain drugs cuts across diagnostic categories, and that normal persons to whom the drugs are given show reduced activity and less response to stimulation (Himwich, 1960). Types of hyperactive patients who secure benefits from tranquilizers are reported to include the manic, the "schizoaffective, in whom abnormal elation is associated with deterioration of mental abilities," and those with a toxic psychosis, such as delirium tremens (Himwich, 1960). Senile patients who are quarrelsome, or show anxiety or irritability, appear to benefit more from these drugs than those who do not show agitation or who are depressed without an accompaniment of anxiety or tension.

Chlorpromazine apparently increases basal skin resistance (L. E. Mitchell and Zax, 1959). Mitchell and Zax found that it was more difficult to produce a conditioned response in patients given chlorpromazine than in a group of control patients, suggesting, as Carran (1960) points out, that the use of tranquilizing drugs should not be undertaken without consideration of the level of autonomic functioning of the patient before the adminstration of the drug, lest the level of activation be altered in an undesirable direction. Carran himself found that tranquilizing drugs lowered the level of activation of patients when this was measured by the galvanic skin response (Uhr, 1960), but Uhr and Miller are said to have found that, throughout a period of experimentally induced stress, the baseline galvanic skin resistance was decreased by meprobamate (Uhr, 1960).

In another study it was found that schizophrenics who were "anxious" (sweat variable) responded best to chlorpromazine, and that treatment with ephedrine prior to chlorpromazine caused significant improvement in total adjustment scores on the MACC Behavioral Adjustment Scale in certain schizophrenic patients, while chlorpromazine alone did not (Ellsworth, 1960).

Turning our attention now to physiological measures in which differences have been found between normal subjects and those with behavior disorders, we shall consider first biochemical differences between the two groups.

BIOCHEMICAL DIFFERENCES

A number of biochemical differences between psychiatric and control subjects have been reported. No survey of studies in this area is attempted, though it seems probable that biochemical differences are an important aspect of differences in activation. Kennard (1953) suggests, for example, that "the sensitivity of the EEG pattern in psychological disorders is due to or is part of, biochemical factors which are known to affect cell respiration."

Among the biochemical differences reported is a difference between psychiatric patients and normal subjects in blood-oxygen-saturation levels under various forms of stimulation—photic, sonic, or tactile (Doust and Schneider, 1952). Differences in hippuric acid excretion have also been reported. Patients with "free anxiety" were found to show a significantly greater amount of hippuric acid excretion than a healthy control group, while catatonic schizophrenic subjects showed significantly less excretion than normal subjects (Persky, Gamm, and Grinker, 1952). Both psychiatric groups showed significantly greater variance than normal controls when the measurements were repeated. It was suggested that the greater variance was due to the fact that hippuric acid excretion varied with the psychiatric condition of the subject which, in turn, was affected by treatment. Successful treatment was said to bring hippuric acid excretion to normal levels.

A number of studies by Hoagland and others have led to the conclusion that schizophrenic patients give subnormal adrenal responses to stress and to ACTH (adrenocorticotrophic hormone) (Hoagland, 1952). This conclusion has been both challenged and defended. One of the challengers reported adrenal cortical responses within the normal range or greater for patients with schizophrenia, manic-depressive psychosis, and involutional psychosis, without regard to the type of psychosis or the length of time during which the patient had been ill (Altschule, 1952). A defender of Hoagland's position points to the larger number of subjects in his investigation, the superior statistical treatment of data, and the more adequate indices of adrenal response employed (Malamud, 1952).

Another group of investigators who found a number of deviations in adrenal cortex function and in thyroid function in psychiatric patients found no specific endocrine disturbance for a particular psychiatric category, but they were critical of the present classification scheme of psychiatric disorders (Reiss, 1955). It was suggested that there was a closer correspondence between psychological disturbances and changes in the total hormone equilibrium, and that successful treatment or spontaneous recovery led to a return to a normal hormonal condition. More recently it has been reported that, in a small group of manic-depressive patients, there was a significantly greater excretion of adrenalin and noradrenalin during the manic than during the depressed phases of the disorder (Ström-Olsen and Weil-Malherbe, 1958).

A number of studies have shown the presence of a toxic substance in the blood of schizophrenics. One group of schizophrenics were found to show conspicuous abnormalities in potassium metabolism under both stress and ACTH administration (Elmadjian and Hoagland, 1949). This fact is of interest since potassium plays a role in nerve excitability and conduction.

Sera from schizophrenics and from other psychotics has been reported to decrease the stimulation of glucose uptake in rat diaphragm (Haavaldsen, Lingjaerde, and Walaas, 1958). This apparently was due to abnormalities in the protein fraction.

A review of certain studies suggests that in schizophrenia there is some disordered metabolic response to stress (Rubin, 1959). This in turn appeared to depend upon a neurohumoral or enzymatic defect. Schizophrenics in general seemed to represent "a generalized disorder of steady-states."

Kennard (1953) suggests the possibility that the changes in the EEG pattern in various disorders may be related to carbohydrate metabolism.

The glutamine/glutamic acid ratio in the plasma of acute schizophrenics and acutely manic patients has been reported to be different from that of normal subjects (Munkvad, 1950). In these patients the mean values of the ratio were found to be ten times higher than the normal average. As the schizophrenia became more chronic, the ratio tended to approach normal values, reaching the normal average in cases of more than ten years' duration.

Other biochemical differences between normal and abnormal subjects, no less important than those mentioned above, have been reported.

DIFFERENCES IN THE ELECTROENCEPHALOGRAM (EEG)

One of the differences between psychiatric patients and control subjects which is receiving considerable attention from investigators at the present time is the difference in the electroencephalogram. Abnormalities of behavior can occur without abnormality of the electroencephalogram,[2] and abnormal electroencephalograms are by no means

[2] The limits of normality in the EEG are not definitely determined; yet, as Kennard (1953) points out, there is wide agreement that certain patterns are normal. Normal patterns remain within roughly defined limits of rate, regularity, amplitude, and wave-complex. The majority of psychiatric patients for whom records have been made are said to have EEG patterns which fall within the normal range.

accompanied always by abnormalities of behavior.[3] Nevertheless, a greater incidence of abnormal EEG's has been found in psychiatric subjects than in the normal population. Some of the abnormal records are related to organic focal disturbances in the central nervous system, but a greater number, in individuals with psychological disorders, show no such relationship to organic pathology.

Characteristics of the EEG which have been reported to be related to abnormalities of behavior include: (1) more activity in very high frequencies or in very low frequencies, (2) less alpha activity, (3) paroxysmal activity, (4) greater variability in EEG frequencies, (5) dysrhythmia, and (6) less inter-relatedness of activity in the various cortical areas. Certain of these characteristics, such as paroxysmal activity, are rather generally regarded as indicative of abnormality. Others, such as moderately slow activity (5 to 8 cycles per second) or higher-voltage fast activity, which represent only slight deviations from the normal, are not so uniformly regarded as constituting an abnormality (Ellingson, 1954). Most of the deviations in the EEG's of psychiatric patients are said to be of the latter, more questionable, sort (Ellingson, 1954).

There is no specific EEG which is related to psychopathology alone. Kennard (1953), in a comprehensive review of electroencephalographic studies, states however that the single EEG characteristic which is most often mentioned in connection with abnormal behavior is that of increased reactivity or lowered threshold to stimulation. Many investigators, variously trained, are said to have found less alpha activity, more fast activity, and greater reactivity to stimuli in the records of patients with a wide variety of psychological disorders. Since these characteristics are found with great frequency in the EEG's of normal individuals who are more excitable or more responsive than the average,[4] it is tempting to suggest that abnormal behavior is behavior occurring at the upper end of the continuum of arousal. Certain findings, to be mentioned later, appear however to challenge this conclusion. In any

[3] The "normal" adult population, without organic pathology or overt psychopathology, is said to have between 5 and 15 or 20 per cent of EEG records which are abnormal (Kennard, 1953; Ellingson, 1954). Selected groups within the normal population have been reported to differ in the percentage of abnormal records (D. Williams, 1941). A highly selected group of R.A.F. pilots had only 5 per cent; a selected group from the medical corps of the air force had 10 per cent; and a group of soldiers of the same units who had developed psychoneurotic symptoms had 26 per cent. A fourth group, with known organic pathology of the nervous system, showed abnormality in 60 per cent of the records.

[4] See Chapter 10.

case, a deviation in the degree of arousal does not in itself constitute a neurosis or a psychosis. Deviation in the directional aspect of behavior appears to be a necessary aspect of these conditions.

Less alpha activity, or alpha activity of a higher frequency, would be the theoretical expectation for excited patients. It has in most, but not in all, instances been the empirical finding. The observation that some individuals tended in general to have "good" alpha waves, characterized by relatively high regularity and amplitude, while others tended to have "poor" waves, or waves which were irregularly present and of low amplitude, was reported by Lemere (1936). A normal alpha rhythm, according to Darrow (1947), would occur only when there was neither a great excess nor great deficiency in the factors favoring cortical activity. He suggests that, in anxious and schizophrenic persons, self-maintained, excessive cortical activity (and low potential EEG's) may persist to the point of exhaustion. A well-developed alpha rhythm, then, should indicate that there was no excessive tension. It might indicate also that there was no extreme deficiency in cortical activity.

Among the studies in which significantly less alpha activity has been found in psychiatric patients than in normal subjects is one by the Davises (P. A. Davis and H. Davis, 1939) in which most subjects in a group of 180 psychotic patients showed only about 20 per cent alpha activity, while 500 normal subjects had, on the average, between 60 and 80 per cent.

A similar difference in alpha activity has been reported between nonanxiety-prone subjects and both anxiety-prone control subjects and patients with manifest anxiety as the predominant system (Ulett, Gleser, Winokur, and Lawler, 1953).[5] Both anxious patients and anxiety-prone controls had a significantly greater proportion of their resting EEG activity in the frequencies between 3 and 7 cycles per second and 16 and 24 cycles per second, and proportionately less in the alpha range. They also showed less response (driving) to photic stimulation at frequencies within or near the alpha range and relatively more response to high or low frequencies. Alpha activity in the "emotionally stable" control group clustered around a modal frequency of 10 to 11 cycles per second. The patients had an almost rectilinear frequency distribution throughout the range from 9 to 12 cycles per second. The emotionally labile control group had a distribution of alpha frequencies midway between that for the patients and that for the stable controls (Brockway, Gleser, Winokur, and Ulett, 1954; Ulett

[5] These findings are based on the use of an electronic brain wave analyser.

et al., 1953). The patients differed significantly from the stable control subjects in dominant alpha frequency, but showed no difference from the total control group in this respect. Evidence of maladjustment was found in 26 out of 45 "normal controls" (Ulett et al., 1953), thus suggesting that the failure to find a reliable difference between psychiatric patients and control subjects may at times be due to the presence in the control group of a large number of unstable persons. Ulett and Gleser (1953) developed scales utilizing the basic EEG record and subjective sensations induced by flicker which identified 65.5 per cent of anxious patients and 59.4 per cent of anxiety-prone normal subjects, with only 11 per cent of false identifications—i.e., the inclusion of nonanxiety-prone subjects. The validating criterion was an 8-point rating scale for anxiety-proneness based on psychiatric interviews and psychological testing. Shagass (1955) has reported that higher frequencies in the EEG were associated with anxiety, while lower frequencies were associated with depression.

Fast activity in the EEG appears to be of common occurrence in psychiatric patients. Often there is an inverse relationship between the percentage of fact activity and the percentage of alpha activity (Finley, 1944). A comparison of the EEG's of 4500 neuropsychiatric patients with those of 300 controls showed that high-frequency patterns were widely distributed throughout all the disorders, and no type of pattern was characteristic of any single clinical category (Finley, 1944). Fast activity was, however, reported to occur especially often in the excited phases of manic-depressive psychosis and in agitated depressions.

Other investigators also have found that high degrees of fast activity occur most often in excited patients (Brazier, Finesinger, and Cobb, 1945; H. Davis and P. Davis, 1936). The majority of manic-depressive manics were reported by one investigator to show mixed fast patterns, with alpha rhythms in the higher frequencies, while a majority of manic-depressive depressed patients were reported to show a dominant alpha rhythm or mixed slow patterns with alpha rhythms in the lower frequencies (P. A. Davis, 1941b). This observation was later confirmed by a different group of investigators (Hurst, Mundy-Castle, and Beerstecher, 1954). Kennard and Schwartzman (1956) have also confirmed the fact that the frequency pattern of the EEG is related to psychological functioning.

Fast activity of a specific type (i.e., 25 to 30 cycles per second in waxing and waning bursts in precentral and prefrontal areas of the brain) has been reported to be related to hyperactivity and instability in both the motor and vegetative systems (J. Schneider, 1957).

That the difference between high-anxiety and low-anxiety subjects may be due to the initial, rather than the continuing reaction to a situation, is suggested by the fact that L. C. Johnson and Ulett (1959) found that, on the first record, the subjects high in anxiety showed significantly less EEG activity, especially in the range of 8 to 12 cycles per second, while on the second and third records there were no significant differences between these subjects and those low in anxiety.

Rapid activity appears to be common also in schizophrenia—a diagnostic category which apparently covers a heterogeneous group of mental disorders (Finley and Campbell, 1941). Finley and Campbell (1941) concluded that if there was anything approaching consistency in the EEG's of schizophrenics, it was the predominance of fast activity. Some investigators have, however, reported less EEG reactivity *to stimulation* in schizophrenics than in the normal population (Blum, 1957; Grinker and Serota, 1941).

Rapid activity has often been found in the psychoneuroses, particularly where anxiety was a major symptom (Faure, 1950; Finley, 1944). A comparison of 100 neurotics with 500 normal adults revealed a significantly greater incidence of fast activity in the neurotics, specifically in the anxiety-neurotics (Brazier, Finesinger, and Cobb, 1945). The records of these subjects were not characterized by abnormal wave-forms such as delta or spike activity. One attempt to correlate deviant EEG patterns with neuroticism led to the conclusion that, as compared with a normal population, neurotics showed (1) more of slow alpha activity (8 cycles per second), (2) more of fast alpha activity (12 cycles per second or faster), (3) excess of theta rhythms, (4) excessive beta activity, (5) occipital delta waves, and (6) exaggerated response both to hyperventilation and to intermittent photic stimulation (M. Dongier and S. Dongier, 1958). Other characteristics were also mentioned.

It must be admitted that the EEG findings in the psychoneuroses have been various, though not more various, Kennard (1953) suggests, than the clinical diagnostic criteria. The frequently reported low voltage, fast activity of psychoneurotics is regarded by one reviewer not as abnormal, but as the result of the subjects' failure to relax during the test (Ellingson, 1954). It would appear, however, that if any group of subjects is characterized by a consistent failure to achieve, under controlled conditions, a degree of relaxation ordinarily achieved by "normal" subjects, that inability to relax may in itself be of significance.

Other evidence suggesting association between excitement and higher frequencies in the EEG is the fact that the photic driving-response in female psychiatric patients with anxiety states showed significantly more driving-response at 15 flashes per second, as compared with 10 flashes per second, than did that for subjects with depressions (Shagass, 1955a). Control subjects occupied an intermediate position. Fluctuations of the driving-response with fluctuations in feeling-state were found in serial studies of a single control subject, the direction of the fluctuations being consistent with the group differences described above. In spite of these facts, the alpha rate of the anxiety group was found to be no more rapid than that of any other group. The greater average age of the depressives suggests the possibility of an artifact since there was a significant correlation ($r = .32$) between age and the frequency of the driving-response. It is entirely possible, however, that the relationship between depression and a greater driving-response at a lower frequency is not an artifact, but instead both phenomena are related to changes in certain organic conditions which occur as the individual grows older.

Other evidence of physiological differences between anxious and depressed patients is seen in the report that the sedation threshold is highest in the most anxious patients, and that it has been found to be low in psychotic depressives (Shagass, 1955b).

Greater excitability in a group of psychiatric children characterized as having a "hyperkinetic impulse disorder" is indicated perhaps by the fact that these children, as compared with a control group of psychiatric patients, had a significantly lower photo-Metrazol threshold (the amount of Metrazol required to produce a myoclonic jerk of the forearms and evoke a burst of EEG spikewaves) (Laufer, Denhoff, and Solomons, 1957). In this disorder, hyperactivity is said to be the most striking characteristic. The subjects were described as impulsive, irritable, and explosive, and as having a short attention span, poor powers of concentration, and low frustration-tolerance. A low photo-Metrazol threshold is reported to have been shown by H. Gastaut to indicate damage to, or dysfunction of, the diencephalon.

A positive relationship between general excitation and fast activity in the EEG is suggested by a number of findings. Among these are the following: (1) Patients in the acute stages of delirium tremens showed in most cases a high incidence of fast activity which, with symptomatic recovery, decreased, and slower alpha activity appeared (Kennard, Beuding, and Wortis, 1945). (2) Fast activity was found likely to be an outstanding characteristic in the EEG records of psychosis (Finley and Campbell, 1941). (3) Adrenalin and Benzedrine have been reported to produce increased fast activity in the EEG (Cutts and Jasper, 1939; Gibbs and Maltby, 1943).

Abnormally slow activity has also been found in the EEG's of psychiatric patients. More theta waves, as well as more of fast activity, than in a normal group were found in the EEG's of a heterogeneous group of psychiatric patients from whom records were taken within 72 hours after admission to the hospital and before any treatment (Rabinovitch, Kennard, and Fister, 1955). In a study of 100 neurotic subjects (M. Dongier, S. Dongier, G. Angel-Villegas, and A. Angel-Villegas, 1957), relatively more of both low and high frequencies were observed than in a group of 113 soldiers (Gallais, Collomb, Miletto, Cardaire, and Blanc-Garin, 1957). The rolandic beta rhythms were, however, regarded as the most characteristic pattern for the neurotic group (H. Gastaut, 1957). In another study, slow rhythms appeared in the records of 46 per cent of neurotic soldiers, while fast rhythms were found in only 18 per cent (Heppenstall, Hill, and Slater, 1945). Golla (1948) says that a number of investigators have shown a relationship between more rhythmic activity slower than the alpha rhythm, on the one hand, and autonomic instability and the recurrence of emotional stress on the other.

Theta waves, or other slow activity, are common in the behavior disorders of children, as will be pointed out later. Delta waves during waking states are said to be found both in functional disorders of the sensorium and in chronic and organic disorders showing psychological deterioration (Kennard, 1953). Some of the records of psychotic patients have been noted to be similar to those found in normal sleep or in epilepsy (P. Davis and H. Davis, 1939).

It appears that there may be an optimal rate of activity in the EEG which is associated with good functioning, while abnormalities of behavior are likely to be associated with an excess of either rapid or slow activity. Some slight support for this hypothesis may perhaps be seen in the fact that moderate to marked clinical improvement following lobotomy has been reported in cases where there was moderate slowing in the EEG after the operation, while little clinical improvement occurred when there was either a slight or a severe degree of slowing (R. D. Walter, Yeager, Margolis, and Simon, 1955).

Great variability in the pattern of the EEG, represented by the presence of activity of many different frequencies or by a tendency toward instability of the EEG pattern, has been reported in a number of psychiatric conditions. Schizophrenics have been said to show activity of many frequencies (Kennard, Rabinovitch, and Fister, 1955; Kennard, 1953); so also have those neurotic soldiers in a neuro-psychiatric rehabilitation center who later showed a poor outcome

(Heppenstall, Hill, and Slater, 1945). Neurotics in general have been said to have a tendency toward instability of the EEG pattern (Lindsley, 1944). Sherman and Jost (1945), for example, reported that the standard deviation of the dominant alpha frequency from second to second was the best single measure of the degree of emotional stability among the physiological measures which differentiated a small group of maladjusted (chiefly neurotic) children from a group of well-adjusted children. The neurotic children were most unstable physiologically.

The degree of synchrony of activity in various parts of the brain appears to be decreased in disturbed conditions. By means of toposcopy it has been shown that there are marked phase differences in alpha activity in different areas during "affective states," and that there is better synchrony of this activity all over the head when the subject is calm (W. G. Walter, 1954a). Psychiatric patients tended to differ from normal controls in having less inter-relatedness of activity between the various cortical areas (Rabinovitch, Kennard, and Fister, 1955).

Paroxysmal activity in the EEG, as previously suggested, is found more frequently in persons with behavior disorders than in the normal population. It occurs often in epileptics and is said to occur in about 20 to 25 per cent of schizophrenics (D. Hill, 1952). Its occurrence in an individual is reported to be variable and apparently to bear a direct relationship to the clinical state at the moment (D. Hill, 1952).

In the behavior disorders (neurotic, psychopathic, delinquent, and problem behavior), there is a relatively high incidence of abnormal EEG's, the incidence varying with age. Abnormal EEG's have been said to decrease with age until the early twenties and to begin to rise again at about the age of fifty-five (Levy and Kennard, 1953).

Jasper, Solomon, and Bradley (1938) found abnormalities of the EEG in 73 per cent of 71 behavior-problem children. There were disturbances of the pattern of the alpha rhythm as well as evidence of slow waves ranging in frequency from 2 to 7 per second. Thirty-nine per cent of the subjects had paroxysmal patterns. Though the irregularities in the records resembled at times those of epileptic children, no seizures had been observed. Subsequent investigations have confirmed the finding of a higher incidence of abnormal EEG records among children with behavior disorders, but the percentage of such records found has differed widely, probably because of differing composition of the groups. Reported rates of abnormality have been said to fall most frequently between 50 and 60 per cent (Ellingson, 1954), the younger the children, the higher the rate of abnormality (Secunda and Finley, 1942).

Lindsley and Cutts (1940) found that a group of children with behavior disorders differed from normal children in having more 2 to 5 and 5 to 8 cycles per second activity as well as in showing more abnormal EEG activity after hyperventilation. The children improved under Benzedrine medication but not under medication with phenobarbital (Lindsley and Henry, 1942).

A number of other investigators have reported an excess of slow activity in the behavior disorders of childhood (C. I. Solomon, Brown, and Deutscher, 1944; Gottlieb, Knott, and Ashby, 1945). While normal children show a certain percentage of abnormal records—C. E. Henry (1944) reports 6.1 per cent—there is less of slow activity and less abnormality in general in their records.

Occurrence of an excess of slow waves, especially theta waves, after the developmental period in which they are usually found, has been attributed by certain British investigators to maturational defect, determined by both genetic and environmental factors (D. Hill, 1950). The influence of an hereditary factor in the production of abnormal EEG's of various kinds has indeed been suggested by a number of other investigators. Some evidence of environmental influence has also been cited.

Gottlieb, Ashby, and Knott (1947) recorded electroencephalograms from 98 parents of 58 patients with behavioral disorders or psychopathic personalities. The patients whose parents had abnormal EEG's showed a significantly higher percentage of abnormal EEG's than the patients whose parents had normal records (72 per cent of abnormal records as compared with 32 per cent). However, factors in the life history of the individual were also shown to be of importance in determining the electroencephalogram since there was a higher incidence of abnormality in the EEG's of patients with a history of severe illness or injury. Approaching the problem from the opposite direction, abnormality of the electroencephalogram in patients was shown to bear a statistically significant relationship to severe maladjustment or convulsive disorders in the direct or collateral family line (Gottlieb, Ashby, and Knott, 1946).

In a later study, it was found that the true parents ($N = 172$) of patients ($N = 86$) with primary behavior disorder or psychopathic personality had a somewhat smaller proportion of normal EEG's than would be expected on the basis of the Gibbses' norms (Knott, Platt, Ashby, and Gottlieb, 1953). The distribution of EEG types among these parents was significantly different from that of the control group of 1000 subjects studied by the Gibbses ($P < .001$). While EEG abnormality in the parents was significantly related to EEG abnormality in their children ($P < .02$), no similar relationship was observed between a small group of patients ($N = 8$) and their foster parents ($N = 16$). Of greater interest is the fact that the type of abnormality in the parents was significantly related to the type of abnormality in the children ($P < .01$), slow EEG's tending to be found in the parents of patients who had slow EEG's, and fast EEG's tending to be found in the parents of patients who had fast EEG's. The patients themselves were described as showing in many instances "deviation in affective control, seen as either an over-reactivity, or as a blandness" (Knott, Platt, Ashby, and Gottlieb, 1953).

Other studies have contributed further evidence of familial similarities in the EEG. In seven pairs of siblings, the per-cent-time-alpha activity showed a correlation of .98 ($P = .01$), and the per-cent-time-3 to 8 cycles per second activity a correlation of .91 ($P = .05$), between the younger and the older sibs of each pair (Ellingson, 1953). Kennard (1949) also has reported a marked similarity in the EEG pattern of the various members of the family when records were taken from the families of children with behavior disorders. The "normal" relatives of these children showed, in 40 per cent of the records, abnormal (dysrhythmic) electroencephalograms, as compared with 60 per cent of such records in the patients, and 10 to 15 per cent of such records in the normal population. Her subjects were 131 patients, 119 of their siblings, and 50 of their parents. Mentioning the higher incidence of abnormal EEG's found by others in psychotic and neurotic patients, as well as an unusual type of EEG found in a large percentage of children with allergies, she suggests that anxiety or tension may be related to dysrhythmia and unstable patterns in the electroencephalogram.

Since certain types of abnormality of the EEG are found, not only in the behavior disorders, but also in epilepsy, some have been tempted to suggest a common neurological basis for epileptoid and problem behavior. If, however, such communality exists, it seems likely that it rests upon a much broader basis than has been suggested. In allergy also, for example, a large percentage of the recorded EEG's show abnormalities as compared with those of a nonallergic control group, even where the allergy is uncomplicated by behavior problems or convulsive disorders (Dees and Lowenbach, 1948). Of 63 children with allergy without convulsions, 45 per cent showed cerebral dysrhythmia. In most cases the dysrhythmia occurred chiefly in the occipital area. Of the total group of 85 patients, those who had a family history of allergy showed a higher percentage of occipital-type dysrhythmia (45 per cent) than those with a negative family history (22 per cent), though normal EEG records were found with about equal frequency in the two groups. Repetition of the measurement from 3 months to 4 years later revealed that the records were unchanged in 25 out of the 36 cases studied. In the other 11 cases the EEG's showed improvement, and all of these patients reported improvement of their allergic symptoms. Clinical improvement was, however, often found without a significant change in the EEG. A combination of allergy, convulsions, and behavior problems did not increase significantly the occurrence of occipital dysrhythmia over that seen in allergy alone.

It appears possible that the common basis, if any, of behavior disorders, allergy, and convulsions may be heightened excitability, or a lack of adequate neural defense against continued excitation, making the organism more susceptible to various forms of disorder. It has been observed that allergic children frequently present behavior problems, especially irritability, and it seems probable that epileptics also tend to be excitable individuals. The forms of abnormality of the EEG most often found in epilepsy, behavior disorders, and allergy are dysrhythmia and, perhaps strangely, from our point of view, a larger than normal proportion of slow waves. It is possible that the source of any common factor in these diverse conditions is to be found in defects of neural organization and integration which predispose toward instability or breakdown. It should be noted that, not only the conditions discussed, but also many others (e.g., periodic stupor, cerebral malaria, encephalitis, syncope, hypoglycemia, and alkalosis) are very likely to be accompanied by a disturbance of cortical rhythms (D. Hill, 1950). It is conceivable, on the other hand, though without adequate empirical support, that the slow waves represent a state of fatigue, manifest during relaxation and deriving from previous overreaction. A significant difference in both alpha frequencies below 10 per second and marked EEG signs of fatigue was found, for example, between 100 behavior-problem boys in a detention home and 100 boys in a trade school (Forssman and Frey, 1953).

In summary, it may be said that the EEG's of subjects showing abnormalities of behavior differ on the average from those of control groups in a number of respects. One of these respects is wavefrequency. It was suggested many years ago that frequency was the aspect of the electrical activity of the cortex most closely correlated with activity of the central nervous system as this was shown in behavior. Studies of both normal and abnormal populations have since that time indicated the strong probability that frequency differences are indeed correlated with differences in behavior. There is considerable evidence that excited or highly aroused patients tend to have less alpha activity, or a higher frequency of alpha activity, or more of fast activity than control groups, though more of slow activity has also at times been reported. There is some, but less, evidence that depressed patients tend to have more of alpha activity, or a lower frequency of alpha activity; and there is considerable evidence that certain patients with behavior disorders, especially children, tend to have more of slow activity (2 to 8 cycles per second) than control subjects.

While the high-frequency, low-amplitude, electrical activity often found in psychological disorders may readily be interpreted as indicative of a high degree of excitation, frequencies below the alpha range offer greater difficulties in interpretation. British electroencephalographers seem inclined in general to accept the suggestion of Denis Hill that such activity is indicative of delay or defect in the maturation of the nervous system. This interpretation finds support in the fact that the incidence of such abnormality decreases with age. Another interpretation invoking constitutional factors is Darrow's (1953), who suggests that, in more stable nervous systems, there is the ability to build up postcentral alpha dominance in defense against repeated, disturbing stimuli, while in less "normal" nervous systems, there is a tendency toward an increase in slow, alpha-like or theta activity in the precentral parts of the brain.

It is not to be expected that differences in frequencies in the EEG would provide the basis for distinguishing one clinical category from another. On the contrary, it appears that many psychiatric disorders have in common considerable "fast activity" such as might be expected in a highly aroused condition. Several clinical categories also have in common a large amount of "slow activity." In psychiatric patients, as in normal subjects, temporary variations in conditions occur. These variations would presumably be accompanied by variations in the EEG.

A clinical category which is based primarily upon the directional aspect of behavior (i.e., the direction taken by an individual's thoughts or overt behavior), and not upon the intensity of response, might be expected to show, in different individuals, diversity in the frequency and amplitude of cortical rhythms. Some "depressions"—for example, agitated depressions—might be expected to show high-frequency, low-amplitude activity, while other "depressions," characterized by a lack of responsiveness, might be expected to show low-frequency, high-amplitude activity. An experimental group composed of both types of patients might show no difference in mean frequency from a control group, or it might show a higher mean cortical frequency, or a lower mean cortical frequency, depending upon the extent to which one type of patient in the group was counterbalanced by the other type of patient. It is at least conceivable that some of the discrepancies in the findings of different investigators are to be accounted for in this fashion, and that not all are due to differences in clinical judgment, or to the absence of a dependable relationship between cortical potentials and basic aspects of behavior. It is possible also that the same clinical disorder—for example, schizophrenia—may tend to be characterized by a high level of arousal in its acute stages and a lower level of arousal after the disorder has persisted for a number of years, the latter condition being perhaps the result of previous excessive response. If such is the case, it might be expected that cortical potentials would be different in the two conditions.

Paroxysmal activity in the EEG, found in epilepsy and in many behavior disorders where no convulsions have been observed, would appear to be the result of a high degree of excitation. The slow waves, which also often occur in these conditions, seem less clear in their significance, though many believe them to be due to defects in neural maturation.

Research in electroencephalography, as in other physiological indicators of excitation, should recognize the fact that, if values characteristic of the individual are to be obtained, repeated measurements under controlled conditions are necessary. Day-to-day variability in the EEG has been found associated with changes in "the blood sugar level, fatigue, emotional status and the like" (D. Hill, 1952).

Changes in the EEG produced by stimulation should, as in the case of other physiological measures, be considered in relation to the base level from which the change occurs. A highly aroused subject may show little EEG change upon stress-stimulation, while a less highly aroused subject may appear to be more responsive if this factor is not taken into account. Perhaps failure to consider the condition of the subject prior to special stimulation is the explanation of some of the reports that certain groups of psychiatric patients were no more responsive, or were less responsive, to various forms of stress than were control subjects.

The nature of the stimulation employed in assessing differential response to stress may also be of significance. Stimuli of basic biological importance, such as pain stimuli, may conceivably fail to reveal a difference between groups which would appear if the stimulus were either the anticipation of pain or the presence of a milder physical stimulus.

It may be concluded that electroencephalographic studies, when employed for purposes for which they are suitable, hold considerable promise in the field of psychiatry. They may, it would appear, be quite useful in indicating the general level of excitation of the psychiatric patient, and may thereby afford clues to, for example, the suitability of a given type of pharmacological treatment or the progress made by the patient toward recovery.

DIFFERENCES IN MUSCLE TENSION

Differences in the degree of muscle tension exist in striking fashion, not only within the normal population, but also between normal and abnormal groups.

Many years ago Jacobson (1928) advanced the hypothesis that "as a rule the neurotic disposition is characterized by habitual hypertension or by frequently hypertensive responses not exhibited by normal individuals." Later studies, in which action potentials from the muscles were recorded, led him to conclude that "when individuals are in a state of 'nervous excitement,' action potentials run high in voltage and frequency as a rule in almost any neuromuscular region tested. No shocks or other test stimuli need be employed by the examiner to induce the high voltages; if the patient is in the state mentioned they are present even if he lies down to rest" (Jacobson, 1941, p. 220). Others also have reported that in some neurotic persons relaxation periods seemed to disappear completely. The electromyogram (EMG) indicated that action currents were constantly present in the muscles (Ruesch and Finesinger, 1943; Lundervold, 1952).

A number of investigators have found that psychiatric patients, as a group, show a higher degree of muscle tension than a normal control group.

Ruesch and Finesinger (1943) found that grip pressure during handwriting was significantly greater for a group of psychiatric patients than for control subjects. When the patients were divided into three separate diagnostic groups, psychoneurosis, psychosis, and neurologic diseases, the difference between each of these groups and normal subjects was found to be reliable. Whereas patients spent about 50 per cent of the time at the third and fourth pressure-levels, control subjects spent about 10 per cent of the time at the third level and no time at the fourth level. Patients more often than control subjects replied that they had feelings of excitement, nervousness, tiredness, trembling inside, shaking and tension in the arms and fingers.

Before the beginning of a task, pressure on a bulb held in the unused hand was reported by Wulfeck (1941b) to be highest in schizophrenics, next highest in manic-depressives, and least in psychoneurotics and normal persons. During the performance of motor tasks, schizophrenics showed a more constant increase in pressure from session to session than any other group, while normal subjects showed the most consistent decrease in pressure. Normality appeared to be characterized by less initial grip pressure and by a consistent decrease in pressure upon successive repetitions of the task.

Perhaps the most extensive investigation of muscle tension in psychiatric patients has been carried out by Malmo and his co-workers at the Allan Memorial Institute of Psychiatry of McGill University. In a series of studies, these investigators have consistently found a higher degree of skeletal muscle tension in neurotics and psychotics than in normal subjects (Malmo and Shagass, 1949a; Malmo, Shagass, and J. F. Davis, 1950; Malmo, Shagass, and J. F. Davis, 1951; Malmo, Shagass, Belanger, and Smith, 1951; Malmo, Shagass, and Smith, 1951). The difference appeared primarily during the response to stimulation, the neurotics, and in most situations, the psychotics, tending to overrespond to pain stimulation, to speeded size-discrimination, to a mirror-drawing task, and to stimulation by sound.[6] Action potentials were recorded from the muscles of the neck and of the forearm, and in some instances from both areas simultaneously. Arm tension was apparently the more differentiating measure. Not merely activity, but also preparation for activity, was accompanied by a reliable difference in tension between psychoneurotic and normal individuals (Malmo, Shagass, and J. F. Davis, 1951). In the case of mirror drawing it appeared that the condition of preparation for activity differentiated more clearly between patients and controls than did the actual performance. However, in almost every situation the physiological responsiveness of the patients, as indicated by muscular tension, was greater than that of the controls.

In later studies, potentials from other muscles, recorded under different stimulating conditions, gave similar results. During listening and talking, patients showed more tension in the chin than did control subjects (A. A. Smith, Malmo, and Shagass, 1954). During pain stimu-

[6] The nature of the stimulation was of some importance. Chronic schizophrenics, for example, were less different from normal subjects in their response to pain stimulation than in their response to situations demanding active contact with the environment (Malmo, Shagass, and J. F. Davis, 1951). Moreover, differences in muscle tension between patients and controls were greater for lower intensities of pain stimulation than for higher intensities.

lation on the forehead or on the forearm, tension of the frontalis muscle was greater in patients than in controls (Malmo and A. A. Smith, 1955). After brief auditory stimulation, tension of the forearm extensors was greater in "anxiety" patients than in control subjects (J. F. Davis, Malmo, and Shagass, 1954). It was observed also that the curve of muscular tension of patients reflected the general course of therapeutic progress, tension in the last five clinical interviews being significantly lower than that in the first four (Shagass and Malmo, 1954). Since, however, it is known that muscle tension under most circumstances decreases with repetition of the stimulus situation, it is possible that this finding reflects merely the familiar phenomenon of adaptation. In this study, concordance between average muscular tension and nursing staff impressions of the patient's mood was noted (Shagass and Malmo, 1954). A "depressed mood" was associated with higher muscle tension than a "cheerful mood."

The emphasis in the McGill studies has been on differences in the response to stimulation. Sainsbury and Gibson (1954), however, have shown that there were differences in muscle tension between anxiety patients and controls even when the subjects were relaxing on a bed and no special stimulation was presented, other than that of having measurements made. Anxiety patients showed greater tension in the frontalis muscle than controls. The difference was significant at the .001 level. Action potentials for the initial 7 minutes of relaxation correlated highly with those of the final 7 minutes. The correlation coefficients were .90 ± .023 for the arms, and .94 ± .002 for the forehead. When the patients were divided into two groups according to whether they scored above or below the median on an inventory of symptoms and bodily complaints, those scoring above the median had significantly higher muscle-tension scores for both the arms and the forehead. In patients who felt tense and anxious, there was widespread muscular tension, while those with head, neck, or arm symptoms showed significantly greater tension in the area to which the symptom was referred.

Both greater anticipatory muscle action potentials and greater residual potentials were found among tense psychiatric patients than among non-tense normal subjects (Davidowitz, Browne-Mayers, Kohl, Welch, and Hayes, 1955).

Bartoshuk (1959) found the slowest habituation rate of the EMG to strong auditory stimulation in neurotic patients with low-amplitude EEG's prior to the stimulation and the most rapid habituation in control subjects with low-amplitude EEG's. Intermediate rates of adaptation were found in both control subjects and patients with high-amplitude alpha.

Almost, if not entirely, alone in reporting more muscle tension in a control group than in psychoneurotics (characterized chiefly by anxiety) is Wishner (1953). In an exploratory study of eleven psychoneurotic subjects and ten normal subjects under various stimulating conditions, he found more muscle action potentials from the frontal muscles in the control subjects. While an explanation of this finding is not readily available (unless it be sought in Wishner's statement that "strict control of timing . . . was impossible owing to clinical exigencies"), the finding runs counter to so much evidence from other studies that it is difficult to accept it without confirmation.

Considerable consistency in the degree of muscular tension shown by an individual in one situation as compared with another has been reported (Malmo, Shagass, and J. F. Davis, 1951; Wishner, 1953). Such consistency supports the hypothesis of a general factor of muscular tension in personality, suggested earlier by the author and others (Duffy, 1946; Freeman, 1948a). Further support for such a factor is seen in the low but statistically reliable correlation found between tension in the arm muscles and tension in the neck (Malmo, Shagass, and J. F. Davis, 1951). Moreover, Sainsbury and Gibson (1954), obtaining from fifteen patients action potentials from the frontalis muscle, the left forearm extensors, the extensors of the left foot, and the posterior cervical muscles, found concordance between the four muscle groups. The coefficient of concordance was 0.45, and this value was significant at the .05 level.

A factor of generalized muscle tension has been questioned, however, by Malmo and A. A. Smith (1955) since tension of the frontalis muscle was found to appear in a different factor from that in which five values for tension in the neck and forearms appeared. This finding need occasion no surprise since the patterning of muscle tension apparently varies with the situation, or with the activity in progress. In fact, Malmo, Shagass, and J. F. Davis (1951) report that, during mirror drawing, when there was diminished focal (arm) activity, there was often increased activity in relatively remote areas of the body, such as the neck or the legs. This circumstance would not appear to deny the existence of some degree of generality in muscle tension, the particular degree present depending upon various factors in the situation and in the individual. Psychiatric patients, for example, were reported to show more diffuse muscular responses to auditory stimulation than a control group (J. F. Davis, Malmo, and Shagass, 1954). Moreover, strong stimulation or vigorous exertion is no doubt accompanied by more generalized muscle tension than weak stimulation or less vigorous response, other factors, such as the degree of habituation, remaining constant. Malmo and his co-workers found that, in one situation, action potentials from the forearm muscles differentiated better between patients and control subjects than those from the masseter and sterno-mastoid muscles (J. F. Davis, Malmo, and Shagass, 1954), while in another situation potentials from the frontalis muscle differentiated better between patients and controls than those from the neck or the forearm (Malmo and A. A. Smith, 1955). In a third situation, in which potentials from the forehead, the neck, the forearm, and the chin were recorded, the only muscle which differentiated between the patients and the controls was the chin muscle (A. A. Smith, Malmo, and Shagass, 1954). Since there is apparently great variability in the "most differentiating" muscle group, it may be suggested that whether or not a given muscle will differentiate well between psychiatric patients and normal subjects will depend at least in part upon the location and function of that muscle in relation to the muscle groups primarily involved in response to the stimulus situation.

Patients in one clinical category have at times been reported to differ from patients in another clinical category in the level of muscular tension, in the change in tension upon the presentation of stimuli, or in both. The relationship between tension measures and clinical classifications is less certainly established, however, than is the relationship between these measures and psychiatric conditions in general. Malmo, Shagass, and J. F. Davis (1951) have reported that the change in muscle tension under pain stress was greatest in a psychoneurotic and an acute psychotic group, intermediate in a control group, and least in a chronic schizophrenic group.

Measures of muscle tension appear, like the electroencephalogram, to be of great potential value in psychiatry and clinical psychology.

DIFFERENCES IN THE ELECTRICAL RESISTANCE OF THE SKIN

Studies of the electrical resistance of the skin have a long history with both normal and psychiatric subjects. Among the many investigations which have been reported, contradictory findings are not infrequent. Some of the apparent contradictions may be explained as due to differences in the conditions and techniques of measurement, and some, no doubt, to problems involved in the psychiatric classification of patients. While a critical survey of these investigations is beyond the scope of the present discussion, a few of the more recent studies and a few of the better known early studies will be mentioned.

Neurotics, as compared with the normal population, have been variously described with respect to both skin resistance and the galvanic skin response. Among those finding no significant difference between normal and neurotic subjects in the level of skin resistance are Wenger (1948) and Jurko, Jost, and Hill (1952), though Wenger did find higher conductance (lower resistance) in operational fatigue patients. Low palmar resistance in "free anxiety," but not where anxiety was relieved through "conversion symptoms," was reported by A. P. Solomon and Fentress (1934). A review of the literature led to the conclusion that measurements of overt palmar sweating in neurotic patients generally showed elevated values, but that there was less consistency in the reports of skin resistance (Altschule, 1953). Silverman and Powell (1944) found either "a strong or intense palmar sweat response" in 83 per cent of 1160 patients in an Army General Hospital. Excessive sweat reactions were found in those discharged from the Army, and especially in those with a diagnosis of psychoneurosis.

Greater reactivity of the galvanic skin response in neurotics than in normal subjects was found by Hoch, Kubis, and Rouke (1944), both in their own study and in their survey of the literature. Altschule (1953), however, in reviewing investigations in this field, reported that the galvanic skin responses of neurotics were variously described. These variations were due, he suggested, not only to differences in technique, but probably also to "the emotional state of the subjects immediately before the test." Two studies were cited to show that, in neurotic patients, anticipation produced abnormally large reactions, and one study was cited to show that the conditioned galvanic response to noise appeared earlier in neurotics than in normal subjects.

Studies of skin-resistance phenomena in psychotics are by no means consistent in their findings. One source of the difficulty may be the fact that psychiatric classifications are not based primarily upon physiological conditions, but rather upon the directional aspect of behavior— attitudes, social orientation, etc.—or upon some combination of the directional and the intensity aspects of response. Under these circumstances no consistent relationship to physiological measures would be expected. Nevertheless it seems clear that psychotic states usually, if not always, involve changes in responsiveness or activation of the organism. It appears probable that some abnormal states are characterized by an unusually high degree of activation (e.g., anxiety, agitation, mania, etc.) and other states by an abnormally low degree of activation (e.g., simple depression). A classification which would place both stuporous and agitated patients in the same group might, if the two types of patients were approximately equal in number and in extent of deviation from the normal, lead to the finding that there was no difference between these patients and a control group in any of the measures which reflected the degree of activation. If, on the other hand, one or the other type of patient was predominant in the experimental group, the finding might well be that psychiatric patients are either more or less reactive than normal subjects, depending upon which type of patient was numerically predominant.

An illustration of the way in which a clinical classification based upon attitudes, or the directional aspect of behavior, may fail to show any correlation with physiological measures is found in data reported by Lockwood (1932) and discussed by D. E. Cameron (1941). Lockwood found that, in patients suffering from mood disorder, there was a correlation between the number of galvanic responses and the hyperglycemic index. In cases which showed no sustained hyperglycemia, and in which the index was zero, the number of galvanic responses was normal or decreased, even in cases apparently showing clinical evidence of agitation and apprehension. She pointed out that other investigators had found that enacting emotional scenes or adopting emotional attitudes did not produce a galvanic skin response in normal subjects or in hysterics. When, on the other hand, the hyperglycemic index was high she found an increase in galvanic activity, not associated with "any particular mental-reaction type but with the degree of emotional tension shown by the subject" (D. E. Cameron, 1941, p. 192). It may be seen from this study that patients classified on the basis of clinical evidence of a certain kind of mental attitude might have diverse physiological responses, representing very different degrees of activation. The clinical group would therefore yield no consistent picture when measured for skin resistance or for certain other physiological responses which presumably reflect the degree of activation. Yet classification on the basis of the degree of activation might be of as much importance in the treatment of the disorders as classification on any other basis.

It would appear that no valid statement can be made about the electrical skin resistance of psychotics as a group. Differences in resistance would be expected between excited and stuporous groups. Moreover, it would not be surprising if schizophrenic patients in the chronic phase differed from those in the acute phase.

Syz (1926) reported high galvanic skin reactivity in paranoid schizophrenics, though many of the galvanic skin responses were "spontaneous." The patients actually showed less direct reaction to the stimuli than normal subjects. Decreased galvanic skin response to stimulation in catatonic and depressive conditions was reported, not only by Syz (1926), but also by Ödegaard (1930) and Westburgh (1929). Darrow and Solomon (1940) reported low skin-resistance levels in both paranoid and depressed patients. Malmo and Shagass (1949a) found a reliably greater decrease in resistance from a pretest to the end of a series of thermal stimulations in a group of unselected psychiatric patients than in a group of control subjects. Among these patients, an anxiety group showed higher resistance than control subjects before the test began and a greater change in resistance from that time to the end of the test.

Comparisons between various psychotic groups and normal subjects were made in a number of early studies from the Phipps Psychiatric Clinic. Richter (1928) found relatively low skin resistance in paranoid schizophrenia, somewhat higher resistance in normal subjects, and still higher skin resistance in catatonic and depressed patients. Syz and Kinder (1928) also reported that normal subjects stood between paranoid schizophrenics on the one hand and catatonic and depressed patients on the other "in skin-resistance behavior and psychogalvanic responsiveness." Paranoid schizophrenics had relatively low skin resistance; catatonic and depressive patients had high initial skin resistance and gave few galvanic responses; normal subjects differed little in initial skin resistance from the schizophrenics but gave rather frequent galvanic responses to stimuli. They showed a smaller decrease in skin resistance during the experimental session than the paranoid schizophrenics, and a greater decrease than the catatonics and the depressives.

Contrary to the Phipps Clinic findings in regard to paranoid schizophrenics are those of Jurko, Jost, and Hill (1952), who reported that both initial skin resistance and resistance at the end of the test were reliably higher in the schizophrenic group than in the control group. Conductance change during the test was significantly smaller for the schizophrenics. These investigators found skin resistance to be one of the measures which differentiated best between control subjects and paranoid schizophrenics and psychoneurotics (hysteria, anxiety reaction, and reactive depression).

There is some evidence that patients with well-formed psychotic states are less reactive than neurotic individuals and that the greatest decrease in reactivity is to be found in the organic and schizophrenic patients (Ödegaard, 1930). Other investigators, finding psychotics less reactive than normal subjects as measured by the galvanic skin response, reported that, as the patient improved, the GSR became more normal (Hoch, Kubis, and Rouke, 1944).

Altschule's review (1953) concludes that the electrical resistance of the skin is generally described as normal or high in psychotic patients. Manic-depressives are said to vary markedly in the galvanic skin response, while schizophrenics are usually, but not always, found to give small galvanic responses, a reaction said to be common in exhaustion, distraction, and illness in general.

A study by Howe (1958) shows, at a high level of confidence, that basal skin resistance is lowest for the chronically anxious, highest for chronic schizophrenics, and intermediate for normal subjects.

More consistent findings in regard to psychotic conditions might be expected if agitated or excited patients were not grouped with stuporous or depressed patients; if acute and chronic stages of the psychoses were distinguished; and if measurement of the individual was repeated on a number of occasions in order to minimize the effect of variations in the condition of the patient. There seems to be no justification for regarding psychotics as a homogeneous group, or even for regarding a particular clinical category such as schizophrenia or manic-depressive psychosis as homogeneous from the point of view of responsiveness.

DIFFERENCES IN OTHER MEASURES

Blood Pressure

Psychoneurotics appear to differ from the normal population, probably in the extent of the blood-pressure rise in response to stimulation and almost certainly in the duration of the elevation in blood pressure. There seems to be no conclusive evidence that they differ in the general level of pressure at all times. Two investigators who have made a number of studies in this field describe the situation as follows:

It would be incorrect to conclude that systolic blood-pressure *level* in the clinical sense is generally elevated in psychoneurosis. . . . The facts indicate that excessively elevated blood-pressure is found in psychoneurotics particularly when they are placed *under stress,* and that this elevation may be interpreted as a greater and more prolonged change of blood-pressure in response to stress in the psychoneurotics than in normal controls (Malmo and Shagass, 1952, p. 91).

This phenomenon was observed in three different stressful situations. There was considerable individual constancy in the blood-pressure response to the various types of stress.

Blood pressure may, apparently, be a relatively sensitive indicator of stress. When several psychomotor tests were given to a group of neurotics and a group of normal subjects, a rise in blood pressure occurred consistently during the performance of the various tasks (Malmo, Shagass, and Heslam, 1951). In fact, it was found in 92 per cent of all individual tests. During a given performance, diastolic blood-pressure changes tended to parallel systolic blood-pressure changes. The chief finding, however, was that systolic pressure in control subjects showed greater adaptation than in patients. The only reliable differences in extent of blood-pressure change during a given test as between neurotics and normal subjects was found in the last psychomotor test and the last cold-pressor test and was interpreted as being due to a difference in adaptation. The mean systolic blood-pressure level of the patients was higher than that of the control subjects in all the tests.

Higher systolic blood pressure in psychoneurotics and acute psychotics than in normal subjects or chronic schizophrenics was found also during a rapid discrimination test (Malmo, Shagass, Belanger, and Smith, 1951). A similar result was not obtained during the instruction period for a mirror-drawing test, both patients and control subjects in this case showing a sharp increase in pressure (Malmo, Shagass, and J. F. Davis, 1951). The patients were differentiated from the normal subjects, however, in having a much greater skeletal muscle response. The investigators suggest that the autonomic preparatory response of the two groups was approximately equal, while the somatic preparatory response of the patients was greater.

In another study from the same laboratory, chronic schizophrenics were reported not to be abnormally sluggish, as has at times been suggested, but to resemble normal control subjects in their systolic blood-pressure reaction to stress. Diastolic blood pressure during pain stress was significantly higher for chronic schizophrenics than for any other group (Malmo, Shagass, and Smith, 1951).

Wenger (1948) found that both systolic and diastolic blood pressure were significantly higher in operational fatigue patients and in hospitalized psychoneurotics (anxiety type or mixed type) than in aviation students.

There is fairly general agreement that psychoneurotics show less adaptation in the blood-pressure response, or slower recovery from the effects of stimulation, than normal subjects. In a number of experimental situations, but not in all, neurotics have shown greater elevation of blood pressure in response to stimulation than was shown by the control groups employed.

It has been suggested that the reactivity of the autonomic nervous system as indicated by blood-pressure changes after the injection of a cholinergic drug, is a valuable tool in predicting behavioral adjustment and spontaneous behavioral changes in schizophrenics (Hirschstein, 1955). A significant correlation coefficient of —.527 was found between poor behavioral adjustment (rated on the Gardner Behavior Chart) and the increase of blood pressure following the injection of Mecholyl Chloride, and a significant coefficient of .425 between good behavioral adjustment and decrease of blood pressure following the injection.

Measures of Heart Rate

Altschule (1953) reviews a number of studies of the heart rate of neurotic and psychotic patients. The conclusions, in general, seem to be that the cardiac rate is either normal or accelerated in patients with neurosis or neurocirculatory asthenia. During psychiatric interviews or other stress situations, it rises markedly. Exercise produces an excessive increase in heart rate.

In studies of manic-depressive patients, the pulse rate has been reported to be either normal or increased, while in schizophrenia it has been reported to be normal, high, or low (Altschule, 1953). It is said that, under conditions of stress, schizophrenic patients, even more than those with other types of psychoses, may show abnormal increases in pulse rate. On standing up, schizophrenics whose disease is of recent origin show excessive increases in pulse rate, while chronic schizophrenics do not show this phenomenon. Altschule concludes that changes in pulse rate in psychosis are either normal or similar to those found in neurosis. A few studies, chosen more or less at random, are the following:

1. Wenger (1948) reported that a group of psychoneurotics, anxiety type or mixed type, had a significantly faster heart rate and less arrhythmia than unselected aviation students. Operational fatigue patients also had a significantly different score for heart period and sinus arrhythmia.

2. Malmo and Shagass (1949a) found that the mean heart rate and the heart-rate variability were lower for control subjects than for a mixed-patient group, an anxiety-patient group, and a group of early

schizophrenics, though the differences were not statistically reliable. The respiratory factor was shown to be important in increasing heart-rate variability. During mirror drawing a group of psychiatric patients and a group of controls both showed a marked increase in heart rate during the period when instructions were being given, but the increase was approximately equal in the two groups (Malmo, Shagass, and J. F. Davis, 1951). Simultaneously recorded muscle tension had shown a considerably greater increase in tension for the patients.

3. Malmo, Shagass, and Smith (1951) found that a small, selected group of chronic schizophrenics had a reliably higher mean heart rate during pain stress than control subjects.

4. Jurko, Jost, and Hill (1952), measuring heart rate during an experimental situation requiring response to the pictures of the Rosenzweig Picture Frustration Study, found that, in the initial period, a psychoneurotic group had a heart rate which was faster, but not significantly faster than that of a control group, while a group of early paranoid schizophrenics had a heart rate significantly faster than that of either psychoneurotics or control subjects. The per cent of change in heart rate from the initial period to the test period was not significantly different for the control and the psychoneurotic groups but was significantly smaller for the schizophrenic group, possibly because this group was already near its ceiling of response.

In general, it may be said that there is some reason to conclude that neurotics have a more rapid heart rate and show greater changes in heart rate than control groups, but the evidence is not very clear. It seems probable that certain types of psychotics resemble neurotics in both respects, but again the evidence is conflicting.

Measures of Respiration

The resting rate of respiration of neurotics appears to be either normal or slightly more rapid than normal, but both emotional upset and exercise increase the rate to an abnormal degree (Altschule, 1953). The findings in regard to the respiratory rate of manic-depressives and psychotics are said to show no consistent difference from normal subjects, except that stress usually produces an excessive increase in respiratory activity (Altschule, 1953).

Wenger (1948) reported that hospitalized psychoneurotics had significantly faster and shallower respiration than preflight students.

Jurko, Jost, and Hill (1952) found that respiratory rate during the initial period of their experiment was significantly greater in both a psychoneurotic group and an early schizophrenic group than in a control group; that during the test period the respiratory frequencies of the three groups showed no differences; and that in the final period of the experiment the initial differences between the groups reappeared. The control group showed the most stable respiratory pattern, the psychoneurotic group a more unstable pattern, and the early schizophrenic group the most unstable pattern of all. These differences were said to be reliable.

Evidence to be presented in a following section suggests that irregularity of respiration is characteristic of neurotics and of certain groups of psychotics.

DIFFERENCES IN FLUCTUATIONS IN ACTIVATION

A large number of functional disorders appear to be characterized by "spontaneous" changes or "irregularities" in the records of various physiological functions. These fluctuations in activation, implying perhaps a certain lack of control, or a deficiency in inhibition, in basic processes are of no less significance than differences in the intensity of response, and they may be of greater behavioral import. In psychiatric patients, they have been studied most intensively in regard to the activity of the muscular system.

Muscle Activity

Irregularities in muscular activity, or the defective regulation of motor responses, has been observed as tremor, as irregular pressure on a key or bulb, as postural unsteadiness, or as restless movements. Luria (1932) reported that 61 per cent of his subjects with "neuropathic symptoms," as compared with 13 per cent of normal subjects, were "reactively labile." Neurotic subjects, as a result of a tendency toward increased "mobilisation of excitation," and "decreased activity of the higher regulative mechanisms" had great difficulty in inhibiting responses. In twenty-five neurotic patients, he found hardly a case in which there was a reasonably well-organized delayed movement. He believed that the greater the ability to inhibit and elaborate a beginning excitation before it reached its motor termination, the fewer were the chances of disorganization of a response as a result of conflicts. According to his point of view, motor irregularities in psychiatric patients would be due to greater responsiveness and deficient inhibitory ability.

While constitutional factors may predispose an individual toward irregularities in motor response, environmental factors also have been shown to be determinants of differences in the degree of organization of behavior. Among the factors which have been reported to decrease motor co-ordination in normal subjects are various forms of stress (Luria, 1932; Altschule, 1953); fatigue from muscular exertion (R. J. Williams, 1946); and the administration of analeptic or depressant drugs (Hauty, 1954).

Though it appears that factors which affect the regulation of motor responses are usually found to affect also the degree of muscle tension, yet as was pointed out in Chapter 8, present evidence suggests that the two variables are not related in linear fashion. Evidence is insufficient to support a curvilinear relationship, but this possibility should not be overlooked. The degree of muscle tension may be indicative of the degree of excitation, while irregularities of motor response may, perhaps, represent deficient inhibition and consequent in-co-ordination (Duffy, 1930, 1932b).

Several studies have found either no evidence, or slight evidence, of a relationship between the degree of muscle tension and fluctuations in tension. A factor analysis of measures of grip pressure, of point pressure, and of fluctuations in grip pressure, as shown in irregularities of the kymograph tracing, revealed that the measure of motor irregularities appeared in a different factor from that designated as the general level of muscular tension (Duffy, 1946). Malmo and his colleagues have reported the two aspects of response to be relatively independent of each other except for the fact that, in one study, tension of the frontalis muscle appeared in the same factor as measures of movement irregularities, and in another study both frontalis and chin tension appeared in a factor which included motor irregularities (Malmo, Shagass, Belanger, and Smith, 1951; Malmo, Shagass, and J. F. Davis, 1951; Malmo and A. A. Smith, 1955). In these investigations curvilinear relationships were not sought. It is probable that the data did not include values of muscle tension sufficiently low to have revealed such a relationship if it exists.

Agents which affect activation may, it appears, not have the same effect upon gross movements as upon fine movements. An analeptic drug, for example, was reported to increase fine manual tremor but to have no significant effect on coarse tremor, while a depressant was reported to reduce fine tremor and increase coarse tremor (Hauty, 1954). Similarly, the use of small muscles as compared with the use of large muscles, was believed by one observer to differentiate "emotionally stable" from "emotionally unstable" children observed on a playground.[7] The unstable children were said to show almost constant play of fine muscles but relatively little activity of large muscle groups. It is conceivable, therefore, that motor irregularities measured as movements of large scope would have a different significance from motor irregularities measured as frequent but relatively small movements. A large change in muscle tension, with the tension sustained for some time at the same level, may be of less behavioral significance than frequent though small oscillations in tension. Instability of function may be better represented by the frequency of change in muscle tension than by the size of the changes. Further investigation is required to determine precisely what measure is the best indicator of defective regulation of motor responses.

Turning to data on the relationship between motor irregularities and various psychiatric conditions, we may consider first a study by Jost (1941) in which hand tremor before and after stimulation was compared in 20 well-adjusted children and 18 children with problems of adjustment, all but two of whom (psychotics) were said to show signs of a neurotic condition. He found that the well-adjusted group showed significantly less tremor both before and after stimulation. Hand tremor before frustration had a correlation coefficient of .56 with rated emotional instability in the group with problems of adjustment.

Changes in grip pressure during handwriting were found by Ruesch and Finesinger (1943) to be significantly greater in number among 40 patients with various psychiatric and neurologic diagnoses than among 12 normal control subjects.

Finger movement during a stress situation was reported by Malmo and Shagass (1949a) to be reliably greater in each of three psychiatric patient groups (mixed patient group, anxiety group, and early schizophrenics) than in a normal control group. The finger movement was measured as oscillation of pressure on a button on which the forefinger rested, and which the subject was instructed to press whenever he thought the heat stimulation applied to the forehead was about to become painful. Since, in the score for finger movement, voluntary pressure on the button was not distinguished from involuntary tremor, these investigators do not have an uncomplicated measure of tremor. They observed that the patients in whom anxiety was predominant showed a much greater amount of finger movement than the less

---

[7] This conclusion, a personal communication from a nursery-school teacher at the Child Development Institute of Teachers College, Columbia University, was based upon general, rather than controlled, observation.

anxious patients or the controls, and that the amount of finger movement was increased by both pain stimulation and questioning.

In a later study, Malmo, Shagass, and J. F. Davis (1951) found no correlation between irregularity of finger movement and total forearm tension, finger movement again including, however, voluntary pressure on a button. They conclude that finger-movement records very likely provide a measure of motor control and that, within limits, motor control may vary independently of muscular tension, though both measures are related to psychoneurosis.

Recording voluntary pressure of the right forefinger during speeded size discrimination, Malmo et al. (Malmo, Shagass, Belanger, and Smith, 1951) reported that control subjects showed significantly less irregular pressure than did psychoneurotics, acute psychotics, or chronic schizophrenics. Left-finger pressure during the same task was also more irregular in the psychiatric patients as a group than in the control group. No reliable difference in this measure was found, however, between controls and acute psychotics (14 Ss) when the latter were considered separately. One of the most striking differences was that between anxiety patients and mixed neurotics, the anxiety patients showing considerably more irregularity of pressure. The coefficient of correlation between the ratings on irregularity of pressure from the right forefinger and that from the left forefinger was only .26, a finding which may be explained in part by the difference in the method of arriving at the two scores. The investigators point out that they have found evidence of deficient regulation of motor responses in psychiatric patients under three different conditions of nonspecific stress, and they suggest that the psychoneurotics may be characterized by an abnormal degree of motor disturbance under any stressful condition. It is not clear why the suggestion is limited to psychoneurotics or why, if so limited, it is not applied specifically to anxiety neurotics since mixed neurotics showed less irregularity of left-finger pressure than any other psychiatric group studied.

In a more recent study from the same laboratory, a group of psychiatric patients, weighted heavily with anxiety states, again showed more motor irregularities than a control group (Malmo and Smith, 1955). Painful thermal stimulation was applied to the forearm or to the forehead. Under both conditions patients showed more head and body movements. Under forehead stimulation they also showed more fluctuations in electric potentials, more irregularity of finger movement, and more withdrawal movements.

Other investigators also have found differences between psychiatric patients and normal controls in various aspects of their motor responses. Sainsbury and Gibson (1954) found more nervous movements (measured electromyographically) in anxiety patients than in control subjects. Commenting that fine movements of the fingers and hands have also been reported to be more marked in anxious subjects, Sainsbury (1955) says that these resemble tremors "which suggests that they result from a disorganization of the central motor coordination mechanisms."

Edwards and Harris (1953) reported greater finger tremor in schizophrenics than in normal subjects. Over a 33-month period, patients who, according to hospital records, had shown improvement were found to have significantly less finger tremor than previously, while patients who, according to the records, had not improved were found to show an increase in tremor. It has been suggested that fine finger tremor is a sign which appears with EEG abnormality (Hodge, 1945).

Forty-three neurotics scheduled to be discharged from the Army on grounds of psychiatric disability were well differentiated from "normal" soldiers by both "small" and "large" motor disturbances in the pressure response to words (Clarke, 1955). Both measures showed significant point-biserial correlations with neuroticism. Normal and neurotic soldiers tended to be disturbed by the same words, thus suggesting that the difference between the two groups was in the degree of response to the word list and not in the fact that certain words tapped areas of conflict in the neurotics but left normal subjects undisturbed.

Neurotics have been reported to have more defective muscular coordination than normal subjects when they attempted to maintain a fixed position of the body and limbs (Himmelweit, Desai, and Petrie, 1946). They had a high static ataxia score. Ingham (1955) also found a statistically significant tendency for neurotics to make more movements than normal subjects as measured by both static ataxia and arm movements—before any suggestion had been given.

Sainsbury (1955) measured electomyographically the shoulder, elbow, wrist, and most finger and thumb movements during a series of psychiatric interviews. He found that the more stressful periods of the interviews were accompanied by more gestural movements and, in most cases, an increase in heart rate.

While both irregularity of motor response and the degree of muscle tension differentiate psychiatric patients from normal subjects, the former measure has been suggested by Malmo et al. as being the more discriminative. It seems reasonable to suppose that a measure indicative of deficient regulation of basic processes, if that is the significance of motor irregularities, would be more closely related to abnormalities of behavior than would a measure indicative of the degree of intensity of response.

Electrical Resistance of the Skin

Syz (1926) reported that "spontaneous and disconnected galvanic waves," which were present in only a small percentage of his normal subjects, occurred in 78 per cent of the paranoid schizophrenic patients, in 38 per cent of the catatonic patients, and in 32 per cent of the depressed patients. Syz and Kinder (1928) also found a high percentage of spontaneous fluctuations in skin resistance in paranoid schizophrenics, but relatively few fluctuations in depressive or catatonic patients, or in normal subjects. Persons with numerous spontaneous waves were said to show, in general, lower palmar resistance and a greater decrease in resistance during stimulation than the average of the group to which they belonged.

Syz (1926) also reported that the galvanic skin-response curve was more regular in normal subjects than in schizophrenics or depressed patients.

Malmo and his associates (Malmo, Shagass, Davis, Cleghorn, Graham, and Goodman, 1948) found a larger number of oscillations in skin resistance during anticipation of pain stimulation in a group of psychoneurotics selected for a high anxiety level than in a group of matched controls. In a subsequent study, Malmo and Shagass (1949a) failed to confirm this finding, perhaps, they suggest, because of a difference in technique.

More fluctuations in skin resistance in the absence of any apparent stimulation were found in a psychopathic group than in a group of normal individuals (Ödegaard, 1930, 1932). As the patient recovered, there was a decrease in the degree of instability of the skin-resistance curve.

A well-known survey of the field (D. E. Cameron, 1941) concludes that "readings obtained from psychopathic patients are more variable than those obtained from normal control groups and that, in general, as the patient improves the variability of the readings becomes less."

The Electroencephalogram

Great variability in the pattern of the EEG, represented by the presence of activity of many different frequencies or by a tendency toward instability of the EEG pattern, has been reported in a number of psychiatric conditions. Schizophrenics have been said to show activity of many frequencies (Kennard, Rabinovitch, and Fister, 1955; Kennard, 1953); so also have those neurotic soldiers in a neuropsychiatric rehabilitation center who later showed a poor outcome (Heppenstall, Hill, and Slater, 1945). Neurotics in general have been said to show a tendency toward instability of the EEG pattern (Lindsley, 1944). Sherman and Jost (1945), it will be recalled, reported that the standard deviation of the dominant alpha frequency from second to second was the best single measure of emotional stability among the physiological measures which differentiated a group of maladjusted (chiefly neurotic) children from a group of well-adjusted children.

Darrow and others are said to have shown that spontaneous fluctuations in the electroencephalogram are paralleled by similar changes in the level of sympathetic tone (Lindsley, 1956).

Respiration

Studies of respiration suggest that neurotic, and in many instances psychotic, individuals show more variable respiration than normal subjects. Finesinger (1944), for example, reported more stable respiratory patterns in normal individuals that in certain groups of neurotic individuals.

Malmo and Shagass (1949a), using two measures of respiratory irregularity, one of which reflected unsteadiness of respiration in the stress situation as a whole, and the other the immediate disturbing effects of pain stimulation, found that both measures showed significantly greater respiratory irregularity in anxiety patients than in a mixed patient group or a control group. An early schizophrenic group proved to be more similar to the anxiety group than to any other. In another study it was found that a group of 17 chronic schizophrenics selected for lobotomy did not differ significantly from a control group and a combined group of psychoneurotics and acute psychotics in regularity of respiration during the stress situation as a whole, but tended to be less responsive (i.e., to show less respiratory irregularity) immediately after pain stimulation (Malmo, Shagass, and Smith, 1951). There was reliably more shallow breathing in the chronic schizophrenic group.

Irregularity of respiration was found by Syz (1926) in both paranoid schizophrenics and catatonics, as compared with depressed patients and normal subjects.

Altschule (1953) concluded that varying degrees of irregularity of respiratory rhythm have been found in psychotic patients, while marked irregularities in rate and rhythm of respiration occur in patients with neurocirculatory asthenia as well as in some other neurotic patients. These irregularities were said to have been found when the patients were at rest and, more markedly, when they were engaged in activity or were upset.

Heart Rate

Stability of heart rate was reported by Whitehorn and Richter (1937) to differentiate neurotic, psychotic, and normal subjects, the psychotic subjects having the most stable heart rate and the neurotic subjects the least stable. Sherman and Jost (1945) found that a more stable heart rate was associated with fewer changes in the EEG during response and less change in skin resistance.

Altschule (1953), however, comments that it is well known that the cardiac rate shows marked variability in psychotic patients without regard to the type of psychosis.

Conclusions

"Spontaneous" changes in activation, irregularities in response, and variability in physiological functioning have frequently been found in certain neurotic and psychotic conditions. Such phenomena may prove to be of greater significance in behavior pathology than differences in the intensity of response.

GROUPS OF MEASURES

In some instances the simultaneous recording of a number of different physiological variables has revealed aspects of the neuroses and psychoses not discernible from the consideration of a single type of measurement.

Jost (1941), using a number of different physiological measures in his comparison of well-adjusted and poorly adjusted children, most of whom were said to show signs of neurosis, concluded that "a better picture of an individual's physiological instability was obtained when all of the measures were considered." Employing as a criterion of physiological instability, scores in which more than half of the measures were outside one sigma of the mean of the control subjects, he found that two-thirds of his experimental (poorly adjusted) subjects fell in the physiologically unstable group. The experimental group responded more violently to a frustration situation and also showed more variable patterns of physiological activity during the control period. In a later study in which a number of physiological measurements were made, including brain potentials, skin resistance, heart rate, and respiration, Sherman and Jost (1945) reported that neurotic subjects were more unstable physiologically than well-adjusted subjects when percentile scores of the two groups were compared. The neurotic subjects scored above the 50 per cent mean of the well-adjusted subjects in all measures except heart rate. When composite standard scores were obtained from the various measures, all of the fifteen emotionally maladjusted children, except three who had been diagnosed as schizophrenic, had negative scores.

Wenger (1948) employed a number of physiological measures in order to study the "autonomic balance" of hospitalized psychoneurotics in the Army Air Force. He found that they differed from aviation students and cadets in having lower and more acid salivary output, faster and shallower respiration, faster heart rate and little sinus arrhythmia, lower finger and sublingual temperature at the beginning of the test, higher systolic and diastolic blood pressure, and lower resting metabolism. However, only ten of the twenty measures employed showed significant differences between the two groups. He concluded, nevertheless, that the patients showed autonomic imbalance "with functional predominance of the sympathetic nervous system."

Patients with anxiety as the predominant characteristic were found to show a higher degree of physiological disturbance under stress (measured by muscle potentials, finger movement, respiration, heart rate, galvanic skin response, and brain potentials) than either normal control subjects or patients in whom anxiety was secondary or absent (Malmo and Shagass, 1949a). The degree of anxiety seemed to be related to the degree of physiologic disturbance, the clearest correspondence between the two being shown in muscle potentials and finger movement. It was concluded that the extent to which the subject's response was confined to autonomic reactions instead of extending into motor response systems seemed to depend largely upon the level of anxiety. A high degree of anxiety appeared to be accompanied by increased discharge into the skeletal muscles involved in responding to the stress stimulation. Less anxious subjects showed better motor control and tended to restrict their activities to appropriate responses. More anxious subjects tended to show excess preparatory activity and to overreact when the stimulus was presented.

Hyperactivity in early schizophrenia has also been reported when measurements were made of muscle potentials, brain potentials, heart rate, respiration, skin resistance, and finger movement (Malmo and Shagass, 1949a). The responses of a group of early schizophrenics were more like those of a group of psychoneurotics with marked anxiety than like those of either control subjects or a mixed patient group (Malmo and Shagass, 1949a). In a later study of chronic schizophrenics, in which however the experimental group was both small and selected, it was found that physiological responsiveness, as indicated by many different measures, was as great as, or greater than, that in normal subjects (Malmo, Shagass, and Smith, 1951). An exception was found in respiratory irregularity immediately after thermal stimulation. According to this measure, the chronic schizophrenics were relatively unresponsive.

Some studies have suggested that responsiveness becomes less and less with longer duration of the disorder. While there is some agreement that there is increased reactivity in early schizophrenia, there are conflicting data with respect to the degree of reactivity in later stages of the psychosis. Malmo et al. suggest that "background physiological responsiveness" in their subjects was by no means low, but that "purposive acts" required in their test situation were "less frequently or less well executed by the schizophrenics" (Malmo, Shagass, and Smith, 1951). This distinction between internal arousal and overt response is an interesting one and may serve to reconcile some of the discrepancies in the reports of other investigators. It does not appear, however, to account for all the findings of hyporeactivity, since many of these findings were based on studies of physiological functioning of what might be called a "background" nature.

It is apparent that the simultaneous recording of a group of physiological measures may bring out aspects of abnormal functioning which would not be observed if a single measure alone were employed.

RECOVERY FROM THE EFFECTS OF STIMULATION

The general finding of investigators has been that maladjusted individuals ordinarily require a longer period of time than well-adjusted persons to recover from the effects of stimulation. They differ from the well adjusted, not only in the extent of response, but also in the persistence of disturbed physiological conditions. Equilibrium is restored less quickly. The time lag in the return to the previous level of physiological functioning is, as was pointed out in Chapter 10, not to be accounted for merely in terms of the extent of disturbance produced, for it has been shown that recovery is slower in relation to the

extent of disturbance. This relationship, it will be recalled, has sometimes been expressed as a "recovery quotient," or RQ, in which the
extent of recovery from the effects of stimulation during a given short
interval after the peak of the reaction is divided by the extent of
change in response which occurred between the time of stimulation
and the time of the peak of reaction.

Early studies of normal subjects by Darrow and Heath (1932), and
by Freeman (1939), revealed that the measure was correlated with
neurotic tendency as indicated by questionnaires.

In a later study, Freeman and Pathman (1942) found that RQ measures for palmar skin conductance (percentage of recovery 5 minutes
after the cessation of stimulation) showed test-retest coefficients of
correlation ranging from .85 to .93, and intercorrelations in four different types of stress situation ranging from .50 to .78. They suggested
that rapid recovery of internal equilibrium was to some extent associated with a greater increase in overt movement during stimulation.
A highly significant correlation coefficient of .53 was obtained between the average RQ score and movement increment scores obtained
through measuring the air displaced from a pneumatic mattress. It
was tentatively suggested that those individuals who "readily discharge aroused excitation by overt muscular action," even though this
action is apparently unadaptive, are the ones who "tend to recover
internal equilibrium most rapidly."

When data from the previous study were related to various other
measures, including a psychiatric rating of emotional stability,[8] the
correlation coefficients between the rating and the recovery quotients
for the four situations ranged from .34 to .49 (Freeman and Katzoff,
1942b). In two of the four situations the conductance RQ was negatively related to the amount of pretest movement (r's of —.50 and
—.65), and in three of the four situations it was negatively related to
the variability in pretest movement (r's ranged from —.45 to —.70),
thus indicating that rapid physiological recovery did not occur in individuals showing numerous or variable restless movements before the
test. Freeman (1948a) has suggested that neuroticism may be related
to "unreleased and self-perpetuating internal nervous excitement."

Freeman and Haggard (1941), selecting from twenty-six children
the ten subjects who had the highest, and the ten subjects who had the
lowest skin conductance, and computing RQ's for these subjects after
exposure to a frustration situation, found no reliable correlation between the RQ and the increment in restless movements during the

[8] The psychiatric ratings were made by Dr. Leon Saul.

test, while variability in restless movements during the frustration period was associated with rapid recovery ($r = .49$). These findings do not appear to offer adequate support for the interpretation suggested by the investigators—i.e., that "a person who does not control or inhibit restless movements during a stressful situation recovers more rapidly" from the physiological effects of frustration than one who does.

Champion (1950), employing the RQ of skin conductance, reported more rapid recovery from an experimentally induced disturbance when there was adaptive movement than when there was no movement.

Individuals showing behavior abnormalities have been compared with normal subjects in the speed of recovery of various physiological functions after stress stimulation. Each of a number of functions has been found to show slower recovery in groups of psychiatric patients than in corresponding normal groups.

Comparing a group of well-adjusted control subjects with a small group of neurotic, psychotic, and behavior-problem children, Jost (1941) concluded that the experimental group showed, not only an exaggerated physiological response, but also a "slower return to the pre-stimulus level of physiological activity." The measures used were heart rate and skin resistance.

Malmo and his co-workers found that psychoneurotics differed from normal control subjects in showing more "residual tension" after the cessation of stimulation. In two studies of the response to strong auditory stimulation, the level of muscle tension reached by the two groups showed less difference in the 0.2-second period of reflex startle than in the "after-response" (Malmo, Shagass, and J. F. Davis, 1950; J. F. Davis, Malmo, and Shagass, 1954). At 0.3 second the tension-level of the control subjects was dropping, while that of the patients was either continuing to rise (Malmo, Shagass, and J. F. Davis, 1950) or was showing a secondary rise (J. F. Davis, Malmo, and Shagass, 1954). After a rapid-discrimination test, there was some indication that acute psychotics, and perhaps psychoneurotics, showed less recovery from the muscular effects of the stimulation (as indicated by forearm tension) [9] than did control subjects (Malmo, Shagass, and J. F. Davis, 1951). Tension level recorded from the chin during questions about feelings was maintained in psychiatric patients (chiefly psychoneurotics) after a point at which, in normal subjects, it was falling rapidly (A. A. Smith, Malmo, and Shagass, 1954). This difference was significant at the .001 level of confidence and was not accounted for by a

[9] Masseter and sternomastoid reactions did not differentiate patients from control subjects.

difference in the percentage of time during which the two groups were talking. Finally, a group of psychiatric subjects, in about half of whom hysterical components were the most prominent feature, showed less decrement of a voluntary response in the course of its repeated elicitation than did a normal control group (Malmo and Wallerstein, 1955). Decrement was measured in terms of the latency and duration of forefinger pressure on a button, and in terms of muscle potentials in the responding arm. Patients failed to show either the increased latency and decreased duration of response or the decreased muscle tension shown by control subjects. On the contrary, they continued to show great responsiveness in both of these respects. In at least one case talking produced a reduction in forehead tension (Malmo, Shagass, and F. H. Davis, 1950).

Blood-pressure studies by Malmo and Shagass (1952) have indicated that psychoneurotics differ from control subjects in the longer continuation of the blood-pressure response to stress. In fact, the investigators report that "the most consistent difference between psychoneurotics and normals was in the psychoneurotics' continuation, or progressive increase of high blood-pressure, during a later phase of the stress situation, when the normals' reaction was showing definite signs of being held in check." There is also some evidence in this study that acute schizophrenics showed a smaller drop in blood pressure, or less recovery from the effects of stimulation, than was shown by normal subjects or by chronic schizophrenics.

In another study from the same laboratory it was reported that, under experimental conditions of "non-specific stress," systolic blood pressure in control subjects showed greater adaptation than in psychoneurotic patients (Malmo, Shagass, and Heslam, 1951). While both groups showed blood-pressure response to stimulation, the response of the control subjects tended to diminish as the experimental session progressed, while the response of the patients tended to persist at the initial high level. The difference between the two groups was more noticeable during a performance and a postperformance period than it was during the preperformance period or the period when instructions were being given.

Jurko, Jost, and Hill (1952), comparing groups of nonpatients, psychoneurotics, and early schizophrenics, reported delayed recovery from physiological response to stimulation in the psychoneurotic and schizophrenic groups as compared with the nonpatient group. Among the measures used were skin conductance, blood pressure, and respiration. The form in which the data are presented makes it somewhat difficult to check this conclusion, but it appears that the conclusion is well justified with respect to skin conductance and somewhat uncertain with respect to the other measures.

Brower (1948) found that, with normal subjects, "peripheral motor discharge tends to reduce tension as manifested in the cardiovascular system."

Relatively slow physiological recovery from the effects of stimulation and a relatively slow decrease in the degree of response to repeated stimulation (i.e., adaptation) appear to characterize individuals with various abnormalities of behavior. Measurement of this aspect of activation, as well as the degree of activation, and fluctuations in the activation of various systems, seems likely to be of considerable significance in the study of the functional disorders.

CONCLUSIONS

In spite of some conflicting evidence, there appears to be considerable support for the conclusion that individuals with various forms of behavior pathology differ from "normal" subjects in various aspects of activation, as well as in the directional aspect of their behavior. The differences between the two groups would probably be greater than those usually reported if control groups did not frequently contain a number of individuals of neurotic or psychotic tendency.

The aspects of activation which appear to be of significance in relation to abnormalities of behavior are the degree of activation, fluctuations in activation, and the speed of physiological recovery from the effects of stimulation. These phenomena may be observed in many different systems, though apparently with more consistency in some systems than in others.

chapter 12

Conclusions

The hypotheses presented here, and the review of the literature undertaken from the point of view of activation theory, have perhaps raised more problems than they have solved. It seems apparent that activation (its degree, its fluctuations, and its speed of return to a prestimulus level) is associated with important differences in behavior. It is apparent that differences in activation may be produced by many different factors, ranging from the genes to hormones, drugs and learned responses to cues. There appears to be both some degree of "generality" and some degree of "specificity" in activation, the extent of each remaining an unsolved problem. It is contended, however, that activation is an organismic phenomenon, and that it is recognized as such when we speak of an individual's being relaxed or being excited rather than of a particular system's showing this condition.

Characteristic individual differences in activation, or responsiveness, are suggested as the basis from which certain other differences in behavior may be derived. Extreme differences in the degree of activation, the variability of activation, or the speed of return of activation to a lower level are suggested as characteristic of the functional disorders. Differences in activation in the same individual at different times have been suggested as a factor in differences in sensory sensitivity, various aspects of motor response, and the general quality of performance.

The purpose of the present discussion has been primarily to point out similarities in phenomena which might, without focus upon them, be overlooked. Critical data which would support or deny many of the hypotheses are lacking; yet, from reading the results of the investigation of a wide range of topics, there emerges the feeling that

the phenomena of activation are of basic significance in the understanding of behavior. Whether the conclusions derived should take the
approximate shape that is presented here remains for futher investigation to determine. If the image proves to be even partially correct, it
will be illuminating in many areas of psychology. If it proves to be
altogether wrong, my colleagues will at least have at hand some references which may prove useful in the construction of a better image.
Naturally, I myself am a convert to my own thinking.

Bibliography

Abel, T. M. Attitudes and the galvanic skin reflex. *J. exp. Psychol.*, 1930, **13**, 47–60.

Abel, T. M. Neurocirculatory reactions and the recall of unfinished and completed tasks. *J. Psychol.*, 1938, **6**, 377–383.

Abraham, K., and Marsan, C. A. Patterns of cortical discharges and their relation to routine scalp electroencephalography. *EEG clin. Neurophysiol.*, 1958, **10**, 447–461.

Abramson, H. A., Jarvik, M. E., and Hirsch, M. W. Lysergic acid diethylamide (LSD-25). X. Effect on reaction time to auditory and visual stimuli. *J. Psychol.*, 1955, **40**, 39–52.

Adams, J. A. Effect of experimentally induced muscular tension on psychomotor performance. *J. exp. Psychol.*, 1954, **48**, 127–130.

Adcock, C. J. Temperament and personality. *Aust. J. Psychol.*, 1952, **4**, 149–165.

Adler, H. F., Burkhardt, W. L., Ivy, A. C., and Atkinson, A. J. Effect of various drugs on psychomotor performance at ground level and at simulated altitudes of 18,000 feet in a low pressure chamber. *J. Aviation Med.*, 1950, **21**, 221–236.

Adrian, E. D. The physiological basis of perception. In J. F. Delafresnaye (Ed.), *Brain mechanisms and consciousness.* Springfield, Ill.: Thomas, 1954.

Adrian, E. D., and Matthews, B. H. C. The Berger rhythm: potential changes from the occipital lobes in man. *Brain*, 1934, **37**, 355–385.

Aird, R. B., and Gastaut, Y. Occipital and posterior electroencephalographic rhythms. *EEG clin. Neurophysiol.*, 1959, **11**, 637–656.

Akimov, N. E. (The effect of adrenalin upon maze learning in white rats.) *Refleksi, Instinkti, Naviki*, 1936, **2**, 111–138. (*Psychol. Abstr.*, 11:1158)

Albino, R. C. The stable and labile personality types of Luria in clinically normal individuals. *Brit. J. Psychol., Gen'l. Sect.*, 1948, **39**, Part I, 54–60.

Alexander, L. Neuropathology and neurophysiology including electroencephalography in wartime Germany. Office of the Publ. Board, Dept. of Commerce, Washington, D. C. Report No. 359. (n.d.)

Allport, G. W. *Personality.* New York: Holt, 1937.

Allport, G. W., and Vernon, P. E. *Studies in expressive movement.* New York: Macmillan, 1933.

Alpers, B. J. Personality and emotional disorders associated with hypothalamic lesions. *Psychosom. Med.*, 1940, **2**, 286–303.

Altmann, M., Knowles, E., and Bull, H. D. A psychosomatic study of the sex cycle in women. *Psychosom. Med.*, 1941, **3**, 199–225.

Altschule, M. D. Discussion of a paper by Hoagland. (See H. Hoagland, Metabolic and physiological disturbances in the psychoses. In Milbank Memorial Fund, *The biology of mental health and disease.* New York: Hoeber, 1952. Pp. 449–453.)

Altschule, M. D. *Bodily physiology in mental and emotional disorders.* New York: Grune and Stratton, 1953.

Anderson, O. D. The role of the glands of internal secretion in the production of behavioral types in the dog. In C. R. Stockard (Ed.), *The genetic and endocrine basis for differences in form and behavior.* Philadelphia: Wistar Institute of Anatomy and Biology, 1941. Pp. 647–753.

Armstrong, H. G. The blood pressure and pulse rate as an index of emotional stability. *Amer. J. Med. Sci.*, 1938, **195**, 211–220.

Arnold, M. B. A study of tension in relation to breakdown. *J. gen. Psychol.*, 1942, **26**, 315–346.

Arnold, M. B. Physiological differentiation of emotional states. *Psychol. Rev.*, 1945, **52**, 35–48.

Ash, I. E. Fatigue and its effects upon control. *Arch. Psychol.*, N. Y., 1914, **4**, Whole No. 31.

Astin, A. W., and Ross, S. Glutamic acid and human intelligence. *Psychol. Bull.*, 1960, **57**, 429–434.

Ax, A. F. The physiological differentiation of fear and anger in humans. *Psychosom. Med.*, 1953, **15**, 433–442.

Ax, A. F., and Colley, W. H. Temporal acuity in psychogenic and neurogenic pathology. *J. consult. Psychol.*, 1955, **19**, 455–461.

Ax, A. F., and Wenger, M. A. *Polygraph Newsletter*, 1955, **1** (2), 5.

Bagby, E. *The psychology of personality.* New York: Holt, 1928.

Bailey, C. J., and Miller, N. E. The effect of Sodium Amytal on an approach-avoidance conflict in cats. *J. comp. physiol. Psychol.*, 1952, **45**, 205–208.

Baker, L. M., and Taylor, W. M. The relationship under stress between changes in skin temperature, electrical skin resistance, and pulse rate. *J. exp. Psychol.*, 1954, **48**, 361–366.

Bard, P. A diencephalic mechanism for the expression of rage, with special reference to the sympathetic nervous system. *Amer. J. Physiol.*, 1928, **84**, 490–513.

Bard, P., and Mountcastle, V. B. Some forebrain mechanisms involved in expression of rage with special reference to suppression of angry behavior. In J. F. Fulton, C. D. Aring, and S. B. Wortis (Eds.), *The frontal lobes.* Baltimore, Md.: Williams and Wilkins, 1948. Pp. 362–404.

Barnes, T. C., and Brieger, H. Biological studies of fatigue. II. Students' electroencephalograms taken at 8 AM and 5 PM. *Fed. Proc. Amer. Soc. exp. Biol.*, 1946, **5** (1), Part 2, 5–6. (Abstract)

Barron, D. H. Vasomotor regulation. In J. F. Fulton (Ed.), *Howell's Textbook of Physiology.* (15th ed.) Philadelphia: Saunders, 1947. Pp. 692–709.

Barsa, J. A. The dual action of the tranquilizers. *Amer. J. Psychiat.*, 1957, **114**, 74–75.

Bartlett, F. C. Fatigue following highly skilled work. *Proc. Royal Soc. London, Biological Sciences*, 1943, B, **131**, 247–257.

Bartley, S. H. Action potentials of the optic cortex under the influence of strychnine. *Amer. J. Physiol.*, 1933, **103**, 203–212.

Bartoshuk, A. K. Electromyographic gradients in goal-directed activity. *Canad. J. Psychol.*, 1955, **9**, 21–28. (a)

Bartoshuk, A. K. Electromyographic gradients as indicants of motivation. *Canad. J. Psychol.*, 1955, **9**, 215–230. (b)

Bartoshuk, A. K. EMG gradients and EEG amplitude during motivated listening. *Canad. J. Psychol.*, 1956, **10**, 156–164.

Bartoshuk, A. K. Electromyographic reactions to strong auditory stimulation as a function of alpha amplitude. *J. comp. physiol. Psychol.*, 1959, **52**, 540–545.

Basowitz, H., Persky, H., Korchin, S. J., and Grinker, R. R. *Anxiety and stress; an interdisciplinary study of a life situation.* New York: McGraw-Hill, 1955.

Beam, J. C. Serial learning and conditioning under real-life stress. *J. abnorm. soc. Psychol.*, 1955, **51**, 543–551.

Belanger, D. "Gradients" musculaires et processus mentaux supérieurs. *Canad. J. Psychol.*, 1957, **11**, 113–122.

Benedict, F. G., and Benedict, C. G. The energy requirements of intense mental effort. *Proc. Nat. Acad. Sci.*, 1930, **16**, 438–443.

Bennett, C. C. The drugs and I. In L. Uhr and J. G. Miller (Eds.), *Drugs and behavior.* New York: Wiley, 1960. Pp. 596–609.

Berger, F. M. Classification of psychoactive drugs according to their chemical structures and sites of action. In L. Uhr and J. G. Miller (Eds.), *Drugs and behavior.* New York: Wiley, 1960. Pp. 86–105.

Berger, H. Über das Elektrenkephalogramm des Menschen. I. *Arch. Psychiat. Nervenkr.*, 1929, **87**, 527–570.

Berger, H. Über das Elektrenkephalogramm des Menschen. VI. *Arch. Psychiat. Nervenkr.*, 1933, **99**, 555–574.

Berrien, F. K. The effects of noise. *Psychol. Bull.*, 1946, **43**, 141–161.

Berry, R. N., and Davis, R. C. Muscle responses and their relation to rote learning. *J. exp. Psychol.*, 1958, **55**, 188–194.

Biesheuvel, S. The nature of temperament. *Trans. Roy. Soc. South Africa*, 1935, **23**, 311–360.

Billingslea, F. Y. Intercorrelational analysis of certain behavior salients in the rat. *J. comp. Psychol.*, 1942, **34**, 203–211.

Bills, A. G. The influence of muscular tension on the efficiency of mental work. *Amer. J. Psychol.*, 1927, **38**, 227–251.

Bills, A. G. Tensions in learning and association. In E. G. Boring (Ed.), *Proceedings and papers of the Ninth International Congress of Psychology.* Princeton, N. J.: Psychological Review Co., 1930. Pp. 75–76.

Bills, A. G. *The psychology of efficiency.* New York: Harper, 1943.

Bills, A. G., and Brown, C. The quantitative set. *J. exp. Psychol.*, 1929, **12**, 301–323.

Bindra, D., Paterson, A. L., and Strzelecki, J. On the relation between anxiety and conditioning. *Canad. J. Psychol.*, 1955, **9**, 1–6.

Bingham, W. E., Jr. A study of the relations which the g.s.r. and sensory reference bear to judgments of the meaningfulness, significance, and importance of 72 words. *J. Psychol.*, 1943, **16**, 21–34.

Birch, H. G. The role of motivational factors in insightful problem-solving. *J. comp. Psychol.*, 1945, **38**, 295–317.

Bishop, G. H. The interpretation of cortical potentials. *Cold Spring Harbor Sympos. quant. Biol.*, 1936, **4**, 305–317.

Bishop, G. H. Review of J. C. Eccles' "The neurophysiology of mind; the principles of neurophysiology." In *EEG clin. Neurophysiol.*, 1953, **5**, 626–627.

Bitterman, M. E., and Holtzman, W. H. Conditioning and extinction of the galvanic skin response as a function of anxiety. *J. abnorm. soc. Psychol.*, 1952, **47**, 615–623.

Bitterman, M. E., and Soloway, E. The relation between frequency of blinking and effort expended in mental work. *J. exp. Psychol.*, 1946, **36**, 134–136.

Blatz, W. E. The cardiac, respiratory, and electrical phenomena involved in the emotion of fear. *J. exp. Psychol.*, 1925, **8**, 109–132.

Block, H. Influence of muscular exertion upon mental performance. *Arch. Psychol., N. Y.*, 1936, **29**, (202), 50–61.

Blough, D. S. Effect of LSD on the absolute visual threshold of the pigeon. *Science*, 1957, **126**, 304–305.

Blough, D. S. New test for tranquilizers. *Science*, 1958, **127**, 586–587.

Blum, Richard H. Alpha rhythm responsiveness in normal, schizophrenic, and brain-damaged persons. *Science*, 1957, **126**, 749–750.

Bonvallet, M., Dell, P., and Hiebel, G. Tonus sympathique et activité électrique corticale. *EEG clin. Neurophysiol.*, 1954, **6**, 103–118.

Boren, J. Behavior profiling and drug evaluation, 1958. Referred to by J. O. Cole, Behavioral toxicity. In L. Uhr and J. G. Miller (Eds.), *Drugs and behavior.* New York: Wiley, 1960. Pp. 166–183.

Bourne, L. E., Jr. An evaluation of the effect of induced tension on performance. *J. exp. Psychol.*, 1955, **49**, 418–422.

Bovet, D. Isosterism and competitive phenomena in drugs. *Science*, 1959, **129**, 1255–1264.

Brackbill, G., and Little, K. B. MMPI correlates of the Taylor Scale of Manifest Anxiety. *J. consult. Psychol.*, 1954, **18**, 433–436.

Brady, J. V. Assessment of drug effects on emotional behavior. *Science*, 1956, **123**, 1033–1034.

Brady, J. V., Schreiner, L., Geller, I., and Kling, A. Subcortical mechanisms in emotional behavior: the effect of rhinencephalic injury upon the acquisition and retention of a conditioned avoidance response in cats. *J. physiol. comp. Psychol.*, 1954, **47**, 179–186.

Brazier, M. A. B. Electroencephalography. In E. A. Spiegel, *Progress in neurology and psychiatry.* New York: Grune and Stratton, 1957. Vol. 12.

Brazier, M. A. B., and Finesinger, J. E. Characteristics of the normal electroencephalogram. I. A study of the occipital cortical potentials in 500 normal adults. *J. clin. Invest.*, 1944, **23**, 303–311.

Brazier, M. A. B., Finesinger, J. E., and Cobb, S. A contrast between the electroencephalograms of 100 psychoneurotic patients and those of 500 normal adults. *Amer. J. Psychiat.*, 1945, **101**, 443–448.

Bremer, F. Considérations sur l'origine et la nature des "ondes" cérébrales. *EEG clin. Neurophysiol.*, 1949, **1**, 177–193.

Brenner, M. W. Continuous stimulation and apparent movement. *Amer. J. Psychol.*, 1953, **66**, 494–495.

Broadhurst, P. L. Emotionality and the Yerkes-Dodson law. *J. exp. Psychol.*, 1957, **54**, 345–352.

Brobeck, J. R. Regulation of energy exchange. *Annu. Rev. Physiol.*, 1948, **10**, 315–328.

Brobeck, J. R., Wheatland, M., and Strominger, J. L. Variations in regulation of energy exchange associated with estrus, diestrus, and pseudopregnancy in rats. *Endocrinology*, 1947, **40**, 65–72.

Brockway, A. L., Gleser, G., Winokur, G., and Ulett, G. A. The use of a control population in neuropsychiatric research (psychiatric, psychological, and EEG evaluation of a heterogeneous sample). *Amer. J. Psychiat.*, 1954, **111**, 248–262.

Brody, E. G. Genetic basis of spontaneous activity in the albino rat. *Comp. Psychol. Monog.*, 1942, **17** (5), 1–24.

Brower, D. The relation between certain Rorschach factors and cardiovascular activity before and after visuo-motor conflict. *J. gen. Psychol.*, 1947, **37**, 93–95.

Brower, D. The relations of visuo-motor conflict to personality traits and cardio-vascular activity. *J. gen. Psychol.*, 1948, **38**, 69–99.

Brown, C. H., and Van Gelder, D. Emotional reactions before examinations. I. Physiological changes. *J. Psychol.*, 1938, **5**, 1–9.

Brown, H. R., Jr., and Pearson, R. Demonstration of a positive relationship between cardiac output and oxygen consumption. *Proc. Soc. exp. Biol. Med.*, 1947, **65**, 307–309.

Brožek, J. Physiological psychology. *Annu. Rev. Psychol.*, 1958, **9**, 71–98.

Brožek, J., and Taylor, H. L. Tests of motor functions in investigations on fitness. *Amer. J. Psychol.*, 1954, **67**, 590–611.

Brudo, C. S., and Darrow, C. W. A preliminary study of per cent-time alpha in the EEG and the human movement response in the Rorschach. *EEG clin. Neurophysiol.*, 1953, **5**, 481. (Abstract)

Bruner, J. S. Neural mechanisms in perception. *Psychol. Rev.*, 1957, **64**, 340–358.

Buchwald, A. M., and Yamaguchi, H. G. The effect of change in drive level on habit reversal. *J. exp. Psychol.*, 1955, **50**, 265–268.

Bujas, Z., and Petz, B. Les modifications des ondes alpha au cours du travail mental prolongé. *Travail hum.*, 1954, **17**, 201–206.

Bülbring, E., and Burn, J. H. An action of adrenaline on transmission in sympa-thetic ganglia, which may play a role in shock. *J. Physiol.*, 1942, **101**, 289–303.

Burch, G. E., Cohn, A. E., and Neuman, C. A study by quantitative methods of spontaneous variations in volume of the finger tip, toe tip, and postero-superior portion of the pinna of resting normal white adults. *Amer. J. Physiol.*, 1942, **136**, 433–447.

Burr, H. S. The meaning of bioelectric potentials. *Yale J. Biol. Med.*, 1944, **16**, 353–360.

Bykow, K. M., Alexandroff, I. S., Wirjikowski, S. N., and Riel, A. V. Influence du travail musculaire sur l'activité de l'écorce cérébrale chez le chien. *C. R. Soc. Biol. Paris*, 1927, **97**, 1398–1400.

Callaway, E., III, and Dembo, E. Narrowed attention: a psychological phenome-non that accompanies a certain physiological change. *A.M.A. Arch. Neurol. Psychiat.*, 1958, **79**, 74–90.

Callaway, E., III, and Stone, G. Re-evaluating focus of attention. In L. Uhr and J. G. Miller (Eds.) *Drugs and behavior*. New York: Wiley, 1960. Pp. 393–398.

Callaway, E., III, and Thompson, S. V. Sympathetic activity and perception. *Psychosom. Med.*, 1953, **15**, 443–455.

Callaway, E., III, and Yeager, C. L. Relationship between reaction time and electroencephalographic alpha phase. *Science*, 1960, **132**, 1765–1766.

Calvin, A. D., Koons, P. B., Jr., Bingham, J. L., and Fink, H. H. A further investigation of the relationship between manifest anxiety and intelligence. *J. consult. Psychol.*, 1955, **19**, 280–282.

Cameron, D. E. *Objective and experimental psychiatry.* (2nd ed.) New York: Macmillan, 1941.

Cameron, D. E. Some relationships between excitement, depression, and anxiety. *Amer. J. Psychiat.*, 1945, **102**, 385–394.

Cannon, W. B. *Bodily changes in pain, hunger, fear and rage.* (2nd ed.) New York: Appleton-Century, 1936.

Cannon, W. B. *The wisdom of the body.* New York: Norton, 1939.

Cantril, H., and Hunt, W. A. Emotional effects produced by the injection of adrenalin. *Amer. J. Psychol.*, 1932, **44**, 300–307.

Carlson, V. R. Effect of lysergic acid diethylamide (LSD-25) on the absolute visual threshold. *J. comp. physiol. Psychol.*, 1958, **51**, 528–531.

Carmena, M. Ist die persönliche Affektlage oder "Nervosität" eine ererbte Eigenschaft? *Z. ges. Neurol. Psychiat.*, 1934, **150**, 434–446.

Carpenter, J. A. The effect of caffeine and alcohol on simple visual reaction time. *J. comp. physiol. Psychol.*, 1959, **52**, 491–496.

Carran, A. Drug effects and activation level. In L. Uhr and J. G. Miller (Eds.), *Drugs and behavior.* New York: Wiley, 1960. Pp. 409–412.

Cason, H. Sensory conditioning. *J. exp. Psychol.*, 1936, **19**, 572–591.

Castaneda, A., and Palermo, D. S. Psychomotor performance as a function of amount of training and stress. *J. exp. Psychol.*, 1955, **50**, 175–179.

Cattell, R. B. *Description and measurement of personality.* Yonkers-on-Hudson, N. Y.: World Book Co., 1946.

Cattell, R. B., Cattell, A. K. S., and Rhymer, R. M. P-technique demonstrated in determining psycho-physiological source traits in a normal individual. *Psychometrika*, 1947, **12**, 267–288.

Champion, R. A. Studies of experimentally induced disturbance. *Aust. J. Psychol.*, 1950, **2**, 90–99.

Chapanis, A., Rouse, R. O., and Schachter, S. The effect of inter-sensory stimulation on dark adaptation and night vision. *J. exp. Psychol.*, 1949, **39**, 425–437.

Chapman, W. P., and Jones, C. M. Variations in cutaneous and visceral pain sensitivity in normal subjects. *J. clin. Invest.*, 1944, **23**, 81–91.

Chappell, M. Blood-pressure changes in deception. *Arch. Psychol., N. Y.*, 1929, **17**, 1–30.

Clark, J. W., and Bindra, D. Individual differences in pain thresholds. *Canad. J. Psychol.*, 1956, **10**, 69–76.

Clarke, A. D. B. Motor and memory responses of neurotics and normals in the Luria association-motor technique. *Brit. J. Psychol.*, 1955, **46**, 38–43.

Clausen, J., Urdal, A., and Gjesvik, A. Relation between galvanic skin resistance and repetition effect in pain stimulation. *J. gen. Psychol.*, 1955, **53**, 29–36.

Cleghorn, R. A. Discussion of a paper by Engel. (See F. L. Engel, 1953.) *Psychosom. Med.*, 1953, **15**, 571–573.

Cleghorn, R. A. The hypothalamic-endocrine system. *Psychosom. Med.*, 1955, 17, 367–376.

Clerc, N. A., Turner, M., and Bérard, E. Modifications de l'électrodermogramme, de la sudation et la température cutanée provoquées par la chlorpromazine (4560 R.P.) chez l'homme. *EEG clin. Neurophysiol.*, 1956, 8, 35–39.

Cohen, B. D., Brown, G. W., and Brown, M. L. Avoidance learning motivated by hypothalamic stimulation. *J. exp. Psychol.*, 1957, 53, 228–233.

Cohen, S. I., Silverman, A. J., and Burch, N. R. A technique for the assessment of affect change. *J. nerv. ment. Dis.*, 1956, 124, 352–360.

Conklin, J. E. Three factors affecting the general level of electrical skin-resistance. *Amer. J. Psychol.*, 1951, 64, 78–86.

Coombs, C. H. Adaptation of the galvanic response to auditory stimuli. *J. exp. Psychol.*, 1938, 22, 244–268.

Corbin, H. P. F., and Bickford, R. G. Studies of the electroencephalogram of normal children: comparison of visual and automatic frequency analyses. *EEG clin. Neurophysiol.*, 1955, 7, 15–28.

Courts, F. A. Relation between experimentally induced tension, muscular tension and memorization. *J. exp. Psychol.*, 1939, 25, 235–256.

Courts, F. A. The influence of practice on the dynamogenic effect of muscular tension. *J. exp. Psychol.*, 1942, 30, 504–511. (a)

Courts, F. A. Relationships between muscular tension and performance. *Psychol. Bull.*, 1942, 39, 347–367. (b)

Cowen, E. L. The influence of varying degrees of psychological stress on problem-solving rigidity. *J. abnorm. soc. Psychol.*, 1952, 47, 512–519.

Crichton-Miller, H. Subjective and objective observations on Benzedrine. *Brit. J. Addict.*, 1947, 44, 46–49.

Cutts, K. K., and Jasper, H. H. Effect of Benzedrine Sulfate and phenobarbital on behavior problem children with abnormal electroencephalograms. *A.M.A. Arch. Neurol. Psychiat.*, 1939, 41, 1138–1145.

Damrau, F. Psychometric evaluation of sedatives. *Med. Rec.*, 1946, 195, 349–351.

Daniel, R. S. The distribution of muscle action potentials during maze learning. *J. exp. Psychol.*, 1939, 24, 621–629.

Daniel, R. S. Some observations on Meyer's study of reaction time and muscle tension. *J. exp. Psychol.*, 1949, 39, 896–898.

Darling, R. P. Autonomic action in relation to personality traits of children. *J. abnorm. soc. Psychol.*, 1940, 35, 246–260.

Darling, R. P., and Darrow, C. W. Determining activity of the autonomic nervous system from measurements of autonomic change. *J. Psychol.*, 1938, 5, 85–89.

Darrow, C. W. The galvanic skin reflex and finger volume changes. *Amer. J. Physiol.*, 1929, 88, 219–229.

Darrow, C. W. The behavior research photopolygraph. *J. gen. Psychol.*, 1932, 7, 215–219.

Darrow, C. W. The galvanic skin reflex (sweating) and blood-pressure as preparatory and facilitative functions. *Psychol. Bull.*, 1936, 33, 73–94.

Darrow, C. W. The equation of the galvanic skin reflex curve. *J. gen. Psychol.*, 1937, 16, 285–309.

Darrow, C. W. Physiological and clinical tests of autonomic function and autonomic balance. *Physiol. Rev.*, 1943, 23, 1–36.

Darrow, C. W. Psychological and psychophysiological significance of the electro-encephalogram. *Psychol. Rev.*, 1947, **54**, 157–168.

Darrow, C. W. A new frontier: neurophysiological effects of emotion on the brain. In M. L. Reymert (Ed.), *Feelings and emotions*. New York: McGraw-Hill, 1950. Pp. 247–260.

Darrow, C. W. Cerebral concomitants of autonomic changes: observations on anterior-posterior cerebral dominance. Paper read at Amer. Psychol. Ass. Meeting, Wash., D. C., September, 1952.

Darrow, C. W. The relation of cerebral to autonomic activity in the conditioned emotional reactions of children. *Ann. NY Acad. Sci.*, 1953, **56**, 289–301.

Darrow, C. W., and Freeman, G. L. Palmar skin-resistance changes contrasted with non-palmar changes and rate of insensible weight loss. *J. exp. Psychol.*, 1934, **17**, 739–748.

Darrow, C. W., and Heath, L. L. Reaction tendencies relating to personality. In K. S. Lashley et al. (Eds.), *Studies in the dynamics of behavior*. Chicago: University of Chicago Press, 1932. Pp. 57–261.

Darrow, C. W., and Henry, C. E. A basis for interpreting autonomic-EEG relationships. *Fed. Proc.*, 1947, **6**, 93.

Darrow, C. W., and Henry, C. E. Psychophysiology of stress. In *Human factors in undersea warfare*. Washington: National Research Council, 1949. Pp. 417–439.

Darrow, C. W., Jost, H., Solomon, A. P., and Mergener, J. C. Autonomic indications of excitatory and homeostatic effects on the electroencephalogram. *J. Psychol.*, 1942, **14**, 115–130.

Darrow, C. W., Pathman, J., and Kronenberg, G. Level of autonomic activity and the electroencephalogram. *J. exp. Psychol.*, 1946, **36**, 355–365.

Darrow, C. W., and Solomon, A. P. Galvanic skin reflex and blood pressure reactions in psychotic states. *A.M.A. Arch. Neurol. Psychiat.*, 1934, **32**, 273–299.

Darrow, C. W., and Solomon, A. P. Mutism and resistance behavior of psychotic patients. *Amer. J. Psychiat.*, 1940, **96**, 1441–1454.

Darrow, C. W., Vieth, R. N., and Wilson, J. Electroencephalographic "blocking" and "adaptation." *Science*, 1957, **126**, 74–75.

Davidowitz, J., Browne-Mayers, A. N., Kohl, R., Welch, L., and Hayes, R. An electromyographic study of muscular tension. *J. Psychol.*, 1955, **40**, 85–94.

Davids, A. Relations among several objective measures of anxiety under different conditions of motivation. *J. consult. Psychol.*, 1955, **19**, 275–279.

Davids, A., and Eriksen, C. W. The relationship of manifest anxiety to association productivity and intellectual attainment. *J. consult. Psychol.*, 1955, **19**, 219–222.

Davis, D. R. *Pilot error—some laboratory experiments*. London: His Majesty's Stationery Office, 1948. Air Ministry, A. P. 3139A.

Davis, H., and Davis, P. A. Action potentials of the brain in normal persons and in normal states of cerebral activity. *A.M.A. Arch. Neurol. Psychiat.*, 1936, **36**, 1214–1224.

Davis, J. F., Malmo, R. B., and Shagass, C. Electromyographic reaction to strong auditory stimulation in psychiatric patients. *Canad. J. Psychol.*, 1954, **8**, 177–186.

Davis, P. A. Technique and evaluation of the electroencephalogram. *J. Neurophysiol.*, 1941, **4**, 94–114. (a)

Davis, P. A. Electroencephalograms of manic-depressive patients. *Amer. J. Psychiat.*, 1941, **98**, 430–433. (b)

Davis, P. A., and Davis, H. The electroencephalograms of psychotic patients. *Amer. J. Psychiat.*, 1939, **95**, 1007–1025.

Davis, R. C. Modification of the galvanic reflex by daily repetition of a stimulus. *J. exp. Psychol.*, 1934, **17**, 504–535.

Davis, R. C. The relation of certain muscle action potentials to "mental work." *Indiana Univer. Publ. Sci. Ser.*, 1937, No. 5.

Davis, R. C. Relation of muscular action potentials to difficulty and frustration. *J. exp. Psychol.*, 1938, **23**, 141–158.

Davis, R. C. Patterns of muscular activity during "mental work" and their constancy. *J. exp. Psychol.*, 1939, **24**, 451–465.

Davis, R. C. Set and muscular tension. *Indiana Univer. Publ. Sci. Ser.*, 1940, No. 10.

Davis, R. C. The pattern of muscular action in simple voluntary movement. *J. exp. Psychol.*, 1942, **31**, 347–366.

Davis, R. C. Motor effects of strong auditory stimuli. *J. exp. Psychol.*, 1948, **38**, 257–275.

Davis, R. C. Motor responses to auditory stimuli above and below threshold. *J. exp. Psychol.*, 1950, **40**, 107–120.

Davis, R. C. The stimulus trace in effectors and its relation to judgment responses. *J. exp. Psychol.*, 1952, **44**, 377–390.

Davis, R. C. Response and adaptation to brief noises of high intensity. *USAF Sch. Aviat. Med. Rep.*, 1953, No. 55–127.

Davis, R. C. Electromyographic factors in aircraft control. The relation of muscular tension to performance. *USAF Sch. Aviat. Med. Rep.*, 1956, No. 55–122. (a)

Davis, R. C. Electromyographic factors in aircraft control. Experimental investigation of the effect of a muscle tension reflex upon simple instructed movements. *USAF Sch. Aviat. Med. Rep.*, 1956, No. 55–123. (b)

Davis, R. C. Electromyographic factors in aircraft control. Muscular activity during steady noise and its relation to instructed responses evoked by auditory signals. *USAF Sch. Aviat. Med. Rep.*, 1956, No. 55–124. (c)

Davis, R. C. Electromyographic factors in aircraft control. Muscular activity during steady noise and its relation to instructed responses evoked by visual signals. *USAF Sch. Aviat. Med. Rep.*, 1956, No. 55–126. (d)

Davis, R. C. Response patterns. *Trans. N. Y. Acad. Sci.*, 1957, **19**, 731–739. (a)

Davis, R. C. Framing experimental problems: some general considerations. APA Symposium Paper, September, 1957. (b)

Davis, R. C. Somatic activity under reduced stimulation. *J. comp. physiol. Psychol.*, 1959, **52**, 309–314.

Davis, R. C., and Buchwald, A. M. An exploration of somatic response patterns: stimulus and sex differences. *J. comp. physiol. Psychol.*, 1957, **50**, 44–52.

Davis, R. C., Buchwald, A. M., and Frankmann, R. W. Autonomic and muscular responses, and their relation to simple stimuli. *Psychol. Monogr.*, 1955, **69**, No. 20 (Whole No. 405).

Davis, R. C., Lundervold, A., and Miller, J. D. The pattern of somatic response during a repetitive motor task and its modification by visual stimuli. *J. comp. physiol. Psychol.*, 1957, **50**, 53–60.

Davis, R. C., and Van Liere, D. W. Adaptation of the muscular tension response to gunfire. *J. exp. Psychol.*, 1949, **39**, 114–117.

Davis, S. W. Auditory and visual flicker-fusion as a measure of fatigue. *Amer. J. Psychol.*, 1955, **68**, 654–657.

Dawson, H. E., and Davis, R. C. The effects of an instructed motor response upon somatic responses to a brief tone. *J. comp. physiol. Psychol.*, 1957, **50**, 368–374.

Dawson, W. M. Inheritance of wildness and tameness in mice. *Genetics*, 1932, **17**, 296–326.

Dees, S. C., and Lowenbach, H. The electroencephalograms of allergic children. *Ann. Allergy*, 1948, **6**, 99–108.

Deese, J., and Lazarus, R. S. The effects of psychological stress upon perceptual-motor performance. *USAF Hum. Resour. Res. Cent. Res. Bull.*, 1952, No. 52–19.

Delafresnaye, J. F. (Ed.), *Brain mechanisms and consciousness.* Springfield, Ill.: Thomas, 1954.

Delgado, J. M. R. Responses evoked in waking cat by electrical stimulation of motor cortex. *Amer. J. Physiol.*, 1952, **171**, 436–446.

Dell, P., and Bonvallet, M. Somatic functions of the nervous system. *Annu. Rev. Physiol.*, 1956, **18**, 309–338.

Denier van der Gon, J. J., and van Hinte, N. The relation between the frequency of the alpha-rhythm and the speed of writing. *EEG clin. Neurophysiol.*, 1959, **11**, 669–674.

De Somer, P. L'influence nocive des petites doses d'alcool. *Arch. Belg. Méd. sociale, Hyg., Méd. Travail, Méd. lég.*, Brussels, 1950, **8**, 635–643.

Dewey, J. The theory of emotion, II. *Psychol. Rev.*, 1895, **2**, 13–32.

Diamond, A. L. A theory of depression and enhancement in the brightness response. *Psychol. Rev.*, 1960, **67**, 168–199.

Di Giorgio, A. M. Modificazioni del punto prossimo, dell'acuità visiva e del potere, di discriminazione dell intensità luminosa, in seguito ad eccitamento del labirinto. *Boll. Soc. ital. Biol. sper.*, 1940, **15**, 391–394.

Dittes, J. E. Extinction during psychotherapy of GSR accompanying "embarrassing" statements. *J. abnorm. soc. Psychol.*, 1957, **54**, 187–191. (a)

Dittes, J. E. Galvanic skin response as a measure of patient's reaction to therapist's permissiveness. *J. abnorm. soc. Psychol.*, 1957, **55**, 295–303. (b)

Dodge, R. Mental work: a study in psychodynamics. *Psychol. Rev.*, 1913, **20**, 1–42.

Domino, E. F. Pharmacology of the central nervous system. In E. A. Spiegel, *Progress in neurology and psychiatry*, 1957, **12**, 92–112. New York: Grune and Stratton, 1957.

Dongier, M., and Dongier, S. Quelques aspects de l'électroencéphalogramme des névroses. *Évolut. Psychiat.*, 1958, No. 1, 1–18.

Dongier, M., Dongier, S., Angel-Villegas, G., and Angel-Villegas, A. Confrontations des données des examens psychologiques et de l'électroencéphalogramme chez 100 névrosés. In H. Fischgold and H. Gastaut (Eds.), *Conditionnement et réactivité en électroencéphalographie.* Paris: Masson, 1957. Pp. 315–320.

Dongier, S., Gastaut, Y., and Dongier, M. Enrégistrement polygraphique de l'effet de surprise. Relations entre des résultats obtenus et les données cliniques. In H. Fischgold and H. Gastaut (Eds.), *Conditionnement et réactivité en électroéncéphalographie.* Paris: Masson, 1957. Pp. 125–132.

Doust, J. W. L., and Schneider, R. A. Studies on the physiology of awareness: the effect of rhythmic sensory bombardment on emotions, blood oxygen saturation and the levels of consciousness. *J. ment. Sci.*, 1952, **98**, 640–653.

DuBois, E. F. *Basal metabolism in health and disease.* (2nd ed.) Philadelphia: Lea and Febiger, 1927.

Duffy, E. Tensions and emotional factors in reaction. *Genet. psychol. Monogr.,* 1930, **7**, (1), 1–79.

Duffy, E. The measurement of muscular tension as a technique for the study of emotional tendencies. *Amer. J. Psychol.,* 1932, **44**, 146–162. (a)

Duffy, E. The relationship between muscular tension and quality of performance. *Amer. J. Psychol.,* 1932, **44**, 535–546. (b)

Duffy, E. Muscular tension as related to physique and behavior. *Child Develpm.,* 1932, **3**, 200–206. (c)

Duffy, E. Emotion: An example of the need for reorientation in psychology. *Psychol. Rev.,* 1934, **41**, 184–198.

Duffy, E. The conceptual categories of psychology: a suggestion for revision. *Psychol. Rev.,* 1941, **48**, 177–203. (a)

Duffy, E. An explanation of "emotional" phenomena without the use of the concept "emotion." *J. gen. Psychol.,* 1941, **25**, 283–293. (b)

Duffy, E. Level of muscular tension as an aspect of personality. *J. gen. Psychol.,* 1946, **35**, 161–171.

Duffy, E. Is there a dichotomy in energy mobilization? *Amer. Psychologist,* 1947, **2**, 398. (Abstract)

Duffy, E. Leeper's "motivational theory of emotion." *Psychol. Rev.,* 1948, **55**, 324–328.

Duffy, E. A systematic framework for the description of personality. *J. abnorm. soc. Psychol.,* 1949, **44**, 175–190.

Duffy, E. The concept of energy mobilization. *Psychol. Rev.,* 1951, **58**, 30–40.

Duffy, E. The psychological significance of the concept of "arousal" or "activation." *Psychol. Rev.,* 1957, **64**, 265–275.

Duffy, E., and Lacey, O. L. Adaptation in energy mobilization: changes in general level of palmar skin conductance. *J. exp. Psychol.,* 1946, **36**, 437–452.

Dusser de Barenne, D., and Gibbs, F. A. Variations in the electroencephalogram during the menstrual cycle. *Amer. J. Obst. Gynec.,* 1942, **4**, 687–690.

DuToit, J. M. Skin conductance and peripheral reactions. *J. exp. Psychol.,* 1956, **52**, 392–397.

Dykman, R. A., Gantt, W. H., and Whitehorn, J. C. Conditioning as emotional sensitization and differentiation. *Psychol. Monogr.,* 1956, **70** (422), 1–17.

Dykman, R. A., Reese, W. C., Galbrecht, C. R., and Thomasson, P. J. Psychophysiological reactions to novel stimuli: measurement, adaptation, and relationship of psychological and physiological variables in the normal human. *Ann. NY Acad. Sci.,* 1959, **79**, 43–107.

Dysinger, W. S., and Ruckmick, C. A. *The emotional responses of children to the motion picture situation.* New York: Macmillan, 1933.

Easterbrook, J. A. The effect of emotion on cue utilization and the organization of behavior. *Psychol. Rev.,* 1959, **66**, 183–201.

Eccles, J. C. Interpretation of action potentials evoked in the cerebral cortex. *EEG clin. Neurophysiol.,* 1951, **3**, 449–464.

Edwards, A. S. Body sway and non-visual factors. *J. Psychol.,* 1947, **23**, 241–254.

Edwards, A. S., and Harris, A. C. Laboratory measurements of deterioration and improvement among schizophrenics. *J. gen. Psychol.,* 1953, **49**, 153–156.

Egdahl, R. H., Richards, J. B., and Hume, D. M. Effect of reserpine on adrenocortical function in unanesthetized dogs. *Science,* 1956, **123**, 418.

Elbel, E. R., and Ronkin, R. R. Palmar skin resistance as a measure of physical fitness. *Amer. J. Physiol.*, 1946, **147**, 1–12.

Ellingson, R. J. Response to physiological stress in normal and behavior problem children. *J. genet. Psychol.*, 1953, **83**, 19–29.

Ellingson, R. J. The incidence of EEG abnormality among patients with mental disorders of apparently nonorganic origin: a critical review. *Amer. J. Psychiat.*, 1954, **111**, 263–275.

Ellingson, R. J. Brain waves and problems of psychology. *Psychol. Bull.*, 1956, **53**, 1–34.

Ellis, D. S., and Brighouse, G. Effects of music on respiration and heart rate. *Amer. J. Psychol.*, 1952, **65**, 39–47.

Ellson, D. G., Davis, R. C., Saltzman, I. J., and Burke, C. J. *Report of research on detection of deception*. Contract No. N6ONR-18011, Office of Naval Research, 1952.

Ellsworth, R. B. Use of behavioral adjustment techniques in evaluating tranquilizers, and their value in social rehabilitation. In L. Uhr and J. G. Miller (Eds.), *Drugs and behavior*. New York: Wiley, 1960. Pp. 555–562.

Elmadjian, F., and Hoagland, H. Endocrinology. In E. A. Spiegel (Ed.), *Progress in neurology and psychiatry: an annual review*. New York: Grune and Stratton, 1949. Pp. 241–254.

Elmgren, J. Significance of individual differences in the human EEG. In G. Ekman et al. (Eds.), *Essays in psychology dedicated to David Katz*. Uppsala: Almqvist and Wiksells, 1951. Pp. 274–283.

Engel, B. T. Some physiological correlates of hunger and pain. *J. exp. Psychol.*, 1959, **57**, 389–396.

Engel, F. L. General concepts of adrenocortical function in relation to the response to stress. *Psychosom. Med.*, 1953, **15**, 565–571.

Enzer, N., Simonson, E., and Blankstein, S. S. The state of sensory and motor centers in patients with hypothyroidism. *Ann. intern. Med.*, 1941, **15**, 659–665.

Eriksen, C. W., and Davids, A. The meaning and clinical validity of the Taylor anxiety scale and the hysteria-psychasthenia scales from the MMPI. *J. abnorm. soc. Psychol.*, 1955, **50**, 135–137.

Evarts, E. V., Landau, W., Freygang, W., Jr., and Marshall, W. H. Some effects of lysergic acid diethylamide and bufotenine on electrical activity in the cat's visual system. *Amer. J. Physiol.*, 1955, **182**, 594–598.

Eysenck, H. J. *Dimensions of personality*. London: Kegan, Paul, 1947.

Eysenck, H. J. *The scientific study of personality*. New York: Macmillan, 1952.

Eysenck, H. J. *The structure of human personality*. New York: Wiley, 1953.

Eysenck, H. J., Casey, S., and Trouton, D. S. Drugs and personality. II. The effect of stimulant and depressant drugs on continuous work. *J. ment. Sci.*, 1957, **103**, 645–649.

Farber, I. E. The role of motivation in verbal learning and performance. *Psychol. Bull.*, 1955, **52**, 311–327.

Farber, I. E., and Spence, K. W. Complex learning and conditioning as a function of anxiety. *J. exp. Psychol.*, 1953, **45**, 120–125.

Farris, E. J., and Yeakel, E. H. Emotional behavior of gray Norway and Wistar albino rats. *J. comp. Psychol.*, 1945, **38**, 109–118.

Faure, J. A une approche bio-électrique des émotions. *J. Physiol.*, Paris, 1950, **42**, 589–590.

Feindel, W., and Gloor, P. Comparison of electrographic effects of stimulation of the amygdala and brain stem reticular formation in cats. *EEG clin. Neurophysiol.*, 1954, **6**, 389–402.

Féré, C. *Sensation et mouvement: études éxperimentales de psychomécanique.* (2nd ed., rev.) Paris: Ancienne Librairie Germer Baillière et Cie, 1900.

Finan, J. L., and Taylor, L. F. Quantitative studies of motivation. I. Strength of conditioning in rats under varying degrees of hunger. *J. comp. Psychol.*, 1940, **29**, 119–134.

Finesinger, J. E. The effect of pleasant and unpleasant ideas on the respiratory pattern (spirogram) in psychoneurotic patients. *Amer. J. Psychiat.*, 1944, **100**, 659–667.

Fink, J. B. Electromyographic factors in aircraft control. The development and loss of a muscle tension set to an incidental stimulus. *USAF Sch. Aviat. Med. Rep.*, 1956, No. 55–130.

Finley, K. H. On the occurrence of rapid frequency potential changes in the human electroencephalogram. *Amer. J. Psychiat.*, 1944, **101**, 194–200.

Finley, K. H., and Campbell, C. M. Electroencephalography in schizophrenia. *Amer. J. Psychiat.*, 1941, **98**, 374–381.

Flecker, R. Skin temperature as a psychophysical variable. *Aust. J. Psychol.*, 1951, **3**, 109–120.

Ford, A. Bioelectrical potentials and mental effort: I. Cardiac effects. *J. comp. physiol. Psychol.*, 1953, **46**, 347–351.

Ford, A. Localization of muscle tone during severe mental effort. *Amer. Psychologist*, 1954, **9**, 369–370. (Abstract) (a)

Ford, A. Bioelectric potentials and mental effort: II. Frontal lobe effects. *J. comp. physiol. Psychol.*, 1954, **47**, 28–30. (b)

Ford, A. Foundations of bioelectronics for human engineering (Research Report No. 761). San Diego: U.S. Navy Electronics Laboratory, 1957.

Forssman, H., and Frey, T. S. Electroencephalograms of boys with behavior disorders. *Acta psychiat. neurol. Scand., Kbh.*, 1953, **28**, 61–73.

Fraisse, P., and Bloch, V. Activité psycho-galvanique et rapidité dans une épreuve sensori-motrice complexe. *Acta Psychol.*, Amsterdam, 1957, **13**, 127–139.

Frank, R. T. *The female sex hormone.* Baltimore: Thomas, 1929.

Franks, C. M., and Laverty, S. G. Sodium Amytal and eyelid conditioning. *J. ment. Sci.*, 1955, **101**, 654–663.

Franks, C. M., and Trouton, D. Effects of amobarbital sodium and dexamphetamine sulfate on the conditioning of the eyeblink response. *J. comp. physiol. Psychol.*, 1958, **51**, 220–222.

Freeman, G. L. The spread of neuro-muscular activity during mental work. *J. gen. Psychol.*, 1931, **5**, 479–494.

Freeman, G. L. The facilitative and inhibitory effects of muscular tension upon performance. *Amer. J. Psychol.*, 1933, **45**, 17–52.

Freeman, G. L. The optimal locus of "anticipatory tensions" in muscular work. *J. exp. Psychol.*, 1937, **21**, 554–564.

Freeman, G. L. The optimal muscular tensions for various performances. *Amer. J. Psychol.*, 1938, **51**, 146–150.

Freeman, G. L. Toward as psychiatric plimsoll mark: physiological recovery quotients in experimentally induced frustration. *J. Psychol.*, 1939, **8**, 247–252.

Freeman, G. L. Cortical autonomous rhythms and the excitatory levels of other bodily tissues. *J. exp. Psychol.*, 1940, **27**, 160–171. (a)

Freeman, G. L. The relationship between performance level and bodily activity level. *J. exp. Psychol.*, 1940, **26**, 602–608. (b)

Freeman, G. L. *The energetics of human behavior.* Ithaca: Cornell University Press, 1948. (a)

Freeman, G. L. *Physiological psychology.* New York: Van Nostrand, 1948. (b)

Freeman, G. L., and Darrow, C. W. Insensible perspiration and the galvanic skin reflex. *Amer. J. Physiol.*, 1935, **111**, 55–63.

Freeman, G. L., and Giffin, L. L. The measurement of general reactivity under basal conditions. *J. gen. Psychol.*, 1939, **21**, 63–72.

Freeman, G. L., and Haggard, E. A. Reactions of children to experimentally induced frustrations. *Psychol. Bull.*, 1941, **38**, 581. (Abstract)

Freeman, G. L., and Hovland, C. I. Diurnal variations in performance and related physiological processes. *Psychol. Bull.*, 1934, **31**, 777–799.

Freeman, G. L., and Katzoff, E. G. Muscular tension and irritability. *Amer. J. Psychol.*, 1932, **44**, 789–792.

Freeman, G. L., and Katzoff, E. T. Methodological evaluation of the galvanic skin response, with special reference to the formula for R.Q. (Recovery Quotient). *J. exp. Psychol.*, 1942, **31**, 239–248. (a)

Freeman, G. L., and Katzoff, E. T. Individual differences in physiological reactions to stimulation and their relation to other measures of emotionality. *J. exp. Psychol.*, 1942, **31**, 527–537. (b)

Freeman, G. L., and Kendall, W. E. The effect upon reaction time of muscular tension induced at various preparatory intervals. *J. exp. Psychol.*, 1940, **27**, 136–148.

Freeman, G. L., and Pathman, J. H. The relation of overt muscular discharge to physiological recovery from experimentally induced displacement. *J. exp. Psychol.*, 1942, **30**, 161–174.

Freeman, G. L., and Simpson, R. M. The effect of muscular tension upon palmar skin resistance. *J. gen. Psychol.*, 1938, **18**, 319–326.

French, J. D., Hernández-Peón, R., and Livingston, R. B. Projections from cortex to cephalic brain stem (reticular formation) in monkeys. *J. Neurophysiol.*, 1955, **18**, 74–95.

French, J. W. A comparison of finger tremor with the galvanic skin reflex and pulse. *J. exp. Psychol.*, 1944, **34**, 494–505.

Fuller, J. L. Individual differences in the reactivity of dogs. *J. comp. physiol. Psychol.*, 1948, **41**, 339–347.

Fulton, J. F. *Physiology of the nervous system.* (3rd ed.) New York: Oxford University Press, 1949.

Fuster, J. M. Effects of stimulation of brain stem on tachistoscopic perception. *Science*, 1958, **127**, 150.

Gallais, P., Collomb, H., Miletto, G., Cardaire, G., and Blanc-Garin, J. Confrontations des données de l'électroencéphalogramme et de l'examen psychologique chez 113 jeunes soldats. In *Conditionnement et réactivité en électroencéphalographie.* Paris: Masson, 1957. Pp. 294–303.

Gastaut, H. The brain stem and cerebral electrogenesis in relation to consciousness. In J. F. Delafresnaye (Ed.), *Brain mechanisms and consciousness.* Springfield, Ill.: Thomas, 1954. Pp. 249–283.

Gastaut, H. Confrontations entre les données de l'électroencéphalogramme et des examens psychologiques chez 522 sujets repartis en trois groupes différents. V. Conclusions d'ensemble. In H. Fischgold and H. Gastaut (Eds.), *Conditionnement et réactivité en électroencéphalographie.* Paris: Masson, 1957. Pp. 321–338.

Gastaut, H., and Bert, J. EEG changes during cinematographic presentation. *EEG clin. Neurophysiol.,* 1954, **6**, 433–444.

Gastaut, H. and Y., Roger, A., Corriol, J., and Naquet, R. Étude électrographique du cycle d'excitabilité corticale. *EEG clin. Neurophysiol.,* 1951, **3**, 401–428. English summary, 427–428.

Gastaut, Y. Les pointes négatives évoquées sur le vertex. Leur signification psychophysiologique et pathologique. *Rev. Neurol.,* 1953, **89**, 382–399.

Gebhard, J. W. Motokawa's studies on electric excitation of the human eye. *Psychol. Bull.,* 1953, **50**, 73–111.

Gelber, B. Electromyographic factors in aircraft control: muscular tension in the learning and unlearning of a simple choice response. *USAF Sch. Aviat. Med. Rep.,* 1957, No. 55–134.

Geldard, F. *The human senses.* New York: Wiley, 1953.

Gellhorn, E. *Autonomic regulations—their significance for psychology and neuropsychiatry.* New York: Interscience, 1943.

Gellhorn, E. *Autonomic imbalance and the hypothalamus.* Minneapolis: University of Minnesota Press, 1957.

Gellhorn, E., and Hailman, H. The parallelism in changes of sensory function and electroencephalogram in anoxia and the effect of hypercapnia under these conditions. *Psychosom. Med.,* 1944, **6**, 23–30.

Gellhorn, E., Koella, W. P., and Ballin, H. M. Interaction on cerebral cortex of acoustic or optic with nociceptive impulses: the problem of consciousness. *J. Neurophysiol.,* 1954, **17**, 14–21.

Gellhorn, E., Koella, W. P., and Ballin, H. M. The influence of hypothalamic stimulation on evoked cortical potentials. *J. Psychol.,* 1955, **39**, 77–88.

Gellhorn, E., and Spiesman, I. G. The influence of hyperpnea and of variations of O_2– and CO_2–tension in inspired air upon hearing. *Amer. J. Physiol.,* 1935, **112**, 519–528.

Gerard, R. W. Drugs for the soul; the rise of psychopharmacology. *Science,* 1957, **125**, 201–203.

Gerard, R. W., Marshall, W. H., and Saul. L. J. Electrical activity of the cat's brain. *A.M.A. Arch. Neurol. Psychiat.,* 1936, **36**, 675–738.

Gesell, A., Castner, B. M., Thompson, H., and Amatruda, C. S. *Biographies of child development.* New York: Hoeber, 1939.

Ghiselli, E. Changes in neuromuscular tension accompanying the performance of a learning problem involving constant choice time. *J. exp. Psychol.,* 1936, **19**, 91–98.

Gibbs, F. A., and Gibbs, E. L. *Atlas of electroencephalography. Vol. I. Methodology and controls.* (2nd ed.) Cambridge, Mass.: Addison-Wesley Press, 1950.

Gibbs, F. A., and Knott, J. R. Growth of the electrical activity of the cortex. *EEG clin. Neurophysiol.,* 1949, **1**, 223–229.

Gibbs, F. A., and Maltby, G. L. Effect on the electrical activity of the cortex of certain depressant and stimulant drugs—barbiturates, morphine, caffeine, Benzedrine and adrenalin. *J. Pharmacol. exp. Therap.,* 1943, **78**, 1–10.

Gilbert, G. M. Inter-sensory facilitation and inhibition. *J. gen. Psychol.,* 1941, **24**, 381–407.

Gildea, E. F., Ronzoni, E., and Trufant, S. A. Results from the use of ACTH and cortisone in psychoses. In Milbank Memorial Fund, *The biology of mental health and disease.* New York: Hoeber, 1952. Pp. 600–613.

Gilliland, A. R., and Nelson, D. The effects of coffee on certain mental and physiological functions. *J. gen. Psychol.,* 1939, **21,** 339–348.

Goldstein, H. The biochemical variability of the individual in relation to personality and intelligence. *J. exp. Psychol.,* 1935, **18,** 348–371.

Goldstone, S. Flicker fusion measurements and anxiety level. *J. exp. Psychol.,* 1955, **49,** 200–202.

Golla, F. L. The objective study of neurosis. *Lancet,* 1921, **2,** 115–122.

Golla, F. L. Physiological psychology. *J. ment. Sci.,* 1944, **90,** 54–63.

Golla, F. Electrophysiology in psychiatry. In N. G. Harris (Ed.), *Modern trends in psychological medicine.* New York: Hoeber, 1948. Pp. 105–121.

Golla, F., Hutton, E. L., and Walter, W. G. Objective study of mental imagery; physiological concomitants. Appendix on new method of electroencephalographic analysis. *J. ment. Sci.,* 1943, **89,** 216–222.

Gonzalez, R. C., and Ross, S. The effects of chlorpromazine on the course of discrimination-reversals in the rat, 1959. Referred to by J. O. Cole, Behavioral toxicity. In L. Uhr and J. G. Miller (Eds.), *Drugs and behavior.* New York: Wiley, 1960. Pp. 166–183.

Gottlieb, J. S., Ashby, M. C., and Knott, J. R. Primary behavior disorders and psychopathic personality; correlations of electroencephalogram with family history and antecedent illness or injury. *A.M.A. Arch. Neurol. Psychiat.,* 1946, **56,** 381–400.

Gottlieb, J. S., Ashby, M. C., and Knott, J. R. Studies in primary behavior disorders and psychopathic personality. II. The inheritance of electrocortical activity. *Amer. J. Psychiat.,* 1947, **103,** 823–827.

Gottlieb, J. S., Knott, J. R., and Ashby, M. C. Electroencephalographic evaluation of primary behavior disorders in children; correlations with age, sex, family history and antecedent illness or injury. *A.M.A. Arch. Neurol. Psychiat.,* 1945, **53,** 138–143.

Gottlober, A. B. The relationship between brain potentials and personality. *J. exp. Psychol.,* 1938, **22,** 67–74.

Graham, B. F. Neuroendocrine components in the physiological response to stress. *Ann. NY Acad. Sci.,* 1953, **56,** 184–199.

Grandjean, E., Egli, R., Diday, F., Bloch, W., and Gfeller, H. Die Verschmelzungsfrequenz intermittierender Lichtreize als Ermüdungsmass. *Helv. Physiol. et Pharmacol. Acta,* 1953, **11,** 355–360.

Granger, G. W. The night visual ability of psychiatric patients. *Brit. J. Physiol. Opt.,* 1954, **11,** 226–232.

Granit, R. *Receptors and sensory perception.* New Haven: Yale University Press, 1955.

Grass, A. M., and Gibbs, F. A. A Fourier transform of the electroencephalogram. *J. Neurophysiol.,* 1938, **1,** 521–526.

Greenberg, P., and Gilliland, A. R. The relationship between basal metabolism and personality. *J. soc. Psychol.,* 1952, **35,** 3–7.

Greenblatt, M. Age and electroencephalographic abnormality in neuropsychiatric patients; a study of 1593 cases. *Amer. J. Psychiat.,* 1944, **101,** 82–90.

Grice, G. R. Discrimination reaction time as a function of anxiety and intelligence. *J. abnorm. soc. Psychol.,* 1955, **50,** 71–74.

Grinker, R. R., and Serota, H. M. Electroencephalographic studies of corticohypothalamic relations in schizophrenia. *Amer. J. Psychiat.*, 1941, **98**, 385–392.

Haavaldsen, R., Lingjaerde, O., and Walaas, O. Disturbances of carbohydrate metabolism in schizophrenics. The effect of serum fractions from schizophrenics on glucose uptake of rat diaphragm in vitro. *Confin. Neurol.* (Norway), 1958, **18**, 270–279.

Hadley, J. M. Some relationships between electrical signs of central and peripheral activity. II. During mental work. *J. exp. Psychol.*, 1941, **28**, 53–62.

Haggard, E. A. Reactions of children to experimentally induced frustration. Unpublished master's essay, Northwestern University, 1941.

Haggard, E. A. Some factors determining adjustment during and readjustment following experimentally induced stress. In S. S. Tomkins (Ed.), *Contemporary psychopathology.* Cambridge: Harvard University Press, 1943. Pp. 529–544.

Haggard, E. A. Experimental studies in affective processes: II. On the quantification and evaluation of "measured" changes in skin resistance. *J. exp. Psychol.*, 1945, **35**, 46–56.

Haggard, E. A. On the application of analysis of variance to GSR data: I. The selection of an appropriate measure. *J. exp. Psychol.*, 1949, **39**, 378–392.

Hall, C. S. Temperament: a survey of animal studies. *Psychol. Bull.*, 1941, **38**, 909–943.

Hall, K. R. L. Studies of cutaneous pain: a survey of research since 1940. *Brit. J. Psychol.*, 1953, **44**, 279–294.

Hall, V. E., and Lindsay, M. The relation of the thyroid gland to the spontaneous activity of the rat. *Endocrinology*, 1938, **22**, 66–79.

Halverson, H. M. Infant sucking and tensional behavior. *J. genet. Psychol.*, 1938, **53**, 365–430.

Hamilton, H. C., and Maher, E. B. The effects of glutamic acid on the behavior of the white rat. *J. comp. physiol. Psychol.*, 1947, **40**, 463–468.

Hammett, F. S. Temperament and bodily constitution. *J. comp. Psychol.*, 1921, **1**, 489–494.

Harris, G. W. The hypothalamus and the endocrine glands. *Brit. Med. Bull.*, 1950, **6**, 345–350.

Harris, R. S., and Thimann, K. W. *Vitamins and hormones.* Vol. IV. New York: Academic, 1947.

Harrison, F. An attempt to produce sleep by diencephalic stimulation. *J. Neurophysiol.*, 1940, **3**, 156–165.

Hartmann, G. W. II. Changes in visual acuity through simultaneous stimulation of other sense organs. *J. exp. Psychol.*, 1933, **16**, 393–407.

Hartmann, G. W. The facilitation effect of strong general illumination upon the discrimination of pitch and intensity differences. *J. exp. Psychol.*, 1934, **17**, 813–822.

Hauty, G. T. The effects of drugs upon the components of hand steadiness. *USAF Sch. Aviat. Med. Proj. Rep.*, 1954, Proj. No. 21-1601-0004 (Rep. No. 5).

Hebb, D. O. The mammal and his environment. *Amer. J. Psychiat.*, 1955, **111**, 826–831. (a)

Hebb, D. O. Drives and the c.n.s. (conceptual nervous system). *Psychol. Rev.*, 1955, **62**, 243–254. (b)

Helson, H., and Quantius, L. Changes in skin temperature following intense stimulation. *J. exp. Psychol.*, 1934, **17**, 20–35.

Hemphill, R. E. Forms of behavior of the electrical resistance of the skin related to certain psychiatric and endocrine conditions. *J. ment. Sci.*, 1942, **88**, 285–305.

Henderson, R. L. Remote action potentials at the moment of response in a simple reaction-time situation. *J. exp. Psychol.*, 1952, **44**, 238–241.

Henry, C. E. Electroencephalographic individual differences and their constancy; I. During sleep. *J. exp. Psychol.*, 1941, **29**, 117–132. (a)

Henry, C. E. Electroencephalographic individual differences and their constancy; II. During waking. *J. exp. Psychol.*, 1941, **29**, 236–241. (b)

Henry, C. E. Electroencephalograms of normal children. *Monogr. Soc. Res. Child Develpm.*, 1944, **9**, No. 3, 1–71.

Henry, C. E., and Darrow, C. W. EEG relationships to five autonomic variables. *Amer. Psychologist*, 1947, **2**, 421.

Henry, C. E., and Knott, J. R. A note on the relationship between "personality" and the alpha rhythm of the electroencephalogram. *J. exp. Psychol.*, 1941, **28**, 362–366.

Henry, G. W. Basal metabolism and emotional states. *J. nerv. ment. Dis.*, 1929, **70**, 598–605.

Heppenstall, M. E., and Greville, G. D. Biochemistry. In J. D. N. Hill and G. Parr (Eds.), *Electroencephalography.* London: Macdonald, 1950. Pp. 127–165.

Heppenstall, M. E., Hill, D., and Slater, E. The EEG in the prognosis of war neurosis. *Brain*, 1945, **68**, 17–22.

Heron, W. The pathology of boredom. *Scient. Amer.*, 1957, **196**, 52–56.

Herren, R. Y. The effect of high and low female sex hormone concentration on the two-point threshold of pain and touch and upon tactile sensitivity. *J. exp. Psychol.*, 1933, **16**, 324–327.

Herrington, L. P. *The psychophysiological profile of introverts and extroverts.* Unpublished Ph.D. thesis, Stanford University, 1930.

Herrington, L. P. The relation of physiological and social indices of activity level. In *Studies in personality, contributed in honor of Lewis M. Terman.* New York: McGraw-Hill, 1942. Pp. 125–146.

Heymans, G. *Inleiding tot de speciale psychologie.* Haarlem: Bohn, 1929.

Hilgard, E. R. Theories of human learning and problems of training. In U. S. Dept. of Defense, Research and Development Board. *Symposium on psychology of learning basic to military training problems.* Washington: U. S. Dept. of Defense, 1953.

Hilgard, E. R., Jones, L. V., and Kaplan, S. J. Conditioned discrimination as related to anxiety. *J. exp. Psychol.*, 1951, **42**, 94–99.

Hill, A. V. Is muscular relaxation an active process? *Nature* (London), 1950, **166**, 646.

Hill, D. Psychiatry. In J. D. N. Hill, and G. Parr (Eds.), *Electroencephalography.* London: Macdonald, 1950. Pp. 319–363.

Hill, D. EEG in episodic psychotic and psychopathic behavior. *EEG clin. Neurophysiol.*, 1952, **4**, 419–442.

Hill, D. Electroencephalography. In R. Brain and E. B. Strauss, *Recent advances in neurology and neuropsychiatry.* London: Churchill, 1955. Pp. 178–231.

Hill, J. D. N., and Parr, G. (Eds.), *Electroencephalography.* London: Macdonald, 1950.

Hill, W. F. Comments on Taylor's "drive theory and manifest anxiety." *Psychol. Bull.*, 1957, **54**, 490–493.

Himmelweit, H. T., Desai, M., and Petrie, A. An experimental investigation of neuroticism. *J. Pers.*, 1946, **15**, 173–196.

Himwich, H. E. Prospects in psychopharmacology. *J. nerv. ment. Dis.*, 1955, **122**, 413–423.

Himwich, H. E. Psychopharmacologic drugs. *Science*, 1958, **127**, 59–72.

Himwich, H. E. Biochemical and neurophysiological action of psychoactive drugs. In L. Uhr and J. G. Miller (Eds.), *Drugs and behavior.* New York: Wiley, 1960. Pp. 41–85.

Hirschstein, R. The significance of characteristic autonomic nervous system responses in the adjustment, change and outcome of schizophrenia. *J. nerv. ment. Dis.*, 1955, **122**, 254–262.

Hoagland, H. Stress and the adrenal cortex with special reference to potassium metabolism. *Psychosom. Med.*, 1950, **12**, 142–148.

Hoagland, H. Metabolic and physiologic disturbances in the psychoses. In Milbank Memorial Fund, *The biology of mental health and disease.* New York: Hoeber, 1952. Pp. 434–449.

Hoch, P., Kubis, J. F., and Rouke, F. L. Psychogalvanometric investigations in psychoses and other abnormal mental states. *Psychosom. Med.* 1944, **6**, 237–243.

Hodge, R. S. The impulsive psychopath: a clinical and electro-physiological study. *J. ment. Sci.*, 1945, **91**, 472–476.

Holliday, A. R., and Dille, J. M. The effects of meprobamate, chlorpromazine, pentobarbital, and a placebo on a behavioral task performed under stress conditions. *J. comp. physiol. Psychol.*, 1958, **51**, 811–815.

Hollingworth, H. L. The influence of caffeine on mental and motor efficiency. *Arch. Psychol., N. Y.*, 1912, No. 22, 1–166.

Horvath, F. E. Psychological stress: a review of definitions and experimental research. Preprint No. 27, Ann Arbor: University of Michigan, 1959.

Hoskins, R. G. *Endocrinology.* New York: Norton, 1941.

Hovland, C. I., and Riesen, A. H. Magnitude of galvanic and vasomotor response as a function of stimulus intensity. *J. gen. Psychol.*, 1940, **23**, 103–121.

Howe, E. S. GSR conditioning in anxiety states, normals, and chronic functional schizophrenic subjects. *J. abnorm. soc. Psychol.*, 1958, **56**, 183–189.

Howie, D. Aspects of personality in the classroom: a study of ratings on personal qualities for a group of schoolboys. *Brit. J. Psychol.*, 1945, **36**, 15–28.

Hughes, H., Epstein, L. J., and Jost, H. The relationship between certain measurable functions of autonomic nervous system activity and color responses on the Rorschach test. *J. clin. Psychol.*, 1951, **7**, 244–249.

Hume, D. M., and Wittenstein, G. J. The relationship of the hypothalamus to pituitary-adrenocortical function. In J. R. Mote (Ed.), *Proceedings of 1st clinical ACTH conference.* Philadelphia: Blakiston, 1950.

Hurst, L. A., Mundy-Castle, A. C., and Beerstecher, D. M. The electroencephalogram in manic-depressive psychosis. *J. ment. Sci.*, 1954, **100**, 220–240.

Huxtable, Z. L., White, M. H., and McCartor, M. A. A re-performance and reinterpretation of the Arai experiment in mental fatigue with three subjects. *Psychol. Monogr.*, 1945, **59**, No. 5 (Whole No. 275).

Ingham, J. G., Psychoneurosis and suggestibility. *J. abnorm. soc. Psychol.*, 1955, **51**, 600–603.

Ingle, D. J. Endocrine function and personality. *Psychol. Rev.*, 1935, **42**, 466–479.

Ingram, W. R., Knott, J. R., Wheatley, M. D., and Summers, T. D. Physiological relationships between hypothalamus and cerebral cortex. *EEG clin. Neurophysiol.*, 1951, **3**, 37–58.

Inman, V. T., Ralston, H. J., Saunders, J. B. de C. M., Feinstein, B., and Wright, E. W., Jr. Relation of human electromyogram to muscular tension. *EEG clin. Neurophysiol.*, 1952, **4**, 186–194.

Iwata, K., and Snider, R. S. Cerebello-hippocampal influences on the electroencephalogram. *EEG clin. Neurophysiol.*, 1959, **11**, 439–446.

Jacobson, E. Further experiments on the inhibition of sensations. *Amer. J. Psychol.*, 1912, **23**, 345–369.

Jacobson, E. Differential relaxation during reading, writing, and other activities as tested by the knee-jerk. *Amer. J. Physiol.*, 1928, **86**, 675–693.

Jacobson, E. *Progressive relaxation.* Chicago: University of Chicago Press, 1929.

Jacobson, E. Electrical measurements of neuromuscular states during mental activities. I. Imagination of movement involving skeletal muscle. *Amer. J. Physiol.*, 1930, **91**, 567–608.

Jacobson, E. *Progressive relaxation.* (2nd ed.) Chicago: University of Chicago Press, 1938.

Jacobson, E. The physiological conception and treatment of certain common "psychoneuroses." *Amer. J. Psychiat.*, 1941, **98**, 219–226.

James, W. T. Morphologic form and its relation to behavior. In C. R. Stockard (Ed.), *The genetic and endocrine basis for differences in form and behavior.* Philadelphia: Wistar Institute of Anatomy and Biology, 1941. Pp. 525–643.

James, W. T. Morphological and constitutional factors in conditioning. *Ann. NY Acad. Sci.*, 1953, **56**, 171–183.

James, W. T., and Ginsburg, B. E. The effect of prostigmine on the conditioned response of "inhibited dogs." *J. comp. physiol. Psychol.*, 1949, **42**, 6–11.

Jasper, H. H. Cortical excitatory state and synchronism in the control of bioelectric autonomous rhythms. *Cold Spring Harbor Sympos. quant. Biol.*, 1936, **4**, 320–338.

Jasper, H. H. Diffuse projection system: the integrative action of the thalamic reticular system. *EEG clin. Neurophysiol.*, 1949, **1**, 405–419.

Jasper, H. H. Electrophysiology and experimental epilepsy. In W. Penfield, and H. Jasper (Eds.), *Epilepsy and the functional anatomy of the human brain.* Boston: Little, Brown, 1954. Pp. 183–238.

Jasper, H. H., Naquet, R., and King, E. E. Thalamocortical recruiting responses in sensory receiving areas in the cat. *EEG clin. Neurophysiol.*, 1955, **7**, 99–114.

Jasper, H. H., Solomon, P., and Bradley, C. Electroencephalographic analyses of behavior problem children. *Amer. J. Psychiat.*, 1938, **95**, 641–658.

Jeffress, L. A. Galvanic phenomena of the skin, *J. exp. Psychol.*, 1928, **11**, 130–144.

Jenkins, R. L. The error of basal metabolism determination and the normal range of basal metabolism. *A.M.A. Arch. Internal Med.*, 1932, **49**, 181–187.

Jenkins, W. L., and Connor, M. B. Some design factors in making settings on a linear scale. *J. appl. Psychol.*, 1949, **33**, 395–409.

Jessor, R., and Hammond, K. R. Construct validity and the Taylor anxiety scale. *Psychol. Bull.*, 1957, **54**, 161–170.

John, R. E., Wenzel, B. M., and Tschirgi, R. D. Differential effects of reserpine on conditioned responses in cats. *Science*, 1958, **126**, 25–26.

Johnson, B. Changes in muscular tension in coördinated hand movements. *J. exp Psychol.*, 1928, **11**, 329–341.

Johnson, H. M. The dynamogenic influence of light on tactile discrimination. *Psychobiology*, 1920, **2**, 351–374.

Johnson, L. C., and Ulett, G. A. Stability of EEG activity and manifest anxiety. *J. comp. physiol. Psychol.*, 1959, **52**, 284–288.

Jones, H. E. Adolescent changes in electrodermal phenomena. *Amer. Psychologist*, 1949, **4**, 390.

Jones, H. E. The study of patterns of emotional expression. In M. L. Reymert (Ed.), *Feelings and emotions*. New York: McGraw-Hill, 1950. Pp. 161–168.

Jost, H. The relationship between certain physiological changes during learning, frustration and sensory stimulation and personality variation. Unpublished doctoral dissertation, University of Chicago, 1940.

Jost, H. Some physiological changes during frustration. *Child Develpm.*, 1941, **12**, 9–15.

Jost, H., and Sontag, L. W. The genetic factor in autonomic nervous system function. *Psychosom. Med.*, 1944, **6**, 308–310.

Judd, C. H. Movement and consciousness. *Psychol. Rev.*, 1905, Monogr. Suppl. No. 29, 199–226.

Jurko, M., Jost, H., and Hill, T. S. Pathology of the energy system: an experimental-clinical study of physiological adaptive capacities in a non-patient, a psychoneurotic, and an early paranoid schizophrenic group. *J. Psychol.*, 1952, **33**, 183–198.

Kaada, B R. Electrical activity of the brain. *Annu. Rev. Physiol.*, 1953, **15**, 39–62.

Kaplan, S. D. Drugs and hypothalamic excitability. In L. Uhr and J. G. Miller (Eds.), *Drugs and behavior*. New York: Wiley, 1960. Pp. 413–419.

Katz, M. M. Projective techniques and drug research. In L. Uhr and J. G. Miller (Eds.), *Drugs and behavior*. New York: Wiley, 1960. Pp. 501–514.

Kausler, D. H., and Trapp, E. P. Motivation and cue utilization in intentional and incidental learning. *Psychol. Rev.*, 1960, **67**, 373–379.

Keeler, C. E. The association of the black (non-agouti) gene with behavior in the Norway rat. *J. Hered.*, 1942, **33**, 371–384.

Kelly, E. L. Theory and techniques of assessment. *Annu. Rev. Psychol.*, 1954, **5**, 281–310.

Kennard, M. A. Autonomic interrelations with the somatic nervous system. *Psychosom. Med.*, 1947, **9**, 29–36.

Kennard, M. A. Inheritance of electroencephalogram patterns in children with behavior disorders. *Psychosom. Med.*, 1949, **11**, 151–157.

Kennard, M. A. The electroencephalogram in psychological disorders: a review. *Psychosom. Med.*, 1953, **15**, 95–115.

Kennard, M. A., Bueding, E., and Wortis, S. B. The relation of the EEG to the pattern of response to environmental stimuli. *Quart. J. Stud. Alc.*, 1945, **6**, 4–14.

Kennard, M. A., Rabinovitch, M. S., and Fister, W. P. The use of frequency analysis in the interpretation of the EEGs of patients with psychological disorders. *EEG clin. Neurophysiol.*, 1955, **7**, 29–38.

Kennard, M. A., and Schwartzman, A. E. A longitudinal study of changes in EEG frequency pattern as related to psychological changes. *J. nerv. ment. Dis.*, 1956, **124**, 8–20.

Kennard, M. A., and Willner, M. D. Correlation between electroencephalograms and deep reflexes in normal adults. *Dis. nerv. System*, 1945, **6**, 337–347.

Kennedy, J. L., and Travis, R. C. Prediction of speed of performance by muscle action potentials. *Science,* 1947, **105,** 410–411.

Kennedy, J. L., and Travis, R. C. Prediction and control of alertness. II. Continuous tracking. *J. comp. physiol. Psychol.,* 1948, **41,** 203–210.

Kerrick, J. S. Some correlates of the Taylor Manifest Anxiety Scale. *J. abnorm. soc. Psychol.,* 1955, **50,** 75–77.

Keys, A. Experimental induction of psychoneuroses by starvation. In Milbank Memorial Fund, *The biology of mental health and disease.* New York: Hoeber, 1952. Pp. 515–525.

King, C. D. Electrometric studies of sleep. *J. gen. Psychol.,* 1946, **35,** 131–159.

Kitzinger, H., Arnold, D. G., Cartwright, R. W., and Shapiro, D. A preliminary study of the effects of glutamic acid on catatonic schizophrenics. *Rorschach res. Exch.,* 1949, **13,** 210–218.

Kleemeier, L. B., and Kleemeier, R. W. Effects of benzedrine sulfate (amphetamine) on psychomotor performance. *Amer. J. Psychol.,* 1947, **60,** 89–100.

Klein, S. J. Muscle action potentials produced in various ways and their relation to quantitative and qualitative measures of ergographic work. Unpublished doctoral dissertation, University of Pennsylvania, 1951.

Klein, S. J. Relation of muscle action potentials variously induced to breakdown of work in task-oriented subjects. *Percept. motor Skills,* 1961, **12,** 131–141.

Kleitman, N. *Sleep and wakefulness.* Chicago: University of Chicago Press, 1939.

Kling, C. The role of the parasympathetics in emotions. *Psychol. Rev.,* 1933, **40,** 368–380.

Kling, J. W., Williams, J. P., and Schlosberg, H. Patterns of skin conductance during rotary pursuit. *Percept. motor Skills,* 1959, **9,** 303–312.

Knott, J. R. Brain potentials during silent and oral reading. *J. gen. Psychol.,* 1938, **18,** 57–62.

Knott, J. R. Electroencephalography and physiological psychology: evaluation and statement of the problem. *Psychol. Bull.,* 1941, **38,** 944–975.

Knott, J. R., Platt, E. B., Ashby, M. C., and Gottlieb, J. S. A familial evaluation of the electroencephalogram of patients with primary behavior disorder and psychopathic personality. *EEG clin. Neurophysiol.,* 1953, **5,** 363–370.

Korchin, S. J., and Basowitz, H. Perceptual adequacy in a life stress. *J. Psychol.,* 1954, **38,** 495–502.

Kornetsky, C. Effects of meprobamate, phenobarbital and dextroamphetamine on reaction time and learning in man. *J. Pharmacol. exp. Therap.,* 1958, **123,** 216–219.

Kornetsky, C. Alterations in psychomotor functions and individual differences in responses produced by psychoactive drugs. In L. Uhr and J. G. Miller (Eds.), *Drugs and behavior.* New York: Wiley, 1960. Pp. 297–312.

Kornetsky, C., and Humphries, O. Psychological effects of centrally acting drugs in man. Effects of chlorpromazine and secobarbital on visual and motor behavior. *J. ment. Sci.,* 1958, **104,** 1093–1099.

Kornetsky, C., Humphries, O., and Evarts, E. V. Comparison of psychological effects of certain centrally acting drugs in man. *A.M.A. Arch. Neurol. Psychiat.,* 1957, **77,** 318–324.

Kosman, M. E., and Gerard, R. W. The effect of adrenaline on a conditioned avoidance response. *J. comp. physiol. Psychol.,* 1955, **48,** 506–508.

Kravkov, S. V. Über die Abhängigkeit der Sehschärfe vom Schallreiz. *Arch. f. Ophthal.*, 1930, **124** (2), 334–339.

Kravkov, S. V. Der Lichtirradiationseffekt im Auge in seiner Abhängigkeit von den Gesichts-, Gehörs-, und Geruchsnebenreizen. *Arch. f. Ophthal.*, 1933, **129** (3), 440–451.

Kravkov, S. V. The influence of caffeine on the color-sensitivity. *Acta ophthal. Kbh.*, 1939, **17**, 89–92.

Kretschmer, E., and Enke, W. *Die Persönlichkeit der Athletiker.* Leipzig: Thieme, 1936.

Kristofferson, A. B., and Cormack, R. H. Preliminary results concerning the galvanic skin response as an indicator of drug effects. In L. Uhr and J. G. Miller (Eds.), *Drugs and behavior.* New York: Wiley, 1960. Pp. 405–408.

Krus, D. M., Wapner, S., and Werner, H. Studies in vicariousness: effect of muscular involvement on visual threshold. *Amer. J. Psychol.*, 1958, **71**, 395–398.

Kubis, J. F. Adaptation of the psychogalvanic response (PGR) to a visual, auditory, and ideational stimulus. *Amer. Psychologist*, 1948, **3**, 256. (Abstract)

Kuno, Y. The significance of sweating in man. *Lancet*, 1930, **218** (1), 912–915.

Kuntz, A. *Visceral innervation and its relation to personality.* Springfield: Thomas, 1951.

Lacey, J. I. Consistency of patterns of somatic response to stress. *Amer. Psychologist*, 1949, **4**, 232–233.

Lacey, J. I. Individual differences in somatic response patterns. *J. comp. physiol. Psychol.*, 1950, **43**, 338–350.

Lacey, J. I. The evaluation of autonomic responses: toward a general solution. *Ann. NY Acad. Sci.*, 1956, **67**, 123–164.

Lacey, J. I. Psychophysiological approaches to the evaluation of psychotherapeutic process and outcome. In *Research in psychotherapy.* Washington: American Psychological Association, 1959. Pp. 160–208.

Lacey, J. I., Bateman, D. E., and Van Lehn, R. Autonomic response specificity and Rorschach color responses. *Psychosom. Med.*, 1952, **14**, 256–260.

Lacey, J. I., Bateman, D. E., and Van Lehn, R. Autonomic response specificity. *Psychosom. Med.*, 1953, **15**, 8–21.

Lacey, J. I., and Lacey, B. C. Verification and extension of the principle of autonomic response-stereotypy. *Amer. J. Psychol.*, 1958, **71**, 50–73. (a)

Lacey, J. I., and Lacey, B. C. The relationship of resting autonomic activity to motor impulsivity. *Res. Publ. Ass. Res. nerv. ment. Dis.*, 1958, **36**, 144–209. (b)

Lacey, J. I., Smith, R. L., and Green, A. Use of conditioned autonomic responses in the study of anxiety. *Psychosom. Med.*, 1955, **17**, 208–217.

Lacey, J. I., and Van Lehn, R. Differential emphasis in somatic response to stress. *Psychosom. Med.*, 1952, **14**, 71–81.

Lacey, O. L., and Siegel, P. S. An analysis of the unit of measurement of the galvanic skin response. *J. exp. Psychol.*, 1949, **39**, 122–127.

Lacey, O. L., Siegel, P. S., and Siegel, H. S. The relation of body morphology to galvanic skin conductance and response. *Amer. J. Psychol.*, 1949, **62**, 430–432.

Lafon, R., and Minvielle, J. Chemotherapy and pharmacodynamic experimentation with schizophrenics. In L. Uhr and J. G. Miller (Eds.), *Drugs and behavior.* New York: Wiley, 1960. Pp. 368–371.

Lairy, G. C., and Dell, P. La régulation de l'activité corticale: aspects psychophysiologiques et psychopathologiques. In H. Fischgold and H. Gastaut, Conditionnement et réactivité en électroencéphalographie. *EEG clin. Neurophysiol.*, 1957, Suppl. No. 6, 341–390.

Lamb, W. M., Ulett, G. A., Masters, W. H., and Robinson, D. W. Premenstrual tension: EEG, hormonal, and psychiatric evaluation. *Amer. J. Psychiat.*, 1953, 109, 840–848.

Landis, C. The electrical phenomena of the skin. *Psychol. Bull.*, 1932, 29, 693–752.

Landis, C. Determinants of the critical flicker-fusion threshold. *Physiol. Rev.*, 1954, 34, 259–286.

Landis, C., and Gullette, R. Studies of emotional reactions. III. Systolic blood pressure and inspiration-expiration ratios. *J. comp. Psychol.*, 1925, 5, 221–253.

Landis, C., and Hamwi, V. The effect of certain physiological determinants on the flicker-fusion threshold. *J. appl. Physiol.*, 1954, 6, 566–572.

Landis, C., and Hunt, W. A. *The startle pattern.* New York: Farrar and Rinehart, 1939.

Lanier, L. H. Variability in the pain threshold. *Science*, 1943, 97, 49–50.

Lansing, R. W. Relation of brain and tremor rhythms to visual reaction time. *EEG clin. Neurophysiol.*, 1957, 9, 497–504.

Lansing, R. W., Schwartz, E., and Lindsley, D. B. Reaction time and EEG activation. *Amer. Psychologist*, 1956, 11, 433. (Abstract)

Lansing, R. W., Schwartz, E., and Lindsley, D. B. Reaction time and EEG activation under alerted and nonalerted conditions. *J. exp. Psychol.*, 1959, 58, 1–7.

Laties, V. G. Effects of meprobamate on fear and palmar sweating. *J. abnorm. soc. Psychol.*, 1959, 59, 156–161.

Lauer, A. E., and Smith, E. A. A quantitative study of the relation between pulse and breathing changes and electro-biochemical responses. *Amer. J. Psychol.*, 1932, 44, 732–739.

Laufer, M. W., Denhoff, E., and Solomons, G. Hyperkinetic impulse disorder in children's behavior problems. *Psychosom. Med.*, 1957, 19, 38–49.

Lazarus, R. S., and Eriksen, C. W. Effects of failure stress upon skilled performance. *J. exp. Psychol.*, 1952, 43, 100–105.

Lee, M. A. M. The relation of the knee-jerk and standing steadiness to nervous instability. *J. abnorm. soc. Psychol.*, 1931, 26, 212–228.

Lehmann, H. E., and Csank, J. Differential screening of phenotropic agents in man: psychophysiologic test data. *J. clin. exp. Psychopath.*, 1957, 18, 222–235.

Lemere, F. Significance of individual differences in the Berger rhythm. *Brain*, 1936, 59, 366–375.

Lennox, W. G., Gibbs, E. L., and Gibbs, F. A. The brain-wave pattern, an hereditary trait; evidence from 74 "normal" pairs of twins. *J. Hered.*, 1945, 36, 233–243.

Lennox, W. G., Gibbs, F. A., and Gibbs, E. L. Relationship in man of cerebral activity to blood flow and to blood constituents. *J. Neurol. Psychiat.*, 1938, 1, 211–225.

Lerman, J. Physiology of the thyroid gland. *J. Amer. Med. Ass.*, 1941, 117, 349–359.

Leuba, C. Toward some integration of learning theories: the concept of optimal stimulation. *Psychol. Rep.*, 1955, 1, 27–33.

Levy, E. Z., Thaler, V. H., and Ruff, G. E. New technique for recording skin resistance changes. *Science*, 1958, 128, 33–34.

Levy, J. R. Changes in the galvanic skin response accompanying the Rorschach test. *Amer. Psychologist*, 1948, **3**, 335.

Levy, S., and Kennard, M. A. The EEG pattern of patients with psychologic disorders of various ages. *J. nerv. ment. Dis.*, 1953, **118**, 416–428.

Lewin, K. *A dynamic theory of personality; selected papers.* Translated by D. K. Adams and K. E. Zener. New York: McGraw-Hill, 1935.

Lewin, K. *The conceptual representation and the measurement of psychological forces.* (*Contributions to Psychological Theory:* Vol. 1, No. 4.) Durham: Duke University Press, 1938.

Li, C., McLennan, H., and Jasper, H. Brain waves and unit discharge in cerebral cortex. *Science*, 1952, **116**, 656–657.

Lindsley, D. B. Brain potentials in children and adults. *Science*, 1936, **84**, 354.

Lindsley, D. B. Electrical potentials of the brain in children and adults. *J. gen. Psychol.*, 1938, **19**, 285–306.

Lindsley, D. B. A longitudinal study of the occipital alpha rhythm in normal children: frequency and amplitude standards. *J. genet. Psychol.*, 1939, **55**, 197–213.

Lindsley, D. B. Electroencephalography. In J. McV. Hunt (Ed.), *Personality and the behavior disorders.* New York: Ronald, 1944. Pp. 1033–1103.

Lindsley, D. B. Emotions and the electroencephalogram. In M. L. Reymert (Ed.), *Feelings and emotions.* New York: McGraw-Hill, 1950. Pp. 238–246.

Lindsley, D. B. Emotion. In S. S. Stevens (Ed.), *Handbook of experimental psychology.* New York: Wiley, 1951.

Lindsley, D. B. Psychological phenomena and the electroencephalogram. *EEG clin. Neurophysiol.*, 1952, **4**, 443–456.

Lindsley, D. B. Physiological psychology. *Annu. Rev. Psychol.*, 1956, **7**, 323–348.

Lindsley, D. B. Psychophysiology and motivation. In M. R. Jones (Ed.), *Nebraska symposium on motivation 1957.* Lincoln: University of Nebraska Press, 1957. Pp. 44–105.

Lindsley, D. B., Bowden, J., and Magoun, H. W. Effect upon the EEG of acute injury to the brain stem activating system. *EEG clin. Neurophysiol.*, 1949, **1**, 475–486.

Lindsley, D. B., and Cutts, K. K. The electroencephalograms of "constitutionally inferior" and behavior problem children: comparison with normal children and adults. *A.M.A. Arch. Neurol. Psychiat.*, 1940, **44**, 1199–1212.

Lindsley, D. B., and Henry, C. E. The effect of drugs on behavior and the electroencephalograms of children with behavior disorders. *Psychosom. Med.*, 1942, **4**, 140–149.

Lindsley, D. B., and Rubenstein, B. B. Relationship between brain potentials and some other physiological variables. *Proc. Soc. exp. Biol.*, 1937, **35**, 558–563.

Lindsley, D. B., Schreiner, L. H., Knowles, W. B., and Magoun, H. W. Behavioral and EEG changes following chronic brain stem lesions in the cat. *EEG clin. Neurophysiol.*, 1950, **2**, 483–498.

Lockwood, M. R. A parallel study of the psychogalvanic reflex and the hyperglycemic index in psychotics. *J. ment. Sci.*, 1932, **78**, 288–301.

London, I. D. Research on sensory interaction in the Soviet Union. *Psychol. Bull.*, 1954, **51**, 531–568.

Loomis, A. L., Harvey, E. N., and Hobart, G. Electrical potentials of the human brain. *J. exp. Psychol.*, 1936, **19**, 249–279.

Loucks, R. The use of muscle action potential measurements in the selection of aircrew trainees. *AAF Sch. Aviat. Med. Proj. Rep.*, 1944, Proj. No. 274, Rep. No. 1.

Lovell, C. A study of personal variation in hand-arm steadiness. *Amer. J. Psychol.*, 1941, **54**, 230–236.

Lucas, W. P., Pryor, H. B., Bost, C., and Pope, S. T., Jr. Growth problems: II. Basal metabolic rate variations in relation to body build, adolescence, and allergy in children. *J. Pediat.*, 1933, **3**, 856–869.

Luchins, A. S. Mechanization in problem solving. *Psychol. Monogr.*, 1942, **54**, No. 6 (Whole No. 248).

Ludlum, S. D. W. Physiologic psychiatry. *Med. Clin. N. Amer.*, 1918, **2**, No. 1, 895.

Lundervold, A. Electro-myography as a test for pilot aspirants. *J. Aviation Med.*, 1950, **21**, 147–149.

Lundervold, A. An electromyographic investigation of tense and relaxed subjects. *J. nerv. ment. Dis.*, 1952, **115**, 512–525.

Luria, A. R. *The nature of human conflicts; or emotion, conflict and will, an objective study of disorganization and control of human behaviour.* Translated from the Russian and edited by W. H. Gantt. New York: Liveright, 1932.

Lybrand, W. A., Andrews, T. G., and Ross, S. Systemic fatigue and perceptual organization. *Amer. J. Psychol.*, 1954, **67**, 704–707.

McCleary, R. A. The nature of the galvanic skin response. *Psychol. Bull.*, 1950, 47, 97–117.

McFann, H. H. Performance on a motor task under differential amounts of physical induced tension. *Proc. Iowa Acad., Sci.*, 1952, **59**, 378–384.

McFarland, R. A. Psycho-acoustical studies at high altitudes in the Andes. Part II. *J. comp. Psychol.*, 1937, **23**, 227–240.

McFarland, R. A., and Huddleson, J. H. Neurocirculatory reactions in the psychoneuroses studied by the Schneider method. *Amer. J. Psychiat.*, 1936, **93**, 567–599.

McTeer, W. Changes in grip tension following electric shock in mirror tracing. *J. exp. Psychol.*, 1933, **16**, 735–742.

Maberly, A. Personality of the problem child. *Brit. J. Psychol.*, 1946, **16**, 5–12.

Mackinnon, P. Variations with age in the number of active palmar digital sweat glands. *J. Neurol. Neurosurg. Psychiat.*, 1954, **17**, 124–126.

Mackworth, N. H. Effects of Benzedrine Sulphate on a visual vigilance test. Report to Royal Naval Personnel Res. Comm., Rep. 47/401, 1947.

Magoun, H. W. Caudal and cephalic influences of the brain stem reticular formation. *Physiol. Rev.*, 1950, **30**, 459–474.

Magoun, H. W. The ascending reticular activating system. *Res. Publ. Ass. nerv. ment. Dis.*, 1952, **30**, 480–492. (a)

Magoun, H. W. An ascending reticular activating system in the brain stem. *A.M.A. Arch. Neurol. Psychiat.*, 1952, **67**, 145–154. (b)

Magoun, H. W. Physiological interrelationships between cortex and subcortical structures. *EEG clin. Neurophysiol.*, 1953, Suppl. 4, 163–167.

Mahut, H. Breed differences in the dog's emotional behavior. *Canad. J. Psychol.*, 1958, **12**, 35–44.

Malamud, W. Hypophyseal-adrenocortical dysfunction in mental disease. In Milbank Memorial Fund, *The biology of mental health and disease.* New York: Hoeber, 1952. Pp. 613–617.

Malmo, R. B. Can muscle tension be used as an "affective index"? Paper read at Amer. Psychol. Ass. Meeting, New York, Sept., 1954. (a)

Malmo, R. B. Research: experimental and theoretical aspects. In E. D. Wittkower and R. A. Cleghorn (Eds.), *Recent developments in psychosomatic medicine.* Philadelphia: Lippincott, 1954. (b)

Malmo, R. B. Activation: a neurophysiological dimension. *Psychol. Rev.,* 1959, 66, 367–386.

Malmo, R. B., Boag, T. J., and Smith, A. A. Physiological study of personal interaction. *Psychosom. Med.,* 1957, 19, 105–119.

Malmo, R. B., and Davis, J. F. Physiological gradients as indicants of "arousal" in mirror tracing. *Canad. J. Psychol.,* 1956, 10, 231–238.

Malmo, R. B., and Shagass, C. Physiologic studies of reaction to stress in anxiety and early schizophrenia. *Psychosom. Med.,* 1949, 11, 9–24. (a)

Malmo, R. B., and Shagass, C. Physiologic study of symptom mechanisms in psychiatric patients under stress. *Psychosom. Med.,* 1949, 11, 25–29. (b)

Malmo, R. B., and Shagass, C. Variability of heart rate in relation to age, sex, and stress. *J. appl. Physiol.,* 1949, 2, 181–184. (c)

Malmo, R. B., and Shagass, C. Electromyographic studies of muscular tension in psychiatric patients under stress. *J. clin. exp. Psychopath.,* 1951, 12, 45–66.

Malmo, R. B., and Shagass, C. Studies of blood pressure in psychiatric patients under stress. *Psychosom. Med.,* 1952, 14, 82–93.

Malmo, R. B., Shagass, C., Belanger, D. J., and Smith, A. A. Motor control in psychiatric patients under experimental stress. *J. abnorm. soc. Psychol.,* 1951, 46, 539–547.

Malmo, R. B., Shagass, C., and Davis, F. H. Symptom specificity and bodily reactions during psychiatric interview. *Psychosom. Med.,* 1950, 12, 362–376.

Malmo, R. B., Shagass, C., and Davis, J. F. A method for the investigation of somatic response mechanisms in psychoneurosis. *Science,* 1950, 112, 325–328.

Malmo, R. B., Shagass, C., and Davis, J. F. Electromyographic studies of muscular tension in psychiatric patients under stress. *J. clin. exp. Psychopath.,* 1951, 12, 45–66.

Malmo, R. B., Shagass, C., Davis, J. F., Cleghorn, R. A., Graham, B. F., and Goodman, A. J. Standardized pain stimulation as controlled stress in physiological studies of psychoneurosis. *Science,* 1948, 108, 509–511.

Malmo, R. B., Shagass, C., and Heslam, R. M. Blood pressure response to repeated brief stress in psychoneurosis: a study of adaptation. *Canad. J. Psychol.,* 1951, 5, 167–179.

Malmo, R. B., Shagass, C., and Smith, A. A. Responsiveness in chronic schizophrenia. *J. Pers.,* 1951, 19, 359–375.

Malmo, R. B., and Smith, A. A. Forehead tension and motor irregularities in psychoneurotic patients under stress. *J. Pers.,* 1955, 23, 391–406.

Malmo, R. B., and Wallerstein, H. Rigidity and reactive inhibition. *J. abnorm. soc. Psychol.,* 1955, 50, 345–348.

Malmo, R. B., Wallerstein, H., and Shagass, C. Headache proneness and mechanisms of motor conflict in psychiatric patients. *J. Pers.,* 1953, 22, 163–187.

Maltzman, I., Fox, J., and Morrissett, L., Jr. Some effects of manifest anxiety on mental set. *J. exp. Psychol.,* 1953, 46, 50–54.

Marquis, D. G., Kelly, E. L., Miller, J. G., Gerard, R. W., and Rapoport, A. Experimental studies of behavioral effects of meprobamate on normal subjects. *Ann. NY Acad. Sci.*, 1957, **67**, 701–712.

Martin, B., and McGowan, B. Some evidence on the validity of the Sarason Test Anxiety Scale. *J. consult. Psychol.*, 1955, **19**, 468.

Martin, I. Personality and muscle activity. *Canad. J. Psychol.*, 1958, **12**, 23–30.

Marx, M. H. Relationship between supranormal glutamic acid and maze learning. *J. comp. physiol. Psychol.*, 1949, **42**, 313–319.

Marzocco, F. N. Production of stress by experimental frustration. Paper presented in Symposium on Psychological and Biological Effects of Stress, Western Psychological Association Sector of A.A.A.S. Meeting, June, 1955. (Reported by A. F. Ax in *Polygraph Newsletter*, 1955, Vol. 1, No. 2.)

Mason, J. W., and Brady, J. V. Plasma 17-hydroxycorticosteroid changes related to reserpine effects on emotional behavior. *Science*, 1956, **124**, 983–984.

Masserman, J. H. Is the hypothalamus a center of emotion? *Psychosom. Med.*, 1941, **3**, 3–25.

Masserman, J. H. *Principles of dynamic psychiatry.* Philadelphia: Saunders, 1946.

Matarazzo, J. D., Guze, S. B., and Matarazzo, R. G. An approach to the validity of the Taylor anxiety scale. *J. abnorm. soc. Psychol.*, 1955, **51**, 276–280.

Matarazzo, J. D., and Phillips, J. S. Digit symbol performance as a function of increasing levels of anxiety. *J. consult. Psychol.*, 1955, **19**, 131–134.

Matarazzo, J. D., Ulett, G. A., and Saslow, G. Human maze performance as a function of increasing levels of anxiety. *J. gen. Psychol.*, 1955, **53**, 79–95.

Matthews, B. H. C., and Luczak, A. K. Some factors influencing dark adaptation. (Flying Personnel Res. Comm. Rep. No. 577.) Farnborough: RAF Physiological Laboratory, 1944.

Max, L. W. An experimental study of the motor theory of consciousness. III. Action current responses in deaf-mutes during sleep, sensory stimulation and dreams. *J. comp. Psychol.*, 1935, **19**, 469–486.

Max, L. W. Experimental study of the motor theory of consciousness. IV. Action-current responses in the deaf during awakening, kinesthetic imagery and abstract thinking. *J. comp. Psychol.*, 1937, **24**, 301–344.

Mayzner, M. S., Jr., Sersen, E., and Tresselt, M. E. The Taylor Manifest Anxiety Scale and intelligence. *J. consult. Psychol.*, 1955, **19**, 401–403.

Melin, K. The EEG in infancy and childhood. *EEG clin. Neurophysiol.*, 1953, Suppl. No. 4, 205–211.

Meyer, D. R. On the interaction of simultaneous responses. *Psychol. Bull.*, 1953, **50**, 204–220.

Miller, J. G. Drugs and human information processing: perception, cognition, and response. In L. Uhr and J. G. Miller (Eds.), *Drugs and behavior.* New York: Wiley, 1960. Pp. 335–351.

Miller, J. G., and Uhr, L. Behavioral toxicity as measured by tests of complex simulated driving and vision. In L. Uhr and J. G. Miller (Eds.), *Drugs and behavior.* New York: Wiley, 1960. Pp. 326–329.

Miller, M. Changes in the response to electric shock by varying muscular conditions. *J. exp. Psychol.*, 1926, **9**, 26–44.

Miller, N. E. Objective techniques for studying motivational effects of drugs on animals. In S. Garattini and V. Ghetti (Eds.), *Proceedings of international symposium on psychotropic drugs.* Amsterdam, Netherlands: Elsevier, 1957.

Miller, N. E., and Miles, W. R. Effect of caffeine on the running speed of hungry, satiated, and frustrated rats. *J. comp. Psychol.*, 1935, **20**, 397–412.

Mirsky, A. F., and Rosvold, H. E. The use of psychoactive drugs as a neuropsychological tool in studies of attention in man. In L. Uhr and J. G. Miller (Eds.), *Drugs and behavior.* New York: Wiley, 1960. Pp. 375–392.

Mirsky, I. A., Miller, R., and Stein, M. Relation of adrenocortical activity and adaptive behavior. *Psychosom. Med.,* 1953, **15**, 574–584.

Mitchell, L. E., and Zax, M. The effects of chlorpromazine on GSR conditioning. *J. abnorm. soc. Psychol.,* 1959, **59**, 246–249.

Mittelmann, B., and Wolff, H. G. Affective states and skin temperature: experimental study of subjects with "cold hands" and Raynaud's syndrome. *Psychosom. Med.,* 1939, **1**, 271–292.

Moldawsky, S., and Moldawsky, P. Digit span as an anxiety indicator. *J. consult. Psychol.,* 1952, **16**, 115–118.

Montague, E. K. The role of anxiety in serial rote learning. *J. exp. Psychol.,* 1953, **45**, 91–96.

Morgan, J. J. B. The overcoming of distraction and other resistances. *Arch. Psychol., N. Y.,* 1916, **5**, Whole No. 35.

Morgan, M. I., and Ojemann, R. H. A study of the Luria method. *J. appl. Psychol.,* 1942, **26**, 168–179.

Morrison, R. S., and Dempsey, E. A study of thalamo-cortical relations. *Amer. J. Physiol.,* 1942, **92**, 135–181.

Moruzzi, G., and Magoun, H. W. Brain stem reticular formation and activation of the EEG. *EEG clin. Neurophysiol.,* 1949, **1**, 455–473.

Motokawa, K. Praktische Methoden der quantitativen Beschreibung des Elektrenkephalogramms. *Tohoku J. exp. Med.,* 1943, **45**, 309–322.

Motokawa, K., Hukuda, M., and Ohinata, S. On the persistence of brain-waves. *Tohoku J. exp. Med.,* 1949, **51**, 87–95.

Motokawa, K., and Huzimori, B. Electroencephalograms and conditioned reflexes. *Tohoku J. exp. Med.,* 1949, **50**, 215–223.

Mountcastle, V. B. Somatic functions of the nervous system. *Annu. Rev. Physiol.,* 1958, **20**, 471–508.

Muller, H. J. Human genetics in Russia. *J. Hered.,* 1935, **26**, 193–196.

Mundy-Castle, A. C. Theta and beta rhythm in the electroencephalogram of normal adults. *EEG clin. Neurophysiol.,* 1951, **3**, 477–486.

Mundy-Castle, A. C. An analysis of central responses to photic stimulation in normal adults. *EEG clin. Neurophysiol.,* 1953, **5**, 1–22. (a)

Mundy-Castle, A. C. Electrical responses of the brain in relation to behavior. *Brit. J. Psychol.,* 1953, **44**, 318–329. (b)

Mundy-Castle, A. C. The relationship between primary-secondary function and the alpha rhythm of the electroencephalogram. *J. Nat. Inst. Personnel Res., Johannesburg,* 1956, **6**, 95–102.

Mundy-Castle, A. C. The electroencephalogram and mental activity. *EEG clin. Neurophysiol.,* 1957, **9**, 643–655.

Mundy-Castle, A. C., Hurst, L. A., Beerstecher, D. M., and Prinsloo, T. The electroencephalogram in the senile psychoses. *EEG clin. Neurophysiol.,* 1954, **6**, 245–252.

Mundy-Castle, A. C., and McKiever, B. L. The psychophysiological significance of the galvanic skin response. *J. exp. Psychol.,* 1953, **46**, 15–24.

Munkvad, I. Determinations of glutamine and glutamic acid in material of mental patients; preliminary report. *Acta psychiat. neurol. Scand., Kbh.,* 1950, **25**, 269–274.

Murphy, J. P., and Gellhorn, E. The influence of hypothalamic stimulation on cortically induced movements and on action potentials of the cortex. *J. Neurophysiol.*, 1945, **8**, 341–364.

Murphy, J. V., and Miller, R. E. The effect of adrenocorticotrophic hormone (ACTH) on avoidance conditioning in the rat. *J. comp. physiol. Psychol.*, 1955, **48**, 47–49.

Murray, H. A. *Explorations in personality.* New York: Oxford University Press, 1938.

Nauta, W. J. H. Hypothalamic regulation of sleep in rats; an experimental study. *J. Neurophysiol.*, 1946, **9**, 285–316.

Neilson, Patricia. Shirley's babies after fifteen years. *J. genet. Psychol.*, 1948, **73**, 175–186.

Nims, L. F. Anoxia in aviation. *Annu. Rev. Physiol.*, 1948, **10**, 305–314.

Notterman, J. M., Schoenfeld, W. N., and Bersh, P. J. Conditioned heart rate response in human beings during experimental anxiety. *J. comp. physiol. Psychol.*, 1952, **45**, 1–8.

Obrist, P. A. GSR conditioning and anxiety as measured by basal conductance. Paper read at Eastern Psychological Association Meeting, Philadelphia, April 11, 1958.

Obrist, P. A. Physiological correlates of serial learning: a longitudinal study. Yellow Springs, Ohio: Fels Research Institute, 1959. (Mimeographed)

Obrist, W. D. Changes in level of palmar skin resistance during adolescence. *Amer. Psychologist*, 1948, **3**, 361. (Abstract)

Obrist, W. D. Skin resistance and electroencephalographic changes associated with learning. Unpublished doctoral dissertation, Northwestern University, 1950.

Obrist, W. D. The electroencephalogram of normal aged adults. *EEG clin. Neurophysiol.*, 1954, **6**, 235–244.

Ödegaard, O. The psychogalvanic reactivity in normals and in various psychopathic conditions. *Acta psychiat. neurol. Scand., Kbh.*, 1930, **5**, 55–103.

Ödegaard, O. The psychogalvanic reactivity in affective disorders. *Brit. J. Med. Psychol.*, 1932, **12**, 132–150.

Oldroyd, C. R., and Moskowitz, B. Optimal tensions for various types of task as a function of proximity to focal musculature. *Proc. Okla. Acad. Sci.*, 1952, **33**, 265.

Olson, W. C. *The measurement of nervous habits in normal children.* Minneapolis, Minn.: University of Minnesota Press, 1929.

Omwake, K. T., Dexter, E. S., and Lewis, L. W. The interrelations of certain physiological measures and aspects of personality. *Character and Pers.*, 1934, **3**, 64–71.

Ostow, M. Flickered light as a provocative test in electroencephalography. *EEG clin. Neurophysiol.*, 1949, **1**, 245. (Abstract)

Paintal, A. S. A comparison of the galvanic skin responses of normals and psychotics. *J. exp. Psychol.*, 1951, **41**, 425–428.

Palermo, D. S., Castaneda, A., and McCandless, B. R. The relationship of anxiety in children to performance in a complex learning task. *Child Develpm.*, 1956, **27**, 333–337.

Pascal, G. R. The effect of relaxation upon recall. *Amer. J. Psychol.*, 1949, **62**, 32–47.

Patrick, J. R. Studies in rational behavior and emotional excitement: II. The effect of emotional excitement on rational behavior in human subjects. *J. comp. Psychol.*, 1934, **18**, 153–195.

Patton, R. M. Electromyographic factors in aircraft control. The effect of induced tension upon muscular activity during simple voluntary movement. *USAF Sch. Aviat. Med. Rep.*, 1957, No. 55–133.

Pavlov, I. P. *Conditioned reflexes: an investigation of the physiological activity of the cerebral cortex.* Translated and edited by G. V. Anrep. Oxford: University Press, 1927.

Payne, R. B., and Hauty, G. T. The effects of experimentally induced attitudes upon task proficiency. *J. exp. Psychol.*, 1954, **47**, 267–273.

Payne, R. B., and Hauty, G. T. Effect of psychological feedback upon work decrement. *J. exp. Psychol.*, 1955, **50**, 343–351.

Pearson, O. P. Metabolism and bioenergetics. *Scient. Month.*, 1948, **66**, 131–134.

Persky, H., Gamm, S. R., and Grinker, R. R. Correlation between fluctuation of free anxiety and quantity of hippuric acid excretion. *Psychosom. Med.*, 1952, **14**, 34–40.

Persky, H., Grinker, R. R., Mirsky, I. A., and Gamm, S. R. Life situations, emotions and the excretion of hippuric acid in anxiety states. In H. G. Wolff (Ed.), *Life stress and bodily disease.* Baltimore: Williams and Wilkins Co., 1950. (*Res. Publ. Ass. nerv. ment. Dis.*, **29**, 297–306.)

Peters, J. E., and Gantt, W. H. Effect of graded degrees of muscular exertion on human heart rate and the role of muscular exertion in cardiac conditional reflexes. *J. gen. Psychol.*, 1953, **49**, 31–43.

Picard, P., Navarranne, P., Laboureur, P., Grousset, G., and Jest, C. Confrontations des données de l'électroencéphalogramme et de l'examen psychologique chez 309 candidats pilotes à l'aéronautique. In H. Fischgold and H. Gastaut (Eds.), *Conditionnement et réactivité en électroencéphalographie.* Paris: Masson, 1957. Pp. 304–314.

Piéron, H. *The sensations: their functions, processes and mechanisms.* New Haven: Yale University Press, 1952.

Plutchik, R., and Greenblatt, M. Temperature changes of the skin: a function of initial level. *Amer. J. Psychol.*, 1956, **69**, 403–409.

Popov, C. Sur l'accroissement de la sensation lumineuse par la stimulation sonore, étudiée par la méthode électroencéphalographique et par la méthode des images consécutives. *C. R. Acad. Sci. Paris*, 1955, **240**, 1268–1271.

Porter, J. M., Jr. Adaptation of the galvanic skin response. *J. exp. Psychol.*, 1938, **23**, 553–557.

Porter, R. W. Hypothalamic involvement in the pituitary-adrenocortical response to stress stimuli. *Amer. J. Physiol.*, 1953, **172**, 515–519.

Porteus, S. D., and Barclay, J. E. A further note on chlorpromazine: maze reactions. *J. consult. Psychol.*, 1957, **21**, 297–299.

Postman, L., and Bruner, J. S. Perception under stress. *Psychol. Rev.*, 1948, **55**, 314–323.

Pribytkova, G. N. (On the influence of various doses of adrenalin on higher nervous activity.) *Bull. Biol. Méd. exp., U.R.S.S.*, 1936, **2**, 110–113. (*Psychol. Abstr.* 12:5220)

Primac, R. B., Mirsky, A. F., and Rosvold, H. E. Effects of centrally acting drugs on two tests of brain damage. *A.M.A. Arch. Neurol. Psychiat.*, 1957, **77**, 328–332.

Purdy, C., Johnson, A. F., and Sheard, C. The relationship between electrical differences of potential in the skin and normal basal metabolism. *Science*, 1931, **73**, 46–49.

Purpura, D. P. Electrophysiological analysis of psychotogenic drug action. I. Effects of LSD on specific afferent systems in the cat. *A.M.A. Arch. Neurol. Psychiat.*, 1956, **75**, 122–131. (a)

Purpura, D. P. Electrophysiological analysis of psychotogenic drug action. II. General nature of lysergic acid diethylamide (LSD) action on central synapses. *A.M.A. Arch. Neurol. Psychiat.*, 1956, **75**, 132–143. (b)

Rabinovitch, M. S., Kennard, M. A., and Fister, W. P. Personality correlates of electroencephalographic patterns: Rorschach findings. *Canad. J. Psychol.*, 1955, **9**, 29–41.

Ramond, C. K. Performance in selective learning as a function of hunger. *J. exp. Psychol.*, 1954, **48**, 265–270.

Rasmus, M. H. Degeneration of emotional response upon reshowing of motion picture situations. *Psychol. Monogr.*, 1936, **48**, 40–56.

Reed, J. D. Spontaneous activity of animals—a review of the literature since 1929. *Psychol. Bull.*, 1947, **44**, 393–412.

Reiss, M. Psychoendocrinology. *J. ment. Sci.*, 1955, **101**, 683–695.

Rémond, A., and Lesèvre, N. Remarques sur l'activité cérébrale des sujects normaux (La typologie électroencéphalographique dans ses rapports avec certains caractères psychologiques). In H. Fischgold and H. Gastaut (Eds.), *Conditionnement et réactivité en électroencéphalographie*. Paris: Masson, 1957. Pp. 235–256.

Reuder, M. E. The relationship between two kinds of instructions and two levels of problem difficulty in their effects on muscular tension levels during problem solution. Unpublished doctoral dissertation, University of Pennsylvania, 1951.

Reymert, M. L., and Speer, G. S. Does the Luria technique measure emotion or merely bodily tension? *Character and Pers.*, 1938–39, **7**, 192–200.

Ribot, T. *The psychology of the emotions*. (2nd ed.) New York: Scribner's, 1911.

Rich, G. I. A biochemical approach to the study of personality. *J. abnorm. soc. Psychol.*, 1928, **23**, 158–175.

Richmond, J. B., and Lustman, S. L. Autonomic function in the neonate: I. Implications for psychosomatic theory. *Psychosom. Med.*, 1955, **17**, 269–275.

Richter, C. P. The significance of changes in the electrical resistance of the body during sleep. *Proc. Nat. Acad. Sci.*, 1926, **12**, 214–222.

Richter, C. P. The electrical skin resistance; diurnal and daily variations in psychopathic and in normal persons. *A.M.A. Arch. Neurol. Psychiat.*, 1928, **19**, 488–508.

Richter, C. P. Physiological factors involved in the electrical resistance of the skin. *Amer. J. Physiol.*, 1929, **88**, 596–615.

Richter, D., and Dawson, R. M. C. Brain metabolism in emotional excitement and in sleep. *Amer. J. Physiol.*, 1948, **154**, 73–79.

Rinaldi, F., and Himwich, H. E. Alerting responses and actions of atropine and cholinergic drugs. *A.M.A. Arch. Neurol. Psychiat.*, 1955, **73**, 387–395. (a)

Rinaldi, F., and Himwich, H. E. Cholinergic mechanism involved in function of mesodiencephalic activating system. *A.M.A. Arch. Neurol. Psychiat.*, 1955, **73**, 396–402. (b)

Rockwell, F. V., Welch, L., Kubis, J., and Fisichelli, V. Changes in palmar skin resistance during the Rorschach test. *Monthly Rev. Psychiat. Neurol.*, 1947, 113, 129–152.

Rosanoff, A. J., Handy, L. M., and Plesset, I. R. The etiology of manic-depressive syndromes with specific reference to their occurrence in twins. *Amer. J. Psychiat.*, 1935, 91, 725–762.

Rose, H. W., and Schmidt, I. Factors affecting dark adaptation. *J. Aviat. Med.*, 1947, 18, 218–230.

Rounds, G. H., Schubert, H. J. P., and Poffenberger, A. T. Effects of practice upon the metabolic cost of mental work. *J. gen. Psychol.*, 1932, 7, 65–79.

Royce, J. R. The factorial analysis of animal behavior. *Psychol. Bull.*, 1950, 47, 235–259.

Rubin, L. S. Recent advances in the chemistry of psychotic disorders. *Psychol. Bull.*, 1959, 56, 375–383.

Ruesch, J., and Finesinger, J. E. Muscular tension in psychiatric patients. *A.M.A. Arch. Neurol. Psychiat.*, 1943, 50, 439–449.

Rundquist, E. A. Inheritance of spontaneous activity in rats. *J. comp. Psychol.*, 1933, 16, 415–438.

Rundquist, E. A., and Bellis, C. J. Respiratory metabolism of active and inactive rats. *Amer. J. Physiol.*, 1933, 106, 670–675.

Russell, J. T. Relative efficiency of relaxation and tension in performing an act of skill. *J. gen. Psychol.*, 1932, 6, 330–343.

Russell, R. W. Drugs as tools in behavioral research. In L. Uhr and J. G. Miller (Eds.), *Drugs and behavior.* New York: Wiley, 1960. Pp. 19–40.

Ryan, A. H., and Ranseen, E. L. Palmar skin resistance (P.S.R.) during a standard period of controlled muscular activity as a measure of physical fitness and fatigue. *Amer. J. Physiol.*, 1944, 142, 68–79.

Ryan, T. A. Interrelations of the sensory systems in perception. *Psychol. Bull.*, 1940, 37, 659–698.

Sainsbury, P. Gestural movement during psychiatric interview. *Psychosom. Med.*, 1955, 17, 458–469.

Sainsbury, P., and Gibson, J. G. Symptoms of anxiety and tension and the accompanying physiological changes in the muscular system. *J. Neurol. Neurosurg. Psychiat.*, 1954, 17, 216–224.

Samuels, I. Reticular mechanisms and behavior. *Psychol. Bull.*, 1959, 56, 1–25.

Sanford, R. N., Adkins, M. M., Miller, R. B., and Cobb, E. A. Physique, personality and scholarship. *Monogr. Soc. Res. Child Develpm.*, 1943, 8, No. 1 (Whole No. 34).

Saul, L. J., Davis, H., and Davis, P. A. Psychologic correlations with the electroencephalogram. *Psychosom. Med.*, 1949, 11, 361–376.

Sayers, G. The adrenal cortex and homeostasis. *Physiol. Rev.*, 1950, 30, 241–320.

Schaffer, H. R. Behavior under stress: a neurophysiological hypothesis. *Psychol. Rev.*, 1954, 61, 323–333.

Schiff, E., Dougan, C., and Welch, L. The conditioned PGR and the EEG as indicators of anxiety. *J. abnorm. soc. Psychol.*, 1949, 44, 549–552.

Schlosberg, H. Three dimensions of emotion. *Psychol. Rev.*, 1954, 61, 81–88.

Schlosberg, H., and Kling, J. W. The relationship between "tension" and efficiency. *Percept. motor Skills*, 1959, 9, 395–397.

Schmidtke, H. Über die Messung der psychischen Ermüdung mit Hilfe des Flimmertests. *Psychol. Forsch.*, 1951, 23, 409–463.

Schneider, J. Activités rapides de type particulier et troubles du comportement. (Fast activities of a specific type and disorders of behavior.) *EEG clin. Neurophysiol.*, 1957, Suppl. 6, 271–281.

Schneider, R. A. The influence of predrug level of functioning on the effects of sedatives, tranquilizers, and stimulants on central autonomic function and reaction time. In L. Uhr and J. G. Miller (Eds.), *Drugs and behavior.* New York: Wiley, 1960. Pp. 420–426.

Schnore, M. M. Individual patterns of physiological activity as a function of task differences and degree of arousal. *J. exp. Psychol.*, 1959, **58**, 117–128.

Scott, J. P., and Charles, M. S. Genetic differences in the behavior of dogs: a case of magnification by thresholds and by habit formation. *J. genet. Psychol.*, 1954, **84**, 175–188.

Secunda, L., and Finley, K. H. Electroencephalographic studies in children presenting behavior disorders. *New England J. Med.*, 1942, **226**, 850–854.

Seltzer, C. C. Body disproportions and dominant personality traits. *Psychosom. Med.*, 1946, **8**, 75–97.

Seward, J. P., and Seward, G. H. The relation of galvanic skin reactions to preceding resistance. *J. exp. Psychol.*, 1935, **18**, 64–79.

Shaffer, L. F. Fear and courage in aerial combat. *J. consult. Psychol.*, 1947, **11**, 137–143.

Shagass, C. The sedation threshold. A method for estimating tension in psychiatric patients. *EEG clin. Neurophysiol.*, 1954, **6**, 221–233.

Shagass, C. Anxiety, depression, and the photically driven EEG. *A.M.A. Arch. Neurol. Psychiat.*, 1955, **74**, 3–10. (a)

Shagass, C. Differentiation between anxiety and depression by the photically activated electroencephalogram. *Amer. J. Psychiat.*, 1955, **112**, 41–46. (b)

Shagass, C., and Malmo, R. B. Psychodynamic themes and localized muscular tension during psychotherapy. *Psychosom. Med.*, 1954, **16**, 295–314.

Sharp, L. H. Effects of residual tension on output and energy expenditure in muscular work. *J. exp. Psychol.*, 1941, **29**, 1–22.

Shaw, W. A. The distribution of muscle action potentials during imagining. *Psychol. Rec.*, 1938, **2**, 195–216.

Shaw, W. A. Facilitating effects of induced tension upon the perception span for digits. *J. exp. Psychol.*, 1956, **51**, 113–117.

Shaw, W. A., and Kline, L. H. A study of muscle action potentials during the attempted solution by children of problems of increasing difficulty. *J. exp. Psychol.*, 1947, **37**, 146–158.

Sheer, D. E. Psychology. In E. A. Spiegel, *Progress in neurology and psychiatry.* New York: Grune and Stratton, 1957. Pp. 399–432.

Sheldon, W. H., and Stevens, S. S. *The varieties of temperament.* New York: Harper, 1942.

Sheldon, W. H., Stevens, S. S., and Tucker, W. B. *The varieties of human physique.* New York: Harper, 1940.

Shepard, J. F. Organic changes and feeling. *Amer. J. Psychol.*, 1906, **17**, 522–584.

Shepard, J. F. *The circulation and sleep, with Atlas.* New York: Macmillan, 1914.

Sherman, M., and Jost, H. Frustration reactions of normal and neurotic persons. *J. Psychol.*, 1942, **13**, 3–19.

Sherman, M., and Jost, H. Quantification of psychophysiological measures. *Psychosom. Med.*, 1945, **7**, 215–219.

Shirley, M. Studies of activity. I. Consistency of the revolving drum method of measuring the activity of the rat. *J. comp. Psychol.*, 1928, **8**, 23–38.

Shirley, M. *The first two years.* Minneapolis: University of Minnesota Press, 1931.

Shock, N. W. Physiological aspects of development. *Rev. Educ. Res.*, 1944, **14** (5), 413–426. (a)

Shock, N. W. Physiological factors in behavior. In J. McV. Hunt (Ed.), *Personality and the behavior disorders.* New York: Ronald Press, 1944. Pp. 582–618. (b)

Shore, M. F. Perceptual efficiency as related to induced muscular effort and manifest anxiety. *J. exp. Psychol.*, 1958, **55**, 179–183.

Silverman, J. J., and Powell, V. E. Studies on palmar sweating. III. Palmar sweating in an army general hospital. *Psychosom. Med.*, 1944, **6**, 243–249.

Silvette, H., and Britton, S. W. The comparative effects on carbohydrate metabolism of exhausting motive and emotive responses and exposure to cold. *Amer. J. Physiol.*, 1932, **100**, 685–692.

Simon, C. W., and Emmons, W. H. EEG, consciousness, and sleep. *Science*, 1956, **124**, 1066–1069.

Simonson, E., and Brožek, J. Flicker fusion frequency: background and applications. *Physiol. Rev.*, 1952, **32**, 349–378.

Sisson, B. D., and Ellingson, R. J. On the relationship between "normal" EEG patterns and personality variables. *J. nerv. ment. Dis.*, 1955, **121**, 353–358.

Skaggs, E. B. Studies in attention and emotion. *J. comp. Psychol.*, 1930, **10**, 375–419.

Skaggs, E. B. Further studies of bodily sway. *Amer. J. Psychol.*, 1937, **49**, 105–108.

Skaggs, E. B., Skaggs, I. S., and Jardon, M. Attention and bodily sway. *Amer. J. Psychol.*, 1932, **44**, 749–755.

Skinner, B. F., and Heron, W. T. Effects of caffeine and Benzedrine upon conditioning and extinction. *Psychol. Rec.*, 1937, **1**, 340–346.

Slonaker, J. R. The normal activity of the albino rat from birth to natural death, its rate of growth, and the duration of life. *J. Animal Behav.*, 1912, **2**, 20–42.

Smith, A. A. An electromyographic study of tension in interrupted and completed tasks. *J. exp. Psychol.*, 1953, **46**, 32–36.

Smith, A. A., Malmo, R. B., and Shagass, C. An electromyographic study of listening and talking. *Canad. J. Psychol.*, 1954, **8**, 219–227.

Smith, W. *The measurement of emotion.* New York: Harcourt, Brace, 1922.

Smock, C. D. The influence of stress on the perception of incongruity. *J. abnorm. soc. Psychol.*, 1955, **50**, 354–356.

Snygg, D., and Combs, A. W. *Individual behavior; a new frame of reference for psychology.* New York: Harper, 1949.

Solomon, A. P., and Fentress, T. L. Galvanic skin reflex and blood pressure reactions in psychoneuroses. *J. nerv. ment. Dis.*, 1934, **80**, 163–182.

Solomon, C. I., Brown, W. T., and Deutscher, M. Electroencephalography in behavior problem children. *Amer. J. Psychiat.*, 1944, **101**, 51–61.

Solomon, R. L., and Wynne, L. C. Traumatic avoidance learning: the principles of anxiety conservation and partial irreversibility. *Psychol. Rev.*, 1954, **61**, 353–385.

Spence, K. W., and Beecroft, R. S. Differential conditioning and level of anxiety. *J. exp. Psychol.*, 1954, **48**, 399–403.

Spence, K. W., and Farber, I. E. The relation of anxiety to differential eyelid conditioning. *J. exp. Psychol.*, 1954, **47**, 127–134.

Spence, K. W., and Taylor, J. A. The relation of conditioned response strength to anxiety in normal, neurotic, and psychotic subjects. *J. exp. Psychol.*, 1953, **45**, 265–272.

Stagner, R. *Psychology of personality.* New York: McGraw-Hill, 1937.

Starr, H. E. The (H) concentration of the mixed saliva considered as an index of fatigue and of emotional excitation, and applied to a study of the metabolic etiology of stammering. *Amer. J. Psychol.*, 1922, **33**, 394–418.

Staudt, V. M., and Kubis, J. F. The psychogalvanic response (PGR) and its relation to changes in tension and relaxation. *J. Psychol.*, 1948, **25**, 443–453.

Stauffacher, J. C. The effect of induced muscular tension upon various phases of the learning process. *J. exp. Psychol.*, 1937, **21**, 26–46.

Stellar, E. The physiology of motivation. *Psychol. Rev.*, 1954, **61**, 5–22.

Stellar, E. Physiological psychology. *Annu. Rev. Psychol.*, 1957, **8**, 415–436.

Stennett, R. G. The relationship of performance level to level of arousal. *J. exp. Psychol.*, 1957, **54**, 54–61. (a)

Stennett, R. G. The relationship of alpha amplitude to the level of palmar conductance. *EEG clin. Neurophysiol.*, 1957, **9**, 131–138. (b)

Stern, M. H. Thyroid function and activity, speed, and timing aspects of behavior. *Canad. J. Psychol.*, 1959, **13**, 43–48.

Stockard, C. R. *The genetic and endocrine basis for differences in form and behavior.* Philadelphia: Wistar Institute of Anatomy and Biology, 1941.

Stone, C. P. Wildness and savageness in rats of different strains. In K. S. Lashley (Ed.), *Studies in the dynamics of behavior.* Chicago: University of Chicago Press, 1932. Pp. 3–55.

Stone, C. P., and Obias, M. D. Effects of hypophysectomy on behavior in rats: II. Maze and discrimination learning. *J. comp. physiol. Psychol.*, 1955, **48**, 404–411.

Stratton, G. M. An experience during danger and the wider functions of emotion. In *Problems of personality; studies presented to Dr. Morton Prince, pioneer in American psychopathology.* New York: Harcourt, Brace, 1925. Pp. 47–62.

Stratton, G. M. The function of emotion, as shown particularly in excitement. *Psychol. Rev.*, 1928, **35**, 351–366.

Ström-Olsen, R., and Weil-Malherbe, H. Humoral changes in manic-depressive psychosis with particular reference to the excretion of catechol amines in urine. *J. ment. Sci.*, 1958, **104**, 696–704.

Strother, G. B., and Cook, D. M. Neurocirculatory reactions and a group stress situation. *J. consult. Psychol.*, 1953, **17**, 267–268.

Stroud, J. B. The role of muscular tensions in stylus maze learning. *J. exp. Psychol.*, 1931, **14**, 606–631.

Surwillo, W. W. Psychological factors in muscle-action potentials: EMG gradients. *J. exp. Psychol.*, 1956, **52**, 263–272.

Syz, H. C. Psychogalvanic studies in schizophrenia. *A.M.A. Arch. Neurol. Psychiat.*, 1926, **16**, 747–760.

Syz, H. C., and Kinder, E. F. Electrical skin resistance in normal and in psychotic subjects. *A.M.A. Arch. Neurol. Psychiat.*, 1928, **19**, 1026–1035.

Taffel, C. Anxiety and the conditioning of verbal behavior. *J. abnorm. soc. Psychol.*, 1955, **51**, 496–501.

Taylor, C. M., Lamb, M. W., Robertson, M. E., and MacLeod, G. The energy expenditure for quiet play and cycling of boys seven to fourteen years of age. *J. Nutrit.*, 1948, **35**, 511–521.

Taylor, J. A. The relationship of anxiety to the conditioned eyelid response. *J. exp. Psychol.*, 1951, **41**, 81–92.

Taylor, J. A. A personality scale of manifest anxiety. *J. abnorm. soc. Psychol.*, 1953, **48**, 285–290.

Taylor, J. A., and Spence, K. W. The relationship of anxiety level to performance in serial learning. *J. exp. Psychol.*, 1952, **44**, 61–64.

Teichner, W. H. Recent studies of simple reaction time. *Psychol. Bull.*, 1954, **51**, 128–149.

Telford, C. W., and Storlie, A. The relation of respiration and reflex winking rates to muscular tension during motor learning. *J. exp. Psychol.*, 1946, **36**, 512–517.

Telford, C. W., and Swenson, W. J. Changes in muscle tension during learning. *J. exp. Psychol.*, 1942, **30**, 236–246.

Terry, R. A. Autonomic balance and temperament. *J. comp. physiol. Psychol.*, 1953, **46**, 454–460.

Thalbitzer, S. *Emotion and insanity.* New York: Harcourt, Brace, 1926.

Theron, P. A. Peripheral vasomotor reactions as indices of basic emotional tension and lability. *Psychosom. Med.*, 1948, **10**, 335–346.

Thiesen, J. W., and Meister, R. K. A laboratory investigation of measures of frustration tolerance of pre-adolescent children. *J. genet. Psychol.*, 1949, **75**, 277–291.

Thorne, F. C. The psychophysical measurement of the temporal course of visual sensitivity. *Arch. Psychol.*, N.Y., 1934, **25**, Whole No. 170.

Thorner, M., Gibbs, F. A., and Gibbs, E. L. Relation between the EEG and flying ability. *War. Med.*, 1942, **2**, 255–262.

Thornton, G. R., Holck, G. O., and Smith, E. L. The effect of Benzedrine and caffeine upon performance in certain psychomotor tasks. *J. abnorm. soc. Psychol.*, 1939, **34**, 96–113.

Tinklepaugh, O. L., and Mitchell, M. B. Monthly and weekly weight cycles in women and their relations to behavioral and physiological functions. *J. genet. Psychol.*, 1939, **54**, 3–16.

Todd, J. W. Reaction to multiple stimuli. *Arch. Psychol.*, N.Y., 1912, **3**, (25).

Tolman, E. C. *Purposive behavior in animals and men.* New York: Century, 1932.

Toman, J. Flicker potentials and the alpha rhythm in man. *J. Neurophysiol.*, 1941, **4**, 51–61.

Tonndorf, J. Combined effects of noise and hypoxia upon the auditory threshold. *USAF Sch. Aviat. Med. Proj. Rep.*, 1953, Proj. No. 21-1203-0001, Rep. No. 1.

Torres, F., and Marshall, C. Reciprocal influence of central responses to visual and auditory stimulation in man. *EEG clin. Neurophysiol.*, 1953, Suppl. 3, 72. (Abstract)

Totten, E. Oxygen consumption during emotional stimulation. *Comp. Psychol. Monogr.*, 1925, **3**, 1–79.

Travis, L. E. Changes in auditory acuity during the performance of certain mental tasks. *Amer. J. Psychol.*, 1926, **37**, 139–142.

Travis, L. E., and Bennett, C. L. The relationship between the electroencephalogram and scores in certain Rorschach categories. *EEG clin. Neurophysiol.*, 1953, **5**, 474. (Abstract)

Travis, R. C., and Kennedy, J. L. Prediction and automatic control of alertness. I. Control of lookout alertness. *J. comp. physiol. Psychol.,* 1947, **40,** 457–461.

Travis, R. C., and Kennedy, J. L. Prediction and control of alertness. III. Calibration of the alertness indicator and further results. *J. comp. physiol. Psychol.,* 1949, **42,** 45–57.

Triplett, N. The dynamogenic factors in pace-making and competition. *Amer. J. Psychol.,* 1898, **9,** 507–533.

Turner, M., Bérard, E., Turner, N., and Franco, N. Modifications électro-encéphalographiques, électrodermographiques et électromyographiques provoquées par la chlorpromazine chez l'homme. *EEG clin. Neurophysiol.,* 1956, **8,** 25–34.

Tuttle, W. W. The effect of sleep upon the patellar tendon reflex. *Amer. J. Physiol.,* 1924, **68,** 345–348.

Tyler, D. B., Goodman, J., and Rothman, T. The effect of experimental insomnia on the rate of potential changes in the brain. *Amer. J. Physiol.,* 1947, **149,** 185–193.

Uhr, L. Objectively measured behavioral effects of psychoactive drugs. In L. Uhr and J. G. Miller (Eds.), *Drugs and behavior.* New York: Wiley, 1960. Pp. 610–633.

Uhr, L., and Miller, J. G. Behavioral toxicity of emylcamate (Striatran) and of meprobamate. *Amer. J. Med. Sci.,* 1960, **240,** 197–203.

Ulett, G. A., and Gleser, G. Psychiatric screening of flying personnel: the development of empirical scales for the prediction of anxiety-proneness from the EEG and reaction of intermittent photic stimulation. *Sch. Aviat. Med. Rep.,* 1953, Proj. No. 21-0202-0007, No. 4.

Ulett, G. A., Gleser, G., Winokur, G., and Lawler, A. The EEG and reaction to photic stimulation as an index of anxiety-proneness. *EEG clin. Neurophysiol.,* 1953, **5,** 23–32.

Valentine, W. L., and Wickens, D. D. *Experimental foundations of general psychology.* (3rd ed.) New York: Rinehart, 1949.

van der Merwe, A. B., and Theron, P. A. A new method of measuring emotional stability. *J. gen. Psychol.,* 1947, **37,** 109–123.

Verplanck, W. S., Collier, G. H., and Cotton, J. W. Nonindependence of successive responses in measurements of the visual threshold. *J. exp. Psychol.,* 1952, **44,** 273–282.

Vogel, W., Baker, R. W., and Lazarus, R. S. The role of motivation in psychological stress. *J. abnorm. soc. Psychol.,* 1958, **56,** 105–112.

Wade, M. The effect of sedatives upon delayed response in monkeys following removal of the prefrontal lobes. *J. Neurophysiol.,* 1947, **10,** 57–61.

Wall, P. D., Rémond, A. G., and Dobson, R. L. Studies on the mechanism of the action of visual afferents on motor cortex excitability. *EEG clin. Neurophysiol.,* 1953, **5,** 385–393.

Waller, A. D. Concerning emotive phenomena. II. Periodic variations of conductance of the palm of the human hand. *Proc. Roy. Soc. Lond., Pt. B,* 1919, **91,** 17–32.

Wallerstein, H. An electromyographic study of attentive listening. *Canad. J. Psychol.,* 1954, **8,** 228–238.

Walter, R. D., Yeager, C. L., Margolis, L. H., and Simon, A. The EEG changes in unilateral and bilateral frontal lobotomy. *Amer. J. Psychiat.,* 1955, **111,** 590–594.

Walter, W. G. Electro-encephalography. *J. ment. Sci.*, 1944, **90**, 64–73.

Walter, W. G. Technique-interpretation. In J. D. N. Hill and G. Parr (Eds.), *Electroencephalography.* London: Macdonald, 1950. Pp. 63–91. (a)

Walter, W. G. Normal rhythms—their development, distribution and significance. In J. D. N. Hill and G. Parr (Eds.), *Electroencephalography.* London: Macdonald, 1950. Pp. 203–227. (b)

Walter, W. G. Theoretical properties of diffuse projection systems in relation to behavior and consciousness. In J. F. Delafresnaye (Ed.), *Brain mechanisms and consciousness.* Springfield, Illinois: Thomas, 1954. Pp. 345–373. (a)

Walter, W. G. In J. M. Tanner and B. Inhelder (Eds.), *Discussions on child development.* Vol. 2. New York: International Universities Press, Inc., 1954. (b)

Wang, G. H. The galvanic skin reflex. A review of old and recent works from a physiologic point of view. Part one. *Amer. J. phys. Med.*, 1957, **36**, 295–320.

Wang, G. H. The galvanic skin reflex. A review of old and recent works from a physiologic point of view. Part two. *Amer. J. phys. Med.*, 1958, **37**, 35–57.

Washburn, R. W. A study of the smiling and laughing of infants in the first year of life. *Genet. psychol. Monogr.*, 1929, **6**, 397–537.

Wechsler, D. The measurement of emotional reaction. *Arch. Psych., N.Y.*, 1925, No. 76.

Welch, L., Diethelm, O., and Long, L. Measurement of hyper-associative activity during elation. *J. Psychol.*, 1946, **21**, 113–126.

Welch, L., and Kubis, J. Conditioned PGR (psychogalvanic response) in states of pathological anxiety. *J. nerv. ment. Dis.*, 1947, **105**, 372–381. (a)

Welch, L., and Kubis, J. The effect of anxiety on the conditioning rate and stability of the PGR. *J. Psychol.*, 1947, **23**, 83–91. (b)

Wendland, John P. Effect of muscular exercise on dark adaptation. *Amer. J. Ophthal.*, 1948, **31**, 1429–1436.

Wenger, M. A. Some relationships between muscular processes and personality and their factorial analysis. *Child Develpm.*, 1938, **9**, 261–276.

Wenger, M. A. The measurement of individual differences in autonomic balance. *Psychosom. Med.*, 1941, **3**, 427–434.

Wenger, M. A. A study of physiological factors: the autonomic nervous system and the skeletal musculature. *Human Biology*, 1942, **14**, 69–84.

Wenger, M. A. An attempt to appraise individual differences in level of muscular tension. *J. exp. Psychol.*, 1943, **32**, 213–225. (a)

Wenger, M. A. A further note on the measurement of autonomic balance. *Psychosom. Med.*, 1943, **5**, 148–151. (b)

Wenger, M. A. Psychophysiological studies: VI. The standard handwriting test, CE 114 A, and its validity for pilot training. Project No. 421, Report No. 1, AAF School of Aviation Medicine, Randolph Field, Texas, 1945.

Wenger, M. A. Preliminary study of the significance of measures of autonomic balance. *Psychosom. Med.*, 1947, **9**, 301–309.

Wenger, M. A. Studies of autonomic balance in Army Air Forces personnel. *Comp. Psychol. Monogr.*, 1948, **19**, No. 4 (Whole No. 101), 1–111.

Wenger, M. A. Autonomic response patterns to four stressors. In A. F. Ax, Report on symposium on psychological and biological effects of stress, Western Psychological Association Sector of AAAS Meeting, June 24, 1955. *Polygraph Newsletter*, 1955, Vol. 1, No. 2.

Wenger, M. A. Pattern analysis of autonomic variables during rest. *Psychosom. Med.*, 1957, **14**, 240–244.

Wenger, M. A., and Ellington, M. The measurement of autonomic balance in children: method and normative data. *Psychosom. Med.*, 1943, **5**, 241–253.

Wenger, M. A., Engel, B. P., and Clemens, D. L. Studies of autonomic response patterns: rationale and methods. *Behav. Sci.*, 1957, **2**, 216–221.

Wenger, M. A., and Irwin, O. C. Fluctuations in skin resistance of infants and adults and their relationship to muscular processes. *Univer. Iowa Studies*, 1936, **12**, 141–179.

Wenger, M. A., Jones, F. N., and Jones, M. H. *Physiological psychology.* New York: Holt, 1956.

Werre, P. F. *The relationships between electroencephalographic and psychological data in normal adults.* Leiden, Netherlands: Universitaire pers Leiden, 1957.

Wertheimer, M. An investigation of the "randomness" of threshold measurements. *J. exp. Psychol.*, 1953, **45**, 294–303.

Wertheimer, M. The variability of auditory and visual absolute thresholds in time. *J. gen. Psychol.*, 1955, **52**, 111–147. (a)

Wertheimer, M. Figural aftereffect as a measure of metabolic efficiency. *J. Pers.*, 1955, **24**, 56–73. (b)

Wertheimer, M., Levin, H., and Wertheimer, N. The effect of experimentally induced changes in metabolism on perceptual measures of metabolic efficiency. *Percept. mot. Skills*, 1955, **5**, 173–176.

Wertheimer, M., and Wertheimer, N. A metabolic interpretation of individual differences in figural aftereffects. *Psychol. Rev.*, 1954, **61**, 279–280.

Westburgh, E. M. Psychogalvanic studies on affective variations in the mentally diseased, *A.M.A. Arch. Neurol. Psychiat.*, 1929, **22**, 719–736.

Westie, F. R., and DeFleur, M. L. Autonomic responses and their relationship to race attitudes. *J. abnorm. soc. Psychol.*, 1959, **58**, 340–347.

White, M. M. The relation of bodily tension to electrical resistance. *J. exp. Psychol.*, 1930, **13**, 267–277.

Whitehorn, J. C., and Richter, H. Unsteadiness of the heart rate in psychotic and neurotic states. *A.M.A. Arch. Neurol. Psychiat.*, 1937, **38**, 62–70.

Wiersma, E. D. *Lectures on psychiatry.* London: Lewis, 1932.

Wikler, A. The uses of drugs in psychiatric research. *Amer. J. Psychiat.*, 1956, **112**, 961–969.

Wilcott, R. C. Correlation of skin resistance and potential. *J. comp. physiol. Psychol.*, 1958, **51**, 691–696.

Wilcott, R. C. Silverman-Powell index of sweating vs. skin conductance and a humidity index of surface moisture. *J. comp. physiol. Psychol.*, 1959, **52**, 33–36.

Wilder, J. The law of initial value in neurology and psychiatry: facts and problems. *J. nerv. ment. Dis.*, 1957, **125**, 73–86.

Williams, A. C., Jr., Macmillan, J. W., and Jenkins, J. G. Preliminary experimental investigations of "tension" as a determinant of performance in flight training. (CAA Div. of Research, Rep. No. 54, 1946; Publ. Bd. No. L 50325.) Washington, D. C.: U. S. Dept. of Commerce, 1947.

Williams, D. The significance of an abnormal electroencephalogram. *J. Neurol. Psychiat.*, 1941, **4**, 257–268.

Williams, R. J. *The human frontier.* New York: Harcourt, Brace, 1946.

William, R. J. Some implications of physiological individuality. In M. L. Reymert (Ed.), *Feelings and emotions.* New York: McGraw-Hill, 1950. Pp. 268–273.

Wishner, J. Neurosis and tension: an exploratory study of the relationships of physiological and Rorschach measures. *J. abnorm. soc. Psychol.*, 1953, **48**, 253–260.

Wolff, H. G. Life stress and bodily disease. In A. Weider, *Contributions toward medical psychology; theory and psychodiagnostic methods.* New York: Ronald Press, 1953. Pp. 315–367.

Wolff, H. G., and Wolf, S. *Pain.* Springfield, Ill.: Thomas, 1948.

Woodbury, D. M., Timiras, P. A., and Vernadakis, A. Influence of adrenocortical steroids on brain function and metabolism. In H. Hoagland (Ed.), *Hormones, brain function and behavior.* New York: Academic Press, Inc., 1957. Pp. 27–54.

Woodworth, R. S. Voluntary phenomena—experimental. *Psychol. Bull.*, 1914, **11**, 402–404.

Woodworth, R. S., and Schlosberg, H. *Experimental psychology.* (Rev. ed.). New York: Holt, 1954.

Wortis, J. Review of psychiatric progress 1948: physiological treatment. *Amer. J. Psychiat.*, 1949, **105**, 528–531.

Wright, S. The physiology of emotions. In N. G. Harris (Ed.), *Modern trends in psychological medicine.* New York and London: Hoeber, 1948. Pp. 19–50.

Wulfeck, W. H. Motor function in the mentally disordered. Part I. A comparative investigation of motor function in psychotics, psychoneurotics, and normals. *Psychol. Rec.*, 1941, **4**, 271–323. (a)

Wulfeck, W. H. Motor function in the mentally disordered. Part II. The relation of muscle tension to the performance of motor tasks. *Psychol. Rec.*, 1941, **4**, 326–348. (b)

Wynne, L. C., and Solomon, R. L. Traumatic avoidance learning: acquisition and extinction in dogs deprived of normal peripheral autonomic function. *Genet. psychol. Monogr.*, 1955, **52**, 241–284.

Yerkes, R. M. The heredity of wildness and savageness in rats. *J. Animal Behav.*, 1913, **3**, 286–296.

Yerkes, R. M., and Dodson, J. D. The relation of strength of stimulus to rapidity of habit-formation. *J. of comp. and Neurol. Psychol.*, 1908, **18**, 459–482.

Zimbardo, P. G., and Barry, H., III. Effects of caffeine and chlorpromazine on the sexual behavior of male rats. *Science*, 1958, **127**, 84–85.

Zimmerman, F. T., Burgemeister, B. B., and Putnam, T. J. A group study of the effect of glutamic acid upon mental functioning of children and adolescents. *Psychosom. Med.*, 1947, **9**, 175–183.

Author index

Subject index

Activation, and alternative terms, 3, 16
and direction, as basic descriptive
concepts, 4–5, 112
as an organismic phenomenon, 49, 82,
113, 118, 322
as a unifying concept, 4
as it appears in other psychological
concepts, 6, 9, 11–13, 15, 16,
112
"basal" level of, 29
behavioral correlates of, 230–268,
271–273
continuum of, 5, 14, 18, 51, 81
consistency of individual differences
in, 197–224, 227–228
definition of, 17–20
degree of, 4–6, 9–10, 12, 14, 17, 20–
29, 33, 50, 110–111, 112, 113,
169–194, 230–255, 278
factors affecting, 9, 34–42, 43–46,
46–49, 50–81, 112, 117, 120–
128, 165–169, 197–198, 218–
219, 220–224, 224–226, 231–
233, 272–275, 278–279, 281–
283
fluctuations in, 24, 26, 29–33, 113,
181–185, 255–266, 308–315
in description of behavior, 112
in relation to goals, 113
in relation to stimulus situation, 50–
81, 109, 112–113
interaction of neural and chemical
agents, 49
interaction with direction, 10–11, 277–
278

Activation, interrelationships of measures of, 91–111
lawfulness of, 85–87, 113
measurement of changes in, 29–32,
255–266, 308–315
measurement of degree of, 20–29, 33,
52–81, 91–111, 113, 207–227,
230–255, 283–308
nature of, 16–20
neurohumoral basis of, 34–46, 118
patterning of, 82–111
recovery time, 113, 266–268
variations, effect upon responses, 117
Activity level, environmental factors in,
199–201, 206
genetic factors in, 197–207
individual differences, in dogs, 202–
207
in infants, 197
in rats, 198–202
sex differences in, 225
Age differences in activation, 220–224
electroencephalogram, 221–224
heart rate, 224
metabolism, 224
skin resistance, 220–221
Anxiety, in relation to autonomic measures, 253–254
to conditioning, 174–175
to the EEG, 238, 241–243
to groups of measures, 316
to motor irregularities, 310–312
to muscle tension, 298
to performance, 132, 175–176, 178,
161–162, 285–286

379